Drinking Water Quality and Contaminants Guidebook

Joseph Cotruvo

CRC Press is an imprint of the
Taylor & Francis Group, an **informa** business

CRC Press
Taylor & Francis Group
6000 Broken Sound Parkway NW, Suite 300
Boca Raton, FL 33487-2742

Printed on acid-free paper

International Standard Book Number-13: 978-0-8153-6305-7 (Hardback)
International Standard Book Number-13: 978-1-351-11047-1 (eBook)

Library of Congress Cataloging-in-Publication Data

Names: Cotruvo, Joseph, author.
Title: Drinking water quality and contaminants guidebook / Joseph Cotruvo.
Description: Boca Raton : Taylor & Francis, a CRC title, part of the Taylor & Francis imprint, a member of the Taylor & Francis Group, the academic division of T&F Informa, plc, 2018.
Identifiers: LCCN 2018018629| ISBN 9780815363057 (hardback : acid-free paper) | ISBN 9781351110471 (e-book)
Subjects: LCSH: Drinking water—Purification—Handbooks, manuals, etc. | Drinking water—Contamination—Handbooks, manuals, etc. | Water—Composition—Handbooks, manuals, etc.
Classification: LCC TD430 .C58 2018 | DDC 628.1/6--dc23
LC record available at https://lccn.loc.gov/2018018629

Visit the Taylor & Francis Web site at
http://www.taylorandfrancis.com

and the CRC Press Web site at
http://www.crcpress.com

Contents

Preface

Drinking water quality and composition are topics of continuing interest among drinking water providers and regulators, and the public is constantly barraged by the works of analytical chemists on the detection of chemicals and other contaminants at lower and lower levels of detection, which are now routinely at parts per trillion for many substances. These reports are headline articles, and the public frequently and mistakenly becomes less confident in the safety of their drinking water and reacts by utilizing bottled water and home treatment devices. The current average per capita bottled water consumption in the United States is about a half liter per day, and bottled beverages account for at least an equivalent amount. This situation is remarkable in developed countries such as the United States because, since the passage of the Safe Drinking Water Act in 1974, public drinking water providers are governed more than ever. These comprehensive regulations include health-based values, monitoring, compliance, and reporting requirements, and water quality and safety in the United States are much better than they have been in at least the past 100 years.

Indeed, since the implementation of the Safe Drinking Water Act, regular reports from the US Centers for Disease Control and Prevention demonstrate that source and treatment-related waterborne disease outbreaks are few and have been in a continuing decline. What is of concern is that distribution and plumbing-related legionellosis from inhalation (not ingestion) of aerosols from indoors, spa, fountain, and cooling tower blowdown account for about two-thirds of the outbreaks and the only drinking water-related deaths over about the past 10 years. This does not necessarily mean that they are increasing, but that these pneumonias are now accurately typed more frequently and recognized by physicians, and reported more assiduously, since their original detection from a cooling tower source at the American Legion Convention in Philadelphia in 1976, and since legionellosis became a reportable disease in 2001.

The watershed of science and technology associated with drinking water began in the early 1970s when chlorine-related disinfection by-products trihalomethanes (THMs) were first detected and then regulated in 1979. Since then, hundreds of potential contaminants have been regulated either individually or in groups (microbial, radionuclides, disinfection by-products). Most of them are virtually never present, and very high percentages of the 50,000 community water supplies and 150,000 public water supplies in the United States are in complete compliance.

Health-based regulatory and World Health Organization (WHO) guideline values are designed to have substantial margins of safety, so a moderate exceedance for some time would have no adverse effect for substances that are not acutely toxic. Substances treated as genotoxic carcinogens are very conservatively assumed to have finite, albeit small, risk at any level above zero; however, this is being challenged more so in parts of the scientific community. There are several currently regulated substances that had been regulated as genotoxic carcinogens that no longer can be classified as functioning in that manner at low drinking water levels. So, properly managed drinking water is actually very safe and likely the safest of the many external exposures that the public experiences from the natural diet and other life experiences.

This volume is a compilation of brief descriptive articles on drinking water quality and regulatory issues reflecting my experiences and judgments from more than 43 years of engagement and evolution in drinking water quality assessments, and regulatory policy decisions. Many of the original articles were published in *Water Technology on Line* over the course of several years. They have been updated and edited for this volume, and others have been added.

This is not intended to be a comprehensive treatise on any of the topics, but rather to focus on a perspective of digested key information that is the basis for regulatory and other water quality issues, and of value to the readers regardless of their roles and interests. The volume of literature on the topics would span many years and usually hundreds or thousands of pages, beyond expectations for any but the most determined reader to absorb. The content of the articles usually concentrates on US Environmental Protection Agency (EPA) standards and guidelines, and WHO Guidelines for Drinking Water Quality, and other published literature. Some of the articles point out significant differences by different water quality management organizations, which demonstrate a degree of judgmental variation in risk assessment, which is not an absolute science. Some of the differences are due to overdue reassessments, and some are due to differences of interpretation of the data. These differences can lead to public confusion with regard to what are actually "safe" levels. Some articles conclude that revisions of some regulatory actions are overdue and should be undertaken to eliminate phantom risks and reduce compliance costs. Some recommend that more actions should be undertaken to address issues such as distribution systems and microbial regrowth in plumbing that provides actuarial cases of illness and death, rather than hypothetical risks that are postulated but undetected for numerous drinking water components, or that are present in drinking water supplies with very low frequency and low concentrations.

Reuse of wastewater for drinking water and desalination are becoming more widely applied in the United States and worldwide. These are numerous successful technological and sustainable approaches for providing drinking water to populations where the capacity of the local natural water sources is being exceeded, usually due to population shifts to water-limited areas. The technologies can produce water that is actually higher quality than most natural water supplies, especially surface water supplies. WHO guidelines have been developed for reuse, and some US states are also producing guidelines and standards. Recycled water and desalinated water are drinking water, and quality specifications for all drinking waters should be the same, with perhaps a few adjustments to reflect local conditions. It is essential that these requirements are reflective of the capabilities of the advanced technologies that are utilized and not so burdensome as to limit the opportunities, or significantly and unnecessarily increase the costs of those advances in provision of high-quality drinking water.

The societal cost of drinking water regulations can be perceived as purchasing insurance that adverse outcomes will not occur; in this regard, the cost of the insurance should be commensurate with the likelihood and magnitude of the risk being addressed. Clearly, protection from microbial disease risks from drinking water must always be predominant, and trace chemicals usually fall farther down the scale of public health risks, but their detections even at very low levels seem to raise the greatest public concerns. To paraphrase the WHO Guidelines for Drinking Water Quality, measures to manage disinfection by-products should never compromise the efficacy of water treatment to control microbial disease risks.

Author

Dr. Joseph Cotruvo, BS, PhD, BCES, is president of Joseph Cotruvo and Associates, LLC, Water, Environment and Public Health Consultants, in Washington, DC. He earned his bachelor of science in chemistry from the University of Toledo, Toledo, Ohio, and PhD in physical organic chemistry from The Ohio State University, Columbus, Ohio. He is board certified in environmental sciences and a research professor in the departments of chemistry and environmental sciences at the University of Toledo, and a member of the School of Green Chemistry and Engineering Science Advisory Board. He is a longtime member of WHO's Guidelines for Drinking Water Quality committee, and he serves on numerous expert advisory panels on drinking water quality and potable water reuse, including Singapore's National Environment Agency Water Standards Technical Advisory Committee, and the Nanyang Technical University Environment and Water Research Institute Advisory Board, and several large-scale wastewater and potable water reuse projects with the National Water Research Institute for Orange County, San Diego, and Los Angeles, California.

At the US Environmental Protection Agency, he was the first director of the Drinking Water Standards Division and also director of the Risk Assessment Division in Pollution Prevention and Toxics. His Drinking Water Standards Division developed risk assessments and comprehensive national drinking water regulations for microbial contaminants, organic and inorganic chemicals and radionuclides, the original regulations for trihalomethane disinfection by-products, surface water filtration rules, and proposed corrosion control, lead, and copper rules. He also initiated EPA's Drinking Water Health Advisory Program providing health risk guidance for unregulated contaminants and emergencies.

His work includes quality specifications and health protection policy for potable water wastewater reclamation and reuse; *legionella* and other biofilm contaminants in distribution systems; novel point-of-use water treatment technologies; nutritional minerals in drinking water; pharmaceuticals and disinfection by-products in water; safe drinking water for emergencies; and Safe Drinking Water Act regulatory policy. He has been principal investigator and co-principal investigator on numerous studies investigating drinking water safety, technology, security, decontamination, nontraditional techniques for water provision, reuse guidelines for the beverage industry, and disinfection by-product formation and health-risk issues. His team has completed research studies on pre-systemic metabolism and the low-dose toxicology and mode of action of bromate, and additional studies are under way on the low-dose toxicology and formation chemistry of bromate in drinking water.

He is an honorary life member of the American Water Works Association and was also chairman of the Water Quality Committee of the Board of Directors of the District of Columbia Water and Sewer Authority (DCWater).

In more than 25 years of service in the WHO Guidelines for Drinking Water Quality committee, he has been engaged in projects producing WHO monographs on numerous water and health risk topics, including most recently the WHO Guidance for Direct and Indirect Potable Reuse (2017).

He is a technical editor for the *Journal of the American Water Works Association*, associate editor of the *AWWA Water Science Journal,* and *Water Technology*, and a peer reviewer for several journals. He has authored more than 300 publications, presentations, and articles on health risk, water quality and safety, and water regulatory policy.

List of Acronyms and Abbreviations

ADI	acceptable daily intake
AI	Adequate Intake
ANSI	American National Standards Institute
Bq	becquerel
BMD	benchmark dose
BTEX	benzene, toluene, ethyl benzene, toluene
bw	body weight
CDC	US Centers for Disease Control
Da	daltons
DBP	disinfection by-product
DWEL	drinking water equivalent level
DWHA	Drinking Water Health Advisory
EPA	US Environmental Protection Agency
FAO	Food and Agricultural Organization of the United Nations
FDA	US Food and Drug Administration
GAC	granular activated carbon
GDWQ	Guidelines for Drinking Water Quality
HAA	haloacetic acid
HPC	heterotrophic plate count
IARC	International Agency for Research on Cancer
ICP-MS	inductively coupled plasma emission spectroscopy-mass spectroscopy
JECFA	FAO/WHO Joint Expert Committee on Food Additives
kg	kilogram
LOAEL	lowest observed adverse effect level
MCL	maximum contaminant level
MCLG	maximum contaminant level goal
mg	milligram
MOA	mode of action
NOEL	no observed effect level
NOAEL	no observed adverse effect level
NTP	National Toxicology Program
μg	microgram
ng	nanogram
pCi	picocurie
PHG	public health goal
RDI	recommended daily intake
RfD	reference dose
RO	reverse osmosis

RSC relative source contribution
TDI tolerable daily intake
THM trihalomethane
TOC total organic carbon
WHO World Health Organization

1 Inorganic Chemicals in Drinking Water

ARSENIC

INTRODUCTION

Arsenic is element 33 in the periodic table with an atomic weight of 75 Da. Natural arsenic is the stable isotope that contains 33 protons and 42 neutrons. Arsenic was formerly used in wood preservatives. Paris Green, perhaps the first commercial pesticide, is a copper arsenite and copper acetate complex originally prepared in 1814 and used as a general insecticide and rodenticide. Many years ago, there were unproven medical uses for arsenic, but one of the visible outcomes was a horny skin keratosis, as well as other toxicity consequences.

PHYSICAL AND CHEMICAL PROPERTIES

Arsenic is a metalloid, neither a metal nor a nonmetal. Arsenic is found in oxidation states of –3 (arsenides), 0 (elemental arsenic), +3 (arsenite and arsenic trichloride), and +5 (arsenate) so it can exist in many inorganic and also organic compounds (e.g., methylarsonic acid and its salts).

OCCURRENCE

Arsenic is widely distributed in the earth's crust. It is found in groundwaters as arsenite (AsO_3^{-3}) or arsenate (AsO_4^{-3}) salts. World water concentrations range from less than 1 μg/L to multiple mg/L amounts. The median level in US drinking water in some studies was 1.5 μg/L, and the 95th percentile was 15.4 μg/L. The 1988 National Inorganics and Radionuclides Survey study of 982 groundwater supplies found 6.52 percent positives above 5 μg/L. The mean of the positives was 13 μg/L, and two exceeded 40 μg/L. There are pockets of high arsenic levels in groundwaters in the northeast and western United States as well as other locations.

Arsenic is found in foods, with fish and shellfish being by far the largest contributors to daily diet. About 99 percent of the seafood arsenic is in organic forms that are likely much less toxic than the inorganic forms.

It is common in cereals, poultry, grains, and vegetables with only trace amounts in milk. Rice can contain on the order of 6.7 μg of inorganic arsenic per cup depending upon where it was grown. Rice is grown in water so it has a greater opportunity to accumulate arsenic from the environment. In the cited Food and Drug Administration (FDA) total diet study, daily intakes ranged from 2 μg/day for infants, 23 μg/day for toddlers, up to a high of 92 μg/day for 60- to 65-year-old men, and 72 μg/day for 60- to 65-year-old women. Seafood contributed 76 to 90 percent for children (2- to 10-year-olds), 79 to 85 percent for 14- to 16-year-olds, and 89 to 96 percent for adults (≥25- to 30-year-olds); rice/rice cereals contributed 4 to 8 percent for children, 8 percent for 14- to 16-year-olds, and 1 to 4 percent for adults (≥25- to 30-year-olds).

Health Effects

Arsenic is acutely toxic at high doses, but it also has chronic toxicity at lower doses and it is a human carcinogen. Inorganic arsenic compounds (arsenate and arsenite) pose greater risks than the organic forms that predominate in the diet.

Skin, bladder, and lung cancer, as well as keratosis have been identified from exposures to inorganic arsenic at high, hundreds of μg/L, water and dietary exposure levels, e.g., Bangladesh and Taiwan.

In Bangladesh, for many years the World Health Organization (WHO) and others had provided thousands of drinking water wells so that microbiologically contaminated surface waters would not be used. However, unfortunately, it was later discovered that many of the wells were heavily contaminated with natural arsenic sometimes in hundreds of μg/L, resulting in high incidences of cancers in the exposed populations.

A 2013 study found no correlations between total arsenic and inorganic arsenic and total cancer risks in Japan. There was a small correlation between total and inorganic arsenic dietary intake and lung cancer with male smokers. Some studies suggest a possibility of lower birth weights at arsenic concentrations in drinking water, somewhat less than 50 μg/L. A US study of male bladder cancer mortality in 133 counties exclusively using groundwater between 1950 and 1979 found no arsenic-related cancer connection over the range of 3–60 μg/L in the drinking water.

Analysis

Commonly available methods for analyzing arsenic in water include inductively coupled plasma mass spectrometry (ICP-MS; detection limit ~0.1 μg/L) (Environmental Protection Agency [EPA] method 200.8). The older hydride generation atomic absorption and flame atomic absorption (detection limits ~ 1–2 μg/L) have been deleted. The standard methods technique is 3500-As.

There are numerous easy-to-use test kits that allow quick on-site colorimetric measurements that can readily detect amounts below 5 μg/L.

They are particularly useful as a presence–absence test for screening and when monitoring the performance of treatment technology.

Water Treatment

Conventional coagulation can achieve less than 10 μg/L in public water plants using either alum or ferric salts. Co-precipitation with iron or aluminum oxides is also effective. Reverse osmosis (RO) (arsenate > arsenite) and anion exchange processes using iron-based products and activated alumina are very effective. Water softening is effective by sorption if magnesium or iron precipitation occurs, but not with calcite alone.

Point-of-use (POU) technologies are particularly cost-effective in home water well or managed small community-wide water supply applications. Anion exchange, RO, and distillation are available for POU/point-of-entry (POE) applications. POU will be most cost-effective because only a few liters of water will be needed each day for drinking and cooking. Community-supplied bottled water is also a viable approach.

A detailed study of a community-wide POU-decentralized treatment for arsenic removal has demonstrated the methodology and success of the concept.

Regulations

Arsenic had been regulated in the United States at 50 μg/L. This standard was lowered to 10 μg/L in 2001. The predominant impact of the standard has been in 3,000–4,000 small groundwater supplies serving about 11,000,000 people that exceed the maximum contaminant level (MCL). All arsenic pesticide registrations in the United States either have been or are being cancelled. The WHO drinking water guideline is also 10 μg/L. California's public health goal (PHG) is 0.004 μg/L for arsenic in drinking water based on their negligible risk (1/1,000,000) estimate for lifetime extra risk of skin and internal cancers, which seems to be unrealistic. Its MCL is also 10 μg/L. By that logic, the risk at the MCL would be 2,500/million, or 2.5/1,000.

Conclusion

It is possible that the current California's PHG and the EPA MCL and WHO Guidelines for Drinking Water Quality (GDWQ) are unnecessarily conservative. The burden for arsenic treatment is significant in some small groundwater systems in the United States that are the most likely exceeders. Centrally managed (by contract) decentralized POU systems might be the most appropriate technical and economic compliance choice, or even community-supplied bottled water for the small-volume drinking water and cooking uses because of the small volumes required.

Sources

California (2004). Public Health Goals For Chemicals in Drinking Water Arsenic. www.waterboards.ca.gov/waterrights/water_issues/programs/bay_delta/california_waterfix/exhibits/docs/SHR/SHR-25.pdf.

Cotruvo JA (2013). Arsenic. Contaminant of the Month. Water Technology on Line. www.watertechonline.com/contaminant-of-the-month-arsenic/ September, 2013.

EPA (2001). Fact Sheet: Drinking Water Standard for Arsenic. www.epa.gov/lawsregs/rulesregs/sdwa/arsenic/regulations_factsheet.cfm Updated 2012. Accessed February 24, 2018.

EPA (2013). Organic Arsenicals. www.epa.gov/oppsrrd1/reregistration/organic_arsenicals_fs.html. Accessed February 24, 2018.

EPA (2017). Drinking Water Contaminants—Standards and Regulations. www.epa.gov/dwstandardsregulations accessed March 25, 2018.

EPA (2012). Drinking Water Health Advisories. www.epa.gov/sites/production/files/2015-09/documents/dwstandards2012.pdf.

EPA (1994). Method 200.8, Revision 5.4: Determination of Trace Elements in Waters and Wastes by Inductively Coupled Plasma Mass Spectrometry. www.epa.gov/sites/production/files/2015-08/documents/method_200-8_rev_5-4_1994.pdf.

Feasibility of an Economically Sustainable Point-of-Use/Point-of-Entry Decentralized Public Water System. EPA Grant X82952301.

Hopenhayn C. et al (2003). Arsenic exposure from drinking water and birth weight. *Epidemiology.* 14(5): pp. 593–602.

Lamm SH, Engel A, Kruse MB, Feinleib M, Byrd DM, Lai S, Wilson R (2004). Arsenic in drinking water and bladder cancer mortality in the United States: An analysis based on 133 U.S. counties and 30 years of observation (1950–1979). *Journal of Occupational and Environmental Medicine.* 46(3): pp. 298–306.

Longtin JP (1988). EPA National Inorganics and Radionuclides Survey (NIRS).

Sawada N. et al (2013). Dietary arsenic intake and subsequent risk of cancer: The Japan Public Health Center-based Prospective Study. *Cancer Causes Control.* 24(7): pp. 1403–14115.

Standard Methods (2017). Standard Methods for the Examination of Water and Wastewater, 23rd Edition. www.techstreet.com/standards/standard-methods-for-the-examination-of-water-and-wastewater-23rd-edition?sid=msn&utm_medium=cpc&utm_source=bing&product_id=1974889.

Tao SH and Bolger PM (1999). Dietary arsenic intakes in the United States: FDA Total Diet Study, September 1991–December 1996. *Food Additives & Contaminants.* 16(11): pp. 465–472.

WHO (2017). World Health Organization Guidelines for Drinking-Water Quality. www.who.int/water_sanitation_health/publications/drinking-water-quality-guidelines-4-including-1st-addendum/en/.

BARIUM

Introduction

Barium is a soft metal with atomic number 56 and atomic weight 137.34 Da. It has some limited commercial uses in electronics and some alloys. It is reactive so it is never found in nature as a metal, but as salts. It provides the green color in firework displays, and insoluble barium sulfate is used as the contrast medium (barium enema) for gastrointestinal (GI) tract X-ray examinations.

Physical and Chemical Properties

Barium is an alkaline earth metal in the same category as magnesium, calcium, strontium, and radium, so it has very similar chemical properties. It forms Ba^{2+} salts with many anions, and many of the salts such as barium sulfate and barium carbonate have low water solubility. However, barium chloride is 37.4 percent water soluble at 25°C.

Occurrence and Exposure

Barium salts have minimal substantial occurrence in surface waters in the United States and thus negligible exposure potential from surface drinking water supplies. Many groundwaters, e.g., hard waters in the Midwest, have detectable amounts of barium along with calcium and magnesium, and some strontium. However, the overall national occurrence significance in drinking water is small. The United States Geological Survey National Water Quality Assessment Program (USGS NAWQA) studies reported 99.8 percent detections in 523 surface waters, but none exceeded the EPA MCL goal (MCLG)/MCL of 2 mg/L. There were 99.6 percent detections in 6,934 groundwaters, but only 5 (0.1 percent) exceeded 2 mg/L and 1 exceeded 6 mg/L.

Human Health Effects

Barium at sufficiently high exposures could affect blood pressure and therefore potentially cardiovascular disease risk. An epidemiology study found no significant differences in health effects while comparing a community with 7.3 mg/L and another with 0.1 mg/L in the drinking water. An EPA health effects assessment for barium considered relevant toxicity studies including developmental and reproductive toxicity, and it revised the reference dose (RfD) for barium from 0.07 to 0.2 mg/kg/day. The assessment also concluded that barium is not likely to be carcinogenic to humans. EPA also determined that the original 20 percent drinking water relative source contribution (RSC) should be raised to 80 percent which raised the drinking water equivalent level (DWEL) to 7 mg/L. The WHO calculated a tolerable daily intake (TDI; similar to an RfD) of 0.21 mg/kg bw/day, to a $BMDL_{05}$ (benchmark dose, 5 percent) of 63 mg/kg/day for nephropathy in mice in a 2-year study, with a 20 percent drinking water RSC and a safety factor of 300.

During the third Six-Year Review cycle, EPA did not identify any changes in health effects information. Therefore, the RfD of 0.2 mg/kg/day remains the appropriate basis for health protection.

Analytical Methods

Analyses of barium in water can be conducted by atomic absorption spectroscopy (EPA 208.1) and ICP-MS (EPA 200.5) and several others, including several Standard Methods 3500-Ba.

Water Treatment Technology

Barium is readily removed from drinking water using water softening technologies. These include lime and lime soda softening in municipal water plants and cation exchange softening in home water softeners. RO membranes, and possibly nanofiltration, would also be effective because barium is a divalent ion. There is a very widespread use of POE cation exchange water softening in homes in locations that have hard water. Barium would be removed somewhat more effectively than calcium or magnesium.

Regulations and Guidelines

The current drinking water MCL and MCLG for barium remain at 2 mg/L. The WHO Guideline is 1.3 mg/L and the current Canadian Guideline is 1 mg/L, but it may be in revision. The EPA health advisory is 0.7 mg/L for 1-day and 10-day consumption of 1 L/day for a 10-kg child which is inconsistent with the RfD. Based on EPA's calculated 0.2 mg/L RfD and assuming 70 kg body weight and 2 L water intake per day, the DWEL is 7.0 mg/L which with an RSC of 80 percent results in a potential MCLG and MCL of 5.6 mg/L, rounded to 6.0 mg/L. However, EPA surprisingly chose not to reconsider and revise the national drinking water standard upward because it concluded that there would not be significant economic benefit to water suppliers.

Conclusion

Barium is not widely distributed in groundwater drinking water sources at levels of concern. It is usually associated with "hard" groundwaters and easily removed by standard water softening techniques. The current health-based MCL/MCLG, WHO GDWQ, and Canadian Guidelines are much lower than they could be based upon the available toxicology information, however, the potential for noncompliance and the potential health risk from public and private drinking water sources are negligible in virtually all locations in the United States.

Sources

Periodic Table. http://periodic-table-of-elements.org/SOLUBILITY/barium_chloride.

EPA (2016). Chemical Contaminant Summaries for the Third Six-year Review of Existing National Primary Drinking Water Regulations. EPA 810-R-16-004.

EPA (2012). Drinking Water Health Advisories. www.epa.gov/sites/production/files/2015-09/documents/dwstandards2012.pdf.

EPA Analytical Methods. www.epa.gov/dwanalyticalmethods and https://nepis.epa.gov/Exe/ZyPDF.cgi?Dockey=P100PHGZ.txt.

EPA (1994). Method 200.8, Revision 5.4: Determination of Trace Elements in Waters and Wastes by Inductively Coupled Plasma Mass Spectrometry. https://www.epa.gov/sites/production/files/2015-08/documents/method_200-8_rev_5-4_1994.pdf.

Standard Methods (2017). Standard Methods for the Examination of Water and Wastewater, 23rd Edition. www.techstreet.com/standards/standard-methods-for-the-examination-of-water-and-wastewater-23rd-

edition?sid=msn&utm_medium=cpc&utm_source=bing&product_id=1974889.
USGS (2011). National Water Quality Assessment Program. https://water.usgs.gov/nawqa/trace/pubs/sir2011-5059/.
WHO (2017). World Health Organization Guidelines for Drinking-water Quality. www.who.int/water_sanitation_health/publications/drinking-water-quality-guidelines-4-including-1st-addendum/en/.

BORON AND BORATES

Introduction

Boron is an element found in nature primarily as water soluble borates and condensed ions such as borax, sodium tetraborate, $Na_2B_4O_7 \cdot 10H_2O$. Uses are in manufacture of glass, soaps, and detergent components and in flame retardants. Borax is a detergent booster that helps to soften hard water, disperse the detergent, improve rinsing, neutralize odors, provide some disinfection, and improve stain removal. Sodium perborate is stable and used in detergents as a mild oxygen bleaching agent. Production of borosilicate glass for insulation and heat stability are major uses. Boron compounds are essential for plant growth, but higher soil concentrations are herbicidal, and some are also registered pesticides for insects.

Physical and Chemical Properties

Boron's atomic number is 5 and its atomic weight is 10.81 Da. The element exists in several different crystalline forms. Elemental boron is borderline between a metal and nonmetal. Even though it is just above aluminum in the periodic table of elements, its chemistry is more similar to silicon than aluminum. In addition to the various oxygen/boron anions and boric acid, boron forms numerous compounds with other elements like BF_3, BH_3, and more complex borohydrides and boranes, which are reactive with water. Borax begins to lose water of hydration at 75°C and completely at 320°C. Boric acid and borates are soluble in water at roughly 6 percent at 25°C–30°C.

Occurrence and Exposure

Borates are found in the ocean, sedimentary rock, soils, and in desert deposits (e.g., Death Valley). The United States and Turkey are major producers along with Chile and China. Recent US production is about 1.3 million metric tons per year, which is declining. Up to about 4 million metric tons are released to the air from seawater, and about 650,000 metric tons are released from anthropogenic sources. Boron compounds are present in food in fruits, vegetables, dairy, wine, and fish. Estimated daily intake in the United States is from 1 mg/day to about 7 mg/day if wine is included, the average is 1.5 mg/day.

The National Inorganic and Radionuclide Survey of 989 groundwater drinking waters indicated that 4.3 percent of the water supplies exceeded 0.7 mg/L; 1.4 mg/L was exceeded in 1.7 percent of the water systems. Surface water concentrations are generally lower than groundwater's concentrations.

Health Considerations

Boron is suspected to be a trace nutrient in humans. Accidental poisoning has been reported in infants with resulting mild diarrhea and vomiting. The half-life after ingestion in infants is about 8 hours. In adults, the lowest adverse effect level was estimated to be 9.6 mg/kg/day as boron (>672 mg/day) in one study for a 70-kg adult. Acute oral exposure symptoms occurred from 3.68 to 70 mg/kg/day as boron. Long-term exposures in patients being treated ranged as high as 24.8 mg/kg/day as boron. One patient at 5 mg/kg/day as boron for 15 days reported indigestion, anorexia, and dermatitis. The symptoms disappeared when the dose was reduced to 2.5 mg/kg/day. Reproductive studies of residents and workers with high boron exposures did not detect adverse effects. Borate compounds are not mutagenic and they are not considered to be carcinogenic. Some animal studies have shown some reproductive and developmental effects from high-dose exposures of borates.

Analytical Methods

Boron is analyzed by ICP-atomic emission spectrometry (AES) (EPA 200.7), and by Standard Method 4500-B. The method detection limit for boron is 0.003 mg/L (3 ppb). The MDL for the Curcumin Method in Standard Methods is 100–1000 Fg/L, but that is much lower than needed for drinking water analyses.

Water Treatment

Boranes, borohydrides and boron halogen compounds react with water to produce borates. Boron-oxygen anions in water are not significantly removed by conventional treatments such as coagulation/flocculation, sedimentation, and media filtration. Anion exchange and RO may be appropriate. Borates are only partially removed by RO unless the pH is raised, so they are in anionic form. Single-pass RO is effective at achieving concentrations well below 2.4 mg/L in sea water desalination processes. Boric acid concentrations in seawater are reported to be in 26–72 mg/L range depending upon the location and also Standard Methods 3500-B.

Regulations

There is no MCL for US drinking water. EPA calculated 1-day and 10-day health advisories for 10-kg child as B of 3 mg/L. The life-time Health Advisory as B is 6 mg/L. The WHO guideline is 2.4 mg/L as B for a 60-kg adult using slightly different assumptions.

Conclusion

Naturally occurring boron/borate chemicals are not a significant concern in US drinking waters. The principal worldwide issue was associated with the limited performance of single pass seawater desalination using RO membranes because they were not capable of meeting the older WHO GDWQ. Costly two-pass RO was being applied. However, that is no longer necessary as the Guidelines have been revised to higher more scientifically supportable values.

Sources

AWWA (American Water Works Association) (1995). Standard Method (SM) 4500-B B in Standard Methods for the Examination of Water and Wastewater, 19th Edition.

Cotruvo JA, Voutchkov N, Fawell J, Payment P, Cunliffe D, Lattemann S (Eds.) (2010). Desalination Technology: Health and Environmental Impacts. CRC Press and IWA Publishing, Taylor and Francis, K11421, ISBN 978-1-4398-2890-8.

EPA (2008). Drinking Water Health Advisory for Boron. www.epa.gov/waterscience/822-R-08-013.

EPA (2017). Methods Approved to Analyze Drinking Water Samples to Ensure Compliance with Regulations. www.epa.gov/dwanalyticalmethods.

EPA (2012). Drinking Water Health Advisories. www.epa.gov/sites/produciton/files/2015-09/documents/dwstandards2012.pdf.

NIRS (1988). EPA National Inorganics and Radionuclides Survey. In EPA/630/P-03/001B.

Standard Methods (2017). Standard Methods for the Examination of Water and Wastewater, 23rd Edition. www.techstreet.com/standards/standard-methods-for-the-examination-of-water-and-wastewater-23rd-edition?sid=msn&utm_medium=cpc&utm_source=bing&product_id=1974889.

WHO (2017). World Health Organization Guidelines for Drinking-water Quality. www.who.int/water_sanitation_health/publications/drinking-water-quality-guidelines-4-including-1st-addendum/en/4th edition.

BROMATE

Introduction

Bromate is an inorganic an ion, bromate (BrO_3^-) and a member of the oxyhalide group of chemicals that includes hypochlorite (OCl^-), chlorate (ClO_3^-), perchlorate (ClO_4^-), and iodate (IO_3^-), and others. It contains bromine in its highest stable oxidation state +5, so it is an oxidizing agent, especially under acidic conditions. It is found in some treated drinking waters at parts per billion (ppb) levels, from residuals in hypochlorite, and from ozonation of bromide. This ion is tasteless at low concentrations, colorless, and has negligible volatility.

Occurrence

Bromate can be present in drinking water from two principal sources: as a residue in hypochlorite solutions produced by electrolysis of sodium chloride salt that contains some bromide, and as a disinfection by-product (DBP) that forms when bromide ion in water reacts with ozone (O_3): $Br^- + O_3 \rightarrow BrO^-/HOBr \rightarrow \rightarrow BrO_3^-$. Bromate can also form from hypochlorite oxidation of bromide in bright sunlight, e.g., in uncovered finished drinking water reservoirs.

Bromate is generally not formed in chlorinated drinking water from oxidation of bromide because the hypobromite (OBr^-) that is initially formed probably is rapidly reactive with the natural organic carbon that is present to form brominated DBPs like bromoform.

During ozonation of water, the rate and extent of bromate formation depends upon the concentration of ozone used, the bromide ion concentration, ozone-to-TOC-to-bromide ratio, pH and contact time. The reaction rate increases with increasing pH and levels off at about pH 8.8.

Salts of bromate include sodium bromate ($NaBrO_3$) and potassium bromate ($KBrO_3$), both white crystalline substances that readily dissolve in water. Both are used in industrial dyeing processes and hair treatments and were used as dough conditioners. In the latter case, the bromate is decomposed during the baking process, but it has been replaced by other chemicals such as ascorbic acid, as a precaution.

Health Effects

Ingestion of very large amounts of bromate (as in acute poisoning from suicide attempts) causes nausea, diarrhea, vomiting and abdominal pain, as well as effects on the kidneys and nervous system and hearing loss.

Sub-chronic toxicity was examined in Fischer 344 rats in a 13-week study of $KBrO_3$ in drinking water. Histopathology was examined in the kidney, lung, liver, thyroid, and tunica vaginalis. Hyaline droplets were observed in renal tubules at 200 and 400 mg/L, but found in no other organs. The no-observed-effect level (NOEL) was 100 mg/kg/day for $KBrO_3$ (8.1 mg/kg/day); bromate equivalent is 6.2 mg/kg/day.

Bromate is an animal carcinogen from high dose testing, causing oxidative DNA damage and, therefore, is considered to be a potential human carcinogen under appropriate dose conditions. DeAngelo (1998) reported that F344 rats (50 rats per group) were administered potassium bromate at concentrations of 0.02, 0.1, 0.2, and 0.4 g/L in drinking water for up to 100 weeks. Bromate doses were calculated to be 1.1, 6.1, 12.9, and 28.7 mg/kg bw/day. Tumors were observed in the kidney, thyroid, and tunica vaginalis, renal cell tumors, at >0.1 g/L (>100 mg/L $KBrO_3$, 6.1 mg/kg/day bromate), and increased at higher doses.

EPA would classify bromate as a B2 probable human carcinogen based upon the original high dose bioassay studies. The International Agency for Research on Cancer (IARC) concluded that there was inadequate evidence for bromate carcinogenicity in humans. On the other hand, more recent chemical reactivity studies have shown that bromate is rapidly decomposed in simulated stomach acid, and stomach acid, and in blood.

Mode of Action (MOA) biochemical studies *in vivo* in rats determined that bromate was not genotoxic to the rat kidney until dosed at least 2 orders of magnitude greater than drinking water concentrations. The kidney cancers found uniquely in male rat testing are also likely not relevant to human risk, because of the hyaline droplet mechanistic effect, which does not occur in humans at low doses. Bromate is metabolized in the GI tract and liver and blood after ingestion, and it was detected in the rat blood only at very high test doses. According to Bull and Cotruvo (2013) and others, the MOA for bromate at low doses as in drinking water is unlikely to be genotoxic (cause DNA damage and genetic mutations) under lower exposure conditions, therefore, likely not a human cancer risk in drinking water, at least with respect to kidney tumors. At a minimum that would change the risk calculations.

Additional studies are underway to determine the MOA for the thyroid and tunica vaginalis tumors. It is hypothesized that the thyroid tumors in the rat carcinogenicity studies are the result of the bromide concentrations produced from the metabolism to bromide from the high bromate doses. The excess bromide formation would compete with transport of iodide to the thyroid thus disrupting thyroid hormone production. The other tumors are postulated to be a secondary effect of the disruption of thyroid hormone production that may occur.

Analytical Methods

Bromate analyses can be conducted by EPA Method 321.8, Ion Chromatography Inductively Coupled Plasma-Mass Spectroscopy. Standard Methods 4110 D is also a method for bromate and bromide.

Water Treatment

Bromate is difficult to remove from water so it is best controlled by preventing its presence in the source or by preventing its generation during water treatment. For example, chlorine gas does not contain bromate, whereas hypochlorite does. Use of purified hypochlorite with low bromate content and not ozonating water that contains bromide are two management possibilities. Some removal treatments include anion exchange and ammonia impregnated granular-activated carbon (GAC). In bottled water production without intervening RO, precise control of the commonly used ozonation process is strongly recommended. Low bromide salts should be used for any taste enhancement additions. Bromide concentration relative to ozone dose is a good predictor of ozone formation. Bromide can be removed prior to ozonation, but that is also expensive.

Lowering pH to less than 8, adding ammonia or controlling ozone reaction time and the ozone/dissolved organic carbon ratio have been recommended, although these methods can have disadvantages as well.

Regulations

The EPA has set the MCL for bromate in public water systems at 0.010 mg/L (10 ppb; 10 μg/L) and the WHO guideline is also 0.010 mg/L. These were based upon calculations using conservative assumptions about human cancer risks (approximately 1/10,000 per lifetime) at low doses without consideration of metabolic chemical reduction, as well as the less sensitive analytical method capabilities at the time. Analytical methods can now achieve quantitation limits below 1 ppb.

Conclusion

Bromate was not included in the 2016 EPA 6-year review of primary drinking water regulations so the MCL is not yet scheduled for reconsideration. The WHO Guideline will likely be reconsidered based upon the then available toxicology data in 2020–2021 for the fifth edition of the Guidelines for Drinking Water Quality. The postulated low-dose genotoxocity MOA in the regulations appears to be at least partially incorrect. Additional mechanistic studies are underway. Even if the original basis for the EPA MCL regulation is shown to be incorrect, there is a provision in the Safe Drinking Water Act, euphemistically called "antibacksliding," which could make it difficult for EPA to raise the MCL; however, WHO is not constrained and it will make its judgment based upon the data that are available at that time. WHO's fourth edition suggests that emerging evidence indicates metabolism at low doses and that there is evidence for a nonlinear dose response for bromate at low doses. If verified by additional mechanistic studies, that would indicate the possible use of a safety factor approach rather than a hypothetical linear low-dose cancer risk calculation.

Sources

Bull RJ and Cotruvo JA (2013). Nongenotoxic mechanisms involved in bromate-induced cancer in rats. *JAWWA*. 105(12): pp. 47–48.

Bull RJ and Cotruvo JA (2006). A Research strategy to improve risk estimates for bromate in rats. *Toxicology*. 221(2–3): pp. 135–248.

Cotruvo JA, Keith J, Bull RJ, Pacey G, Gordon G (2010). Bromate reduction in simulated gastric juice. *Journal of American Water Works Association*. 102(11): pp. 77–86.

Cotruvo JA (2013). Contaminant of the Month: Bromate. www.watertechonline.com/contaminant-of-the-month-bromate/.

DeAngelo AB, George MH, Kilburn SR, Moore TM, Wolf DC (1998). Carcinogenicity of potassium bromate administered in the drinking water to male B6C3F1 mice and F344/N rats. *Toxicologic Pathology*. 26(5): pp. 587–594.

Dodd D. et al (2013). Subchronic toxicity evaluation of potassium bromate in Fischer 344 rats. *Environmental Toxicology and Pharmacology*. 36(3): pp. 1227–1234.

EPA (1997). Determination of Bromate in Drinking Water by Ion Chromatography Inductively Coupled Plasma-Mass Spectroscopy. www.epa.gov/dwanalyticalmethods/method-3218-determination-bromate-drinking-waters-ion-chromatography.

EPA (2012). Drinking Water Health Advisories. www.epa.gov/sites/produciton/files/2015-09/documents/dwstandards2012.pdf.

EPA (2017). Drinking Water Contaminant Human Health Effects Information. www.epa.gov/dwstandardsregulations/drinking-water-contaminant-human-health-effects-information.

NTP (2007). Toxicology Studies of Sodium Bromate in Genetically Modified (FVB Tg.AC HEMIZYGOUS) Mice and Carcinogenicity Studies of

Sodium Bromate in Genetically Modified (N5) HAPLOINSUFFICIENT] Mice https://ntp.niehs.nih.gov/ntp/htdocs/gmm_rpts/gmm6.pdf.
Standard Methods (2017). Method 4110-D. Standard Methods for the Examination of Water and Wastewater, 23rd Edition. www.techstreet.com/standards/standard-methods-for-the-examination-of-water-and-wastewater-23rd- edition?sid=msn&utm_medium=cpc&utm_source=bing&product_id=1974889.
WHO (2017). World Health Organization Guidelines for Drinking-water Quality. www.who.int/water_sanitation_health/publications/drinking-water-quality-guidelines-4-including-1st-addendum/en/.
Yamaguchi T. et al (2008). Lack of mutagenic and toxic effects of low dose potassium bromate on kidneys in the big blue rat. *Mutation Research.* 652(1): pp. 1–11.

CADMIUM

Introduction

Cadmium is a silvery white metal found in ores in combined forms concurrently with other metals, especially zinc. It is present in plants, rocks, and foods in small amounts and in the air from combustion. There are several cadmium-based pigments in glass, plastics, ceramics, and paints that provide bright yellow, orange, red, and maroon coloring. It also used in nickel-cadmium rechargeable batteries as the anode metal. In electroplating it is a coating on screws and bolts; cadmium telluride is used in solar panels.

Physical and Chemical Properties

Cadmium is in the same chemical family as zinc and they have similar chemical properties, but cadmium is significantly more toxic than zinc. Its atomic number is 48 and its atomic weight is 112.4 Da. The metal's melting point is 321°C (610°F). Its primary oxidation state in salts is +2. Cadmium forms numerous salts, e.g., cadmium chloride, $CdCl_{2,}$ which is soluble in water, and cadmium sulfide, CdS, which is insoluble. Because of their chemical similarities, zinc, including galvanized coatings, often contains small amounts of cadmium.

Occurrence and Exposure

Recent US annual production is about 600 metric tons per year, which is declining. Cadmium oxide is formed and dispersed into the air when fossil fuels and municipal wastes are combusted. Occupational exposure to cadmium mostly by inhalation is significant in many manufacturing activities including metal refining and welding. Sources include phosphate fertilizers, and combustion, and iron and steel, nonferrous metals and cement production. Tobacco is an important source for smokers; 2–4 μg is inhaled by smoking a pack of cigarettes.

Many foods including plants, animal livers, and kidneys contain traces of cadmium. Daily intake from food in the United States and Europe is in the range of 8–30 μg (0.008–0.030 mg/day). Estimates are that food accounts for more than 95 percent of total intake for a nonsmoker, and about 50 percent for a smoker. Some foods like sunflower seeds and shellfish contain elevated cadmium but do not produce elevated blood levels because they probably also contain substances that inhibit uptake, or the cadmium may be bound in forms that are not assimilated. Water is a minor source of exposure; only two of 983 drinking water groundwaters exceeded the 0.005 mg/L (5 ppb) MCL in the 1988 National Inorganics and Radionuclides Survey, and 979 of 983 supplies had less than 0.002 mg/L (2 ppb).

Health Considerations

Cadmium compounds are considered to be carcinogenic by inhalation, but not by ingestion. It is estimated that only 2–6 percent of ingested cadmium is taken up by the body compared to 30–64 percent of inhaled cadmium. The kidney is the general target organ where cadmium accumulates, as well as the lung from inhaled cadmium. Cumulative exposure to cadmium is tracked by its concentration in urine. Irreversible kidney damage occurs from excess acute and chronic exposure, leading to kidney failure and also indirect consequences of kidney damage such as hypertension, muscle weakness, and gout. Most of the epidemiological information on cadmium is from occupational exposure settings and studies in Japan. Itai-itai disease in Japan was associated with cadmium in the 1960s and is one of the frequently cited examples of disease from environmental contamination. It had probably occurred for over 100 years because of uncontrolled mining and manufacturing waste releases in that area.

Analytical Methods

Cadmium is analyzed by ICP-MS (EPA 200.8) as well as by graphite furnace atomic absorption spectrometry (EPA 200.9 or 213.2). Detection levels are low, in the sub-ppb. Cadmium can also be analyzed by ion chromatography. The Standard Methods procedure is 3500-Cd.

Water Treatment

Cadmium is removable by conventional coagulation filtration treatment and lime softening. Cation exchange water softening by POE units and POU RO are also effective.

Regulations

The US drinking water MCL is 0.005 mg/L; the WHO guideline is 0.003 mg/L. The Drinking Water Health Advisories for short-term exposure are 0.040 mg/L for 1- and 10-day exposures and 0.005 mg/L for lifetime exposure. Very few drinking water supplies have been reported to be exceeding the MCL, e.g., one in California.

Conclusion

Cadmium is generally not commonly present in public drinking water supplies at frequencies and levels of concern.

Sources

ATSDR (2011). Cadmium. www.atsdr.cdc.gov/substances/toxsubstance.asp?toxid=15.

Cadmium Exposure and Human Health. www.cadmium.org/index.php.

Cotruvo JA (2015). Water Technology on Line. Cadmium, Contaminant of the Month. February, 2015.

EPA Analytical Methods. www.epa.gov/dwanalyticalmethods.

EPA Basic Information about Cadmium in Drinking Water. http://water.epa.gov/drink/contaminants/basicinformation/cadmium.cfm.

EPA (2017). Drinking Water Contaminant Human Health Effects Information. www.epa.gov/dwstandardsregulations/drinking-water-contaminant-human-health-effects-information.

EPA (2012). Drinking Water Health Advisories. www.epa.gov/sites/production/files/2015-09/documents/dwstandards2012.pdf.

NIRS (1988). EPA National Inorganics and Radionuclides Survey. In EPA/630/P-03/001B.

Scientific World Journal. www.hindawi.com/journals/tswj/2012/729430/.

Standard Methods (2017). Method 3500-CD. Standard Methods for the Examination of Water and Wastewater, 23rd Edition. www.techstreet.com/standards/standard-methods-for-the-examination-of-water-and-wastewater-23rd-edition?sid=msn&utm_medium=cpc&utm_source=bing&product_id=1974889.

World Health Organization Guidelines for Drinking-water Quality (2017). www.who.int/water_sanitation_health/publications/drinking-water-quality-guidelines-4-including-1st-addendum/en/4th edition.

CALCIUM AND CALCIUM SALTS

Introduction

Calcium is called an alkaline earth metal. The name is derivative of the Latin *calx* (lime). It is a ductile and silvery metal and forms numerous Ca^{2+} salts, such as calcium chloride ($CaCl_2$) and calcium carbonate ($CaCO_3$), by losing two electrons. Its atomic number is 20 and its most common form has an atomic weight of 40.08 Da.

Chemistry

Calcium metal is less dense than magnesium metal (1.55 g/cc^3 compared to 1.74 g/cc^3) even though its atomic weight is much greater. Calcium reacts with water to form calcium hydroxide and hydrogen, but it is less reactive than sodium in that regard. It is always found in nature in combined salt form. Calcium salts and their water solutions are colorless, but the salts burn at very high temperatures with an orange-red flame, making the salts useful in fireworks. Calcium is commonly found as calcium carbonate (limestone, marble, chalk), which can be converted to calcium oxide (CaO, lime) by heating (calcining) and loss of carbon dioxide, and then to calcium hydroxide (slaked lime) by controlled water addition. These seemingly simple processes are basic to the applications of lime in water treatment.

Occurrence

Calcium is the fifth most abundant element in the earth's crust at 5 percent, after oxygen, silicon, aluminum, and iron. Mortar is a combination of lime and sand. In water, calcium and magnesium ions are the primary components of "hard water." Calcium in some form is likely present in all natural terrestrial waters. In the National Inorganics and Radionuclides Survey, all of the 989 groundwater drinking water supplies had detectable calcium. Nine of them exceeded 250 mg/L; the maximum was 1,112 mg/L and the average was 49.2 mg/L.

Health Effects

Calcium is a major component in bones and teeth. The mineral component of bone consists mainly of hydroxyapatite ($Ca_{10}(PO_4)_6(OH)_2$), consisting of calcium, phosphorus, hydrogen, and oxygen. A person typically carries about 1,200 g (more than 2.6 lbs.) of calcium. About 99 percent is in the bones and teeth.

Calcium salts have very low toxicity. Calcium carbonate is also used as an acid neutralizer in medicinal antacids. High dietary calcium intake seems to result in reduced risk of kidney stones. Calcium deficiency causes rickets in children and osteoporosis.

Calcium is an important essential dietary mineral and it is present in substantial amounts in dairy products as well as numerous vegetables like kale, soy beans, broccoli, and nuts. Vitamin D3 is involved in the absorption of calcium from the diet, and is therefore important for bone building. Calcium in combination with magnesium, sodium, and potassium is important for cardiac function. The recommended daily intake (RDI) for calcium ranges from about 1,000 mg/day for children to about 1,200 mg/day for adults.

Calcium supplementation can reduce the risk of high blood pressure and preeclampsia in pregnant women. The WHO advises that all pregnant women in areas of low calcium intake (i.e., low-income countries with intakes around 300–600 mg/day) be given supplemental calcium (and magnesium) starting in the 20th week of pregnancy.

There is a long-standing hypothesis that consumption of hard water reduces the risk of cardiovascular mortality. Literally hundreds of correlational studies have reported that benefit in the epidemiological literature. However, more sophisticated analyses have led to the conclusion that if there is a hard water cardiovascular benefit effect, it is most likely due to the presence of magnesium, and not hardness per se.

There is some indication that excess calcium intake (e.g., ~2,000 mg/day) can be harmful. Some recent studies have raised questions about the benefits and risks of consuming high-dose calcium supplements. Results have been mixed with some studies indicating lower risks of some types of cancer, but others indicating slightly higher mortality.

Analytical Methods

The EPA analytical method is 200.7. The Standard Methods procedure is 3500-Ca.

Water Treatment (See "Hard Water" in This Volume)

Water softening is a common practice both in the home and in larger-scale facilities. Precipitative lime softening with calcium hydroxide and lime-soda ash softening are used by municipal water plants that soften. POE softening with a cation exchange resin is a common practice. Cation exchanged softened water is not necessarily aggressive to metal pipe because the total ionic composition remains high. POU RO softening is not a good option in the home. POE RO softening would cause the water to be aggressive toward metal pipe and fixtures.

Regulations

There are no known direct health-based regulations or guidelines for calcium or calcium hardness in drinking water. However, excess hardness can cause heat transfer problems due to calcium carbonate scale with hot water heaters and cooling systems and can interfere with operations and service life.

Conclusion

Drinking water calcium is a beneficial serendipitous source of total calcium intake, because calcium uptake from drinking water and dairy is more efficient than from foods. Consumers of softened water should consider calcium (and magnesium) supplementation in consultation with their physicians unless they have adequate dietary intakes.

Sources

Calcium. Linus Pauling Institute, Oregon State University. http://lpi.oregonstate.edu/mic/minerals/calcium Accessed February 23, 2018.

Cotruvo JA (2013) Contaminant of the Month. Water Technology on Line. January. www.watertechonline.com/contaminant-of-the-month-calcium/.

Cotruvo J and Bartram J (Eds.) (2009). Calcium and Magnesium in Drinking Water: Public Health Significance. World Health Organization, Geneva. Also online at whqlibdoc.who.int/publications/2009/9789241563550_eng.pdf. ISBN 978 92 4 156355 0.

EPA (1994). Method 200.7, Revision 4.4: Determination of Metals and Trace Elements in Water and Wastes by Inductively Coupled Plasma-Atomic Emission Spectrometry. www.epa.gov/sites/production/files/2015-08/documents/method_200-7_rev_4-4_1994.pdf.

NIRS (1988). EPA National Inorganics and Radionuclides Survey. In EPA/630/P-03/001B.

Standard Methods (2017). Standard Methods for the Examination of Water and Wastewater, 23rd Edition. www.techstreet.com/standards/standard-methods-for-the-examination-of-water-and-wastewater-23rd-edition?sid=msn&utm_medium=cpc&utm_source=bing&product_id=1974889.

CHROMIUM AND CHROMIUM VI IN DRINKING WATER

Introduction

Chromium is a transition element, the 21st most abundant element in the earth's crust and widely distributed. It is found in plants, rocks, foods, and animals in small amounts. The two most common forms are Cr(III) and Cr(VI). Chromium VI is a component of chromium stainless steel; Cr(VI) on the steel surface prevents rust formation. Chromium is generally present in the environment from the natural geology in both forms, and also from industrial discharges in some locations. The chromate and dichromate salts are used as pigments and colorants in glazes, paints and in pyrotechnic displays, giving characteristic yellow colors.

Physical and Chemical Properties

Chromium (atomic number 24, atomic weight 51.99 Da) can exist in nine oxidation states; trivalent, Cr(III) (or Cr+3), and hexavalent, Cr(VI) (or Cr+6) are the most common chromium-containing ions found in water and the environment and often as complex anions. Cr(VI) is in the highest oxidation state and soluble in water although usually at low or fractional ppb levels. Chromium forms chromate (CrO_4^{-2}) and dichromate ($Cr_2O_7^{-2}$) anions that are good oxidizing agents, especially in acidic solution. The solubility of chromium compounds varies, depending primarily on the oxidation state. Trivalent chromium compounds, except acetate, chloride, and nitrate salts, are generally insoluble in water, but if present Cr(III) can be oxidized to Cr(VI) by chlorination and ozonation.

The zinc and lead salts of chromic acid have low solubility; calcium and strontium salts are slightly soluble in water. Sodium, potassium, ammonium salts are soluble. Hexavalent chromium compounds are reduced to the trivalent form in the presence of oxidizable organic matter, but hexavalent chromium compounds are more stable when reducing conditions are absent.

Occurrence in Water

A Water Research Foundation funded study of 407 source waters found total chromium at concentrations from <0.2 to 47.1 μg/L. Average and median values were 1.1 μg/L. California geology seems to have unusual concentrations of natural Cr(VI). California reported that 5 percent of its drinking water sources had Cr(VI) at > 10 μg/L. The National Inorganics and Radionuclide Survey measured total chromium above 0.010 mg/L in 8 of 989 groundwater drinking water supplies. The maximum was 0.041 mg/L and the mean of the positives was 0.007 mg/L. EPA's third Unregulated Contaminant Monitoring Rule (UCMR 3) included analyses for total chromium and for Cr(VI). The minimum reporting levels (MRLs) were 0.2 μg/L for total chromium, and 0.03 μg/L for Cr(VI). Interestingly, 3,660 of 4,911 water supplies reported detections of total chromium above its MRL, but 4,401 of 4,919 water supplies reported Cr (VI) exceeding its MRL. In numerous cases, the total chromium value was lower than the Cr(VI) value, causing some interpretation problems.

Health Considerations

Cr(III) is nontoxic and a likely essential nutrient, but that issue is unresolved. In 2001, the NAS Institute of Medicine produced Adequate Intake (AI) recommendations in the range of 20–45 μg/day for Cr(III).

Cr(VI) is rapidly reduced to Cr(III) after ingestion in the reducing conditions of the GI tract. Occupational epidemiological studies have been mixed. A 2010 meta-analysis of 32 occupational studies among highly exposed workers who swallowed chromium salts did not detect increases of GI cancers, as well as a meta-analysis of 49 studies in 2005. A 2015 study of 56 studies concluded that they "suggest" that Cr (VI) is a stomach carcinogen in humans.

Cr(VI) is considered to be an occupational carcinogen by inhalation, although Cole et al. stated that it was a weak cause of lung cancer. Concern about systemic cancers was initiated by a National Toxicology Program (NTP) high-dose ingestion study in rats and mice. There were oral and intestinal cancers at the high doses (rats, 1.4 mg/kg/day), and mice (>2.4 mg/kg/day), but not lower doses. NTP suggested that the differences might be due to exceeding of the animals' natural capacity to reduce Cr(VI) to Cr(III).

Assuming genotoxicity and non-threshold risk models, both California and US EPA carried out hypothetical quantitative risk assessments that arrived at cancer risks at sub-ppb doses; however, both assessments ignored the NTP suggestion and natural chemical reduction processes that spontaneously occur at large doses well above drinking water concentrations.

The American Chemistry Council funded numerous independent mechanistic studies that concluded that Cr(VI) is not carcinogenic at drinking water exposure levels. The data support a non-genotoxic MOA that involves cytotoxicity in the small intestine villi resulting in chronic regenerative hyperplasia, thus, in disagreement with genotoxicity assumptions used in the risk calculations.

Analytical Methods

Total chromium is measurable by ICP-MS (EPA 200.8) as well as by Graphite Furnace Atomic Absorption (EPA 200.9). Detection levels are sub-ppb. CrVI can be analyzed by ion chromatography EPA 218.7 (MRL/detection level 0.02 ppb).

Apparently there are problems with the total chrome analytical method, because it is subject to interferences from carbon and it requires a correction for the carbon, which was not done in the UCMR 3 analyses. The Standard Methods procedure is 3500-Cr.

Water Treatment

Total Chromium and Cr(III) are removable by conventional treatment and lime softening, involving reduction coagulation filtration and strong base anion exchange. Cr(VI) must first be reduced to Cr(III), such as by sulfite, sulfide, or ferrous or stannous salts. Anion exchange is effective since the chromium is in an oxychromium anionic form.

POU and POE technologies are available for removal of chromium in home water supplies by products that have been certified to ANSI/NSF Standards 53, 58, and 62. Current challenges and removals are pegged to the 0.050–0.1 mg/L

Regulations and Guidelines

Cr(VI) has been regulated in drinking water for many years. The original 1946 US Public Health Service chromium standard was 0.050 mg/L (50 μg/L). It conservatively assumed that all of the chromium might be in the VI state. The subsequent USEPA Interim Primary Drinking Water MCL was also 0.050 mg/L, and later raised to 0.100 mg/L in the revised regulations, also assuming Cr(VI). So, it is apparent that CrVI has been regulated in drinking water nationally for at least 72 years.

California has a PHG of 0.02 ppb (0.00002 mg/L) assuming genotoxicity and a non-threshold mechanism, and proposed an MCL of 0.010 mg/L in 2013; however, the regulation was rescinded because the analysis did not examine small systems impact as was required by the California statute.

Conclusion

After reexamination of the toxicology data base and considering the latest toxicology and MOA data, Canada has conservatively issued a draft guideline for comment of 50 ppb (0.050 mg/L) to 100 ppb (0.100 mg/L) for CrVI, using a threshold and safety factor approach rather than low-dose genotoxicity (Moffat et al, 2018). All the parameter options that they examined arrived at drinking water values of 50–100 ppb range. So, considering the MOA, it is extremely unlikely that there is any cancer risk for CrVI at the sub-ppb levels computed in the California risk assessments, or at the current 50–100 ppb MCL levels.

Sources

Canada (2015). Chromium Review Document. www.canada.ca/en/health-canada/programs/chromium-drinking-water/chromium-drinking-water.html.

Cole P and Rodu G (2005). Epidemiologic studies of chrome and cancer mortality: a series of meta-analyses. *Regulatory Toxicology and Pharmacology.* 43(3): pp. 225–231.

Cotruvo JA (2014). Water Technology on Line. Chromium VI. Contaminant of the Month. www.watertechonline.com/contaminant-of-the-month-chromium-vi/.

Cotruvo JA (2013). Tempest in a Chromium Teapot: Is there a health risk from drinking water? Processing. www.processingmagazine.com/tempest-in-a-chromium-teapot/.

Chromium (2015). ATSDR Toxicological Profile. www.atsdr.cdc.gov/toxprofiles/tp7-c4.pdf.

Chromium (2001). *In: Dietary Reference Intakes for Vitamin A, Vitamin K, Arsenic, Boron, Chromium, Iodine, Iron, Manganese, Molybdenum, Nickel, Silicon, Vanadium, and Chromium*. National Academy Press, pp. 197–223.

Eaton A (2017). *Eaton Eurofins Analytical*. Personal Communications.

EPA (1994). Method 200.8, Revision 5.4:Determination of Trace Elements in Waters and Wastes by Inductively Coupled Plasma Mass Spectrometry. www.epa.gov/sites/production/files/2015-08/documents/method_200-8_rev_5-4_1994.pdf.

EPA (1994). Method 200.9, Revision 2.2: Determination of Trace Elements by Stabilized Temperature Graphic Furnace Atomic Absorption. www.epa.gov/sites/production/files/2015-08/documents/method_200-9_rev_2-2_1994.pdf.

EPA (2011). Method 218.7: Determination of Hexavalent Chromium in Drinking Water by Ion Chromatography with Post-Column Derivatization and UV-Visible Spectroscopic Detection. EPA 815-R-11–005.

Gatto NM. et al (2010). Occupational exposure to hexavalent chromium and cancers of the gastrointestinal tract: A meta-analysis. *Cancer Epidemiology*. 34(4): pp. 388–399.

McNeill L. et al (2013). *Trace Level Hexavalent Chromium. Occurrence and Analysis*. Water Research Foundation, Denver, CO (Project No. 4404).

Moffat I, Martinova N, Seidel C, Thompson CM (2018). Hexavalent Chromium in Drinking Water. *JAWWA*, 110:5, p. 35.

NIRS (1988). EPA National Inorganics and Radionuclides Survey. In EPA/630/P-03/001B.

NTP (2008). NTP technical report of the toxicology and carcinogenesis of sodium dichromate dihydrate (CAS No. 7789-12-0) in F344/N rats and B6C3F1 mice (drinking water studies). (NTP TR 546). Available at: http://ntp.niehs.nih.gov/ntp/htdocs/LT_rpts/tr546.pdf.

Standard Methods (2017). Standard Methods for the Examination of Water and Wastewater, 23rd Edition. www.techstreet.com/standards/standard-methods-for-the-examination-of-water-and-wastewater-23rd-edition?sid=msn&utm_medium=cpc&utm_source=bing&product_id=1974889.

Welling R. et al (2015) Chromium VI and stomach cancer: a meta-analysis of the current epidemiological evidence. *Occupational and Environmental Medicine*. 72: pp. 151–159. http://asrg.berkeley.edu/Index_files/Publications_PDF/Welling%202015%20Chromium%20OEM.pdf.

COPPER

Introduction

Copper is a soft, ductile, and reddish metal found widely in nature as salts such as chlorides, sulfides, and arsenides, but also as elemental copper. It has many uses in plumbing, electrical wiring, and in alloys. Copper has herbicidal properties and it is an essential nutrient in humans.

Physical and Chemical Properties

Copper forms Cu^{1+}, Cu^{2+}, and Cu^{3+} compounds with the first two being most common. Its atomic weight is 63.54 Da and its atomic number is 29. It is a transition metal; even though it has +1 and +2 oxidation states, its chemistry is quite different from the alkali metals (e.g., sodium) and alkaline earth metals (e.g., calcium). The metal has multiple uses and oxidizes in air to a green patina.

Copper pigments have several colors depending upon the associated groups and ions, and oxidation states. They include blue (Egyptian Blue, Han Blue, Azurite), purple (Han Purple), and red hair color dye shades are copper based. The metal is widely used in electrical wiring where its conductivity is second only to silver. Its principal uses in the water context are in copper pipe but also in copper/zinc alloy brass fittings.

Occurrence and Exposure

Copper is commonly detected in virtually all drinking water sources as well as in drinking water at the tap. The concentrations range from less than a few tenths mg/L, but it can easily exceed 1 mg/L if the water is corrosive. The higher concentrations are usually caused by the action of some waters on a copper pipe or brass fixtures, if the corrosivity is not controlled. This occurs if the water is acidic or in high carbonate waters with alkaline pH.

Excess copper can impart a metallic taste to drinking water. The taste threshold for copper sulfate and copper chloride in tap water is reported as 2.6 mg/L Cu, and 2.4 and 2.5 mg/L for distilled deionized water. It was 3.5–3.8 mg/L in uncarbonated (still) mineral water, which could occur in some domestic well waters. The National Inorganics and Radionuclides Survey measured copper above 1 mg/L in 7 of 989 groundwater drinking water supplies. The maximum was 2.37 mg/L and the mean of the positives was 0.063 mg/L.

Copper is commonly present in many foods. The median intake of copper from food in the United States is approximately 1.0–1.6 mg/day for adult men and women. Some foods with substantial concentrations include: beef liver (4.1 mg/ounce), seafood (from 0.2 to 0.3 mg/ounce), various nuts (from 0.3 to 0.6 mg/ounce), chocolate (0.2 mg/ounce), and seeds, wheat, kale, and mushrooms.

Copper has biocidal properties, copper sulfate is used as an algaecide in source waters, and other copper compounds are used as fungicides and in wood preservatives. It has been considered a water disinfectant or bacteriostat since at least

400B.C., but it is slow acting. Copper/silver ionization systems are used for controlling *legionella* in plumbing. Some microorganisms can develop resistance to metal toxicity.

Health Considerations

Copper is an essential dietary micronutrient important for functioning of numerous proteins and metalloenzymes that involve growth, bone, brain and heart maintenance, red cell formation, iron absorption as well as cholesterol and glucose metabolism. Recommended dietary allowances (RDAs) from the NAS Institute of Medicine to prevent deficiency range from 0.2 mg/day for infants to 0.34 mg/day for toddlers, 0.7 mg/day 9–13 years, 0.9 mg/day for 19 year and adults, with somewhat higher levels for pregnancy and breast-feeding. The median intake of copper from food in the United States is approximately 1.0–1.6 mg/day for adult men and women. Mineral supplements typically contain 0.9–2 mg of copper. The Tolerable Upper Intake Level (UL) for adults is 10,000 μg/day (10 mg/day), a value based on protection from liver damage as the critical adverse effect.

About 30–40 percent of dietary copper is absorbed in the GI tract with water uptake being more efficient than from foods. Copper is very toxic at doses approaching 5 mg/kg body weight/day, and the absorption plateau occurs at about 100 μg/kg/day. AI ranges about 11–34, and 8.5 μg/kg/day is considered to be deficient. Deficiency is not common but it can occur in severe malnutrition as well as from some genetic conditions that can be causal. Wilson's and Menkes are among several rare hereditary genetic diseases that involve the inability to appropriately manage and use copper. The incidence of Wilson's disease is one per 30,000 births and is now treatable; Menkes incidence is about one per 200,000 and is fatal.

The MCLG is 1.3 mg/L but it is based marginally on GI upset which is an individual matter and subject to dose rate and also whether the water ingestion is in combination with food consumption which would mitigate an effect, and with acidic fruit juices which might exacerbate the effect.

Analytical Methods

Copper is analyzed by ICP-MS (EPA 200.8) as well as by graphite furnace atomic absorption (EPA 200.9). Detection levels are low ppb to sub-ppb. There are also numerous test kits for copper in water that are fast and low in cost per test. The Standard Methods analytical method is 3500-Cu.

Water Treatment

Aggressive water acting on copper plumbing can produce blue water in extreme cases, and pipe pitting can also occur. Copper corrosion is often associated with soft acidic waters (pH less than 6.5), and calcium carbonate hardness less than 60 mg/L. Hot water systems are more vulnerable. Copper corrosion is also often associated with hard groundwaters with carbon dioxide above 5 mg/L and high dissolved oxygen. Langlier and Ryzner indices are not necessarily good indicators of copper corrosion. Raising pH to 8–8.5 will usually overcome the problem. Copper should be controllable by pH and alkalinity adjustment for corrosion control if the source is copper pipe corrosion. Treatment techniques include municipal softening with lime or lime soda. In home treatment include POE cation exchange water softening and POU RO.

Regulations and Guidelines

The primary MCLG is 1.3 mg/L and the action level in the Lead and Copper Rule treatment technique is 1.3 mg/L. The US drinking water Secondary MCL (SMCL) is 1 mg/L; the WHO guideline is 2 mg/L. Both are based upon taste and potential gastric upset, which can occur at a few mg/L and are probably mitigated by food and exacerbated by consumption in acidic juices.

The Lead and Copper Rule in the United States uses the measurement of lead and copper in a 1 L, overnight, first-draw stagnant water sample as indicative of excessive corrosivity of the water. The action level (not MCL) for copper is 1.3 mg/L and lead is 0.015 mg/L.

Conclusions

Copper is not a significant health risk in drinking water. There are standards and guidelines that address copper as an indicator of excessive water corrosivity affecting copper pipe that should be corrected, as well as aesthetic taste concerns.

Sources

Cotruvo JA (2015). Copper. Water Technology on Line. www.watertechonline.com/contaminant-of-the-month-copper/.

EPA (1994). Method 200.8, Revision 5.4: Determination of Trace Elements in Waters and Wastes by Inductively Coupled Plasma Mass Spectrometry. www.epa.gov/sites/production/files/2015-08/documents/method_200-8_rev_5-4_1994.pdf.

EPA (2015). Method 200.9: Determination of Trace Elements in Waters—US EPA www.epa.gov/sites/production/files/2015-08/.

Krishnamoorthy L, Cotruvo JA Jr, Chan J. et al (2016). Copper regulates cyclic-AMP-dependent lipolysis. *Nature Chemical Biology*. 12(8): pp. 586–92.

Linus Pauling Institute. Lpi.oregonstate.edu/mic/minerals/copper.

List of Inorganic Pigments. En.wkipedia.org/wiki/List_of_inorganic_pigments.

National Academy of Sciences/Institute of Medicine. DRI Nutrient Reports. www.nal.usda.gov/fnic/dri-nutrient-reports.

National Institutes of Health Determinants of Copper Needs Across the Life Span. Ods.od.nih.gov/News/Copper.aspx.

NIRS (1988). EPA National Inorganics and Radionuclides Survey. In EPA/630/P-03/001B.

Standard Methods (2017). Standard Methods for the Examination of Water and Wastewater, 23rd Edition. www.techstreet.com/standards/

standard-methods-for-the-examination-of-water-and-wastewater-23rd-edition?sid=msn&utm_medium=cpc&utm_source=bing&product_id=1974889.
WHO (2017). World Health Organization Guidelines for Drinking-water Quality. www.who.int/water_sanitation_health/publications/drinking-water-quality-guidelines-4-including-1st-addendum/en/4th edition.
Zacarias I. et al (2001). Determination of the taste threshold of copper in water. *Chemical Senses*. 26(1): pp. 85–89. www.researchgate.net/publication/31327462_Determination_of_the_Taste_Threshold_of_Copper_in_Water.

FLUORIDE AND FLUORIDATION OF DRINKING WATER

Fluorine is the most active halogen chemical and element 9 in the periodic table. Fluoride is its anion with a charge of –1. Fluoride is ubiquitous in the environment in water, rocks, plants, and animals in small amounts. It deposits in bone and in teeth as the fluorapatite mineral $Ca_5(PO_4)_3F$—a very hard crystalline compound where the OH group in mineral apatite has been replaced by an F atom. Many types of toothpaste are fluoridated with sodium fluoride or stannous (tin II) fluoride.

What Is the Fluoride/Fluoridation Issue?

Beginning in 1941, tooth decay studies in several Midwestern communities noted reduced incidence of dental caries when higher levels of fluoride were present in their drinking water. Many communities began to add fluoride to their drinking waters at about 1 ppm, either as sodium fluoride or fluosilicic acid. Some have argued that fluosilicic acid which is stable at very low pH has not been tested for chronic toxicity. That is not possible because fluosilic acid rapidly hydrolyses 100 percent to fluoride and silicate at drinking water pH, so a test of fluosilic acid would be a fluoride test.

Numerous dental organizations advocate controlled fluoridation of drinking water; some states require fluoridation of water, and others have it as a community option. By statute, the federal government cannot require the addition of fluoride to drinking water for therapeutic purposes. However, governmental organizations such as the Centers for Disease Control and Prevention (CDC) and the National Institute for Dental Research (NIDR) advocate its addition to reduce tooth decay in children.

Some advocacy groups have consistently opposed drinking water fluoridation as an involuntary medication, a possible health risk and unnecessary because dental decay rates have been dropping even in non-fluoridated communities.

Health Considerations

Excessive natural fluoride in some world drinking water sources can cause crippling skeletal fluorosis or osteomalacia, which are serious bone and joint malformations. Drinking water levels on the order of 1 or 2–4 mg/L can cause dental fluorosis ranging from very mild purely aesthetic, to moderate to severe with dark staining and brittle teeth, depending upon the amount of water consumed daily, which is affected by climate, as well as total fluoride intake from all sources. Fluoride has been tested in animals extensively without significant negative outcomes that could be associated with low ppm exposures as in regulated drinking water. The cancer bioassay in rats and mice showed no increased cancer risk, but some equivocal evidence. Therapeutic high doses of fluoride have been used in osteoporosis treatment, however beneficial effects have been marginal and sometimes increased risk of bone fracture was noted.

There are numerous independent Cochrane studies addressing fluoride and its effects on dental caries. Their general conclusions are that brushing with fluoridated toothpaste, consumption of fluoridated water or milk, and topical dental fluoride treatments are effective in reducing children's tooth decay. One of their studies concluded, however, that the supportive epidemiological studies on fluoridated water were usually not well designed.

Analytical Methods

Fluoride can be analyzed by ion selective electrodes and ion chromatography. EPA Methods 300.0 Rev 2.1 and 300.1 Rev 1.0 are approved. Methods 340.1, 340.2 and 340.3 have been deleted. The Standard Methods procedure is 4500 F C, along with several others.

Water Treatment

Fluoride can be removed from water by lime precipitation, anion exchange with activated alumina, bone char and RO. Activated alumina and RO are available POU methods.

National Fluoridation Trends

Fluoridation is widely practiced around the world but some countries such as Sweden, Holland and Czech Republic, have banned it. The Israeli Health Minister had announced a ban a few years ago, but the then current Prime Minister had endorsed fluoridation when he was health minister and advocated for a community option.

Regulations and Guidelines

The National Primary Drinking Water Regulation MCL for total fluoride is 4 mg/L; the aesthetic (mild dental fluorosis) Secondary (SMCL) regulation is 2 mg/L. The WHO Guideline is 1.5 mg/L, which should be adjusted relative to local climate and water consumption. The CDC and EPA recommend that practiced fluoridation should be at 0.7 mg/L to minimize mild dental fluorosis while maintaining dental benefits.

Conclusions

Fluoride is an effective contributing factor for reducing dental caries. Fluoridation of drinking water is still debated by some who claim health risks without benefits, but most public health authorities support it because of the benefits of reduced tooth decay among children, especially among lower income groups who do not receive regular dental care, or do not regularly use fluoridated toothpaste. Regulated drinking water fluoridation does not produce adverse health effects. The current recommended balanced recommendation for fluoridation is at 0.7 mg/L as the optimal value for dental benefits with minimal potential for mild dental fluorosis, which in itself is not a significant aesthetic or heath effect.

The impact of the regulations is predominantly in small communities using groundwaters that happen to have excessive fluoride because of geological conditions. Those communities typically are not capable of funding or operating defluoridation treatment technology in their water supplies. The most practical and rational approach for them would likely be providing bottled water for children during the years when their teeth are being formed so that the teeth will not be fluorosed when they erupt.

Sources

Cochrane (2015). Fluoridated Milk for Preventing Tooth Decay. www.cochrane.org/CD003876/ORAL_fluoridated-milk-preventing-tooth-decay.

Cochrane (2015). Water Fluoridation to Prevent Tooth Decay. www.cochrane.org/CD010856/ORAL_water-fluoridation-prevent-tooth-decay.

Cotruvo JA (2014). Fluoride and Fluoridation. www.watertechonline.com/contaminant-of-the-month-fluoride-and-fluoridation/.

EPA Drinking Water Contaminants- Regulations. www.epa.gov/dwstandardsregulations.

EPA (2011). Fluoride Risk Assessment and Relative Source Contribution. www.epa.gov/dwstandardsregulations/fluoride-risk-assessment-and-relative-source-contribution.

EPA (1993). Fluoride. Methods for the Determination of Inorganic Substances in Environmental Samples. EPA/600/R-93/100.

EPA (2000). Fluoride. Methods for the Determination of Organic and Inorganic Substances in Environmental Samples. EPA 815-R-00–014.

Finney WF, Wilson E, Callender A, Morris MD, Beck LW (2006). Reexamination of hexafluorosilicate hydrolysis by ^{19}F NMR and pH measurement. *Environmental Science and Technology*. 40(8): pp. 2572–2577.

Haneke et al (2001). Sodium Hexafluorosilicate [CASRN 16893-85-9] and Fluorosilicic Acid [CASRN 16961-83-4] Review of Toxicological Literature" (PDF). ntp.niehs.nih.gov. Accessed March 3, 2018.

Jerusalem Post (2014). www.jpost.com/Israel-News/Health-Minister-German-outlaws-fluoridation-of-all-tap-water-371332. Accessed March 3, 2014.

Standard Methods (2017). Standard Methods for the Examination of Water and Wastewater, 23rd Edition. www.techstreet.com/standards/standard-methods-for-the-examination-of-water-and-wastewater-23rd-edition?sid=msn&utm_medium=cpc&utm_source=bing&product_id=1974889.

WHO (2017). World Health Organization Guidelines for Drinking-water Quality. www.who.int/water_sanitation_health/publications/drinking-water-quality-guidelines-4-including-1st-addendum/en/4th edition.

IODINE, IODIDE, AND IODATE

Introduction

The element I_2 is a black crystalline solid, but its vapors are violet and solutions are brown to purple. It is reactive and found in nature in brines as iodides and iodates. It forms a blue complex with starch. Iodine has been used as a water disinfectant and as a biocide as tincture of iodine in medical applications.

Physical and Chemical Properties

Iodine is a halogen element in the same series as fluorine, chlorine, and bromine. Its atomic number is 53, and its atomic weight is 127 Da. It has several synthetic isotopes including some that are radioactive with short half-lives.

Iodine reacts with water under basic conditions to produce hypoiodous acid (HOI) which is chemically reactive. Iodine is easily oxidized to form numerous oxyanions, including hypoiodite (OI^-), iodate (IO_3^-), and periodate (IO_4^-) at basic pH. It also forms complexes such as I_3^- and I_5^- Neutral and reactive I_2O_4, I_2O_5, and I_4O_9 are also among the oxide products.

The melting point of iodine is 113.5°C (236.3°F) and its boiling point is 184°C (363.2), and its density is 4.93 g/cc. Iodide and iodate are very soluble in water. Iodine is a nonmetal, but its chemistry is very complex forming many products in several oxidation states. It also displays some metallic properties.

Iodine is chemically similar to chlorine and bromine, but much less reactive as an oxidizer, but it is reactive with many organic molecules to form iodoorganic compounds. Iodide (I^-) is an excellent reducing agent. Like the other halogen-oxygen ions, hypoiodite disproportionates (reacts with itself by oxidation-reduction) to produce iodide and iodate.

Occurrence and Exposure

As an essential nutrient, dairy, seafood, and some algae are excellent dietary sources of iodine, but grains and other food sources depend on the iodine levels of soil in which they are grown. Iodine forms have very low occurrence in drinking water. Seawater averages about 1 mg/L whereas surface freshwaters have much less iodine content. Some localized groundwaters can have microgram to low milligram per liter concentrations of iodides and some other forms.

DBPs

Chlorination and chloramination and other oxidant disinfectants produce iodinated DBPs when iodide is present. Iodinated trihalomethanes and haloacetic acids and others have been occasionally detected at parts per trillion or low ppb levels in disinfected waters. Some are chemically and biologically active or are cytotoxic in cell culture testing, but interpretations of *in vitro* activity are problematic when trying to interpret *in vivo* effects. Iodoform (CHI_3) has been tested by the NTP and found not to be carcinogenic. Potential human risk from exposures to trace levels of iodinated DBPs has not been determined, but iodo compounds are labile, meaning that the iodine atom is readily transferred between molecules.

Health Considerations

Iodine is an essential nutrient that is toxic, but only at high doses. Iodide or iodate are provided in nutritional supplement tablets to compliment inadequate dietary intake, and used to treat hypothyroidism. Thyroid hormones, triiodothyroxine (T_3), and thyroxine (T_4) are important in protein synthesis, enzymatic activity and metabolism, as well as for neurological and skeletal development in fetuses and infants. Dietary iodide is transported in the blood stream to the thyroid by the NIS (sodium iodide symporter protein). Many other common anions such as perchlorate, bromate, bromide, thiocyanate, and nitrate are also transported competitively by the same transporter. Inadequate iodine intake can result in thyroid hormone deficiency, and goiter, so it is essential that there be sufficient iodine daily consumption of iodine species to compensate.

Adequate iodine intake is critical for pregnant women and infants. Recommended daily intakes (RDIs) range from about 100 to 150 μg/day for young children to adults, 220 μg/day during pregnancy, and 290 μg/day during lactation. A healthy adult stores about 15–20 mg of iodine, mostly in the thyroid. The tolerable UL for adults is 1,100 μg/day (1.1 mg/day), based on serum thyroptropin concentration in response to varying levels of ingested iodine.

Iodized (as iodate) table salt was introduced in the United States in 1924 to reduce the risk of goiter (hypothyroidism), but people are consuming less iodized salt now, partly because some cooking fads and chefs suggest use of seasoning salts that are not iodized, ostensibly for taste reasons.

Iodine chemicals have many commercial and medical uses as biocides. Tincture of iodine is a topical treatment for small cuts. Providone/Betadine is iodine complexes with polyvinylpyrrolidone in a solution used as surgical scrubs and surface swab disinfectants.

Iodine contrast media (iodophors), such as iopamidol, are used in some X-ray diagnoses.

Radioactive iodine (I-131) is released during nuclear plant accidents. It is also used in some medical diagnostic applications. Its half-life is about eight days. Potassium iodide tablets are temporary thyroid protecting agents. The thyroid becomes saturated with iodide, and the radioactive iodine uptake by the thyroid is reduced, thus reducing the risk of thyroid cancer, while the radioactive iodine is decomposing in its short half-life.

The WHO and government health agencies recommend use of several iodine products for water disinfection in traveling and emergency situations. See pp. 108–111 in the WHO 2011 GDWQ. Long-term high level exposures are discouraged because excess iodine can also have thyroid toxicity problems; however, these are generally reversible when the exposure is reduced. There are many world locations with significant iodine dietary deficiency resulting in neurological deficits.

Analytical Methods

There are numerous analytical methods for several iodine species. They include catalytic reduction photometric (<80 μg/L) and leucocrystal violet methods (>50 μg/L) are used in water analyses, as well as inductively couple plasma emission spectrometry (<1 μg/L), and ion chromatography (MDL 7.58 μg/L. Iodometric methods are used in chlorine analyses. The EPA published methods for iodine and iodine include 300 320.1 although iodine is not regulated. Standard Methods are: iodide, 4500-I; iodide, 4500-I^-, and iodate, 4500-IO_3^-.

Water Treatment

Removal of iodine from drinking water is not practiced. The iodine species in water are dependent on pH and vary in disinfection efficacy when used as temporary use biocides in contaminated drinking waters.

Iodine is used in some POU and POE treatment systems for water disinfection. These are regulated in the United States as pesticides or pesticidal devices.

Regulations and Guidelines

Iodine species and iodinated organics are not currently regulated, and their future regulatory status is unknown. Perchlorate is regulated in a few US states because it competes with iodide for transport to the thyroid, and EPA has been considering possible perchlorate regulation for many years. However, sufficient iodine intake compensates for perchlorate exposure. The WHO has not established a drinking water guideline value for iodine in water, because of questions about potential thyroid risks from long-term use beyond emergencies and excessive exposures.

Conclusions

Iodine species are not regulated in drinking water. Iodinated DBPs can be formed in very small amounts when drinking water containing iodide is disinfected. Iodine is an essential nutrient and there are very large populations in the world including parts of the United States where insufficient iodine is being consumed from the diet, and many people are not consuming iodized salt. There are detectable risks to pregnant women and fetuses/infants due to inadequate thyroid hormone production. The adverse effects are manifested in impaired neurological development as well as thyroid deficiency toxicology. In many countries, pregnant women are routinely advised to take iodine supplements. The WHO recommends iodine as an interim water disinfectant in emergencies. While WHO acknowledges that very large world populations in some areas are seriously deficient in iodine intake it has not established recommended upper value in drinking water. On balance, controlled iodination of drinking water or iodination of bottled water might be worthy of consideration in those seriously deficient areas where adverse effects are being observed.

Sources

Cotruvo JA (2016). Iodine, Iodide, Iodate. Water Technology on Line. www.watertechonline.com/contaminant-of-the-month-iodine-iodide-iodate/. Accessed February 25, 2018.

Cotruvo JA (2015). Perchlorate in US drinking water: Is a federal regulation needed to protect public health? *Journal American Water Works Association*. 107(6): pp. 66–71. www.awwa.org/publications/journal-awwa/abstract/articleid/52991491.aspx.

EPA/CDPR (2012). Iodine by Ion Chromatography. www.cdpr.ca.gov/docs/emon/pubs/anl_methds/iodide_by_ion_chromatography.pdf.

Iodine by ICP-MS (2012). EPA Method 300. www.cdpr.ca.gov/docs/emon/pubs/anl_methds/total_iodine_by_icp.pdf.

NAS (2001). *Institute of Medicine, Food and Nutrition Board. Dietary Reference Intakes: Vitamin A, Vitamin K, Arsenic, Boron, Chromium, Copper, Iodine, Iron, Manganese, Molybdenum, Nickel, Silicon, Vanadium, and Zinc.* National Academy Press, Washington, D.C. www.nap.edu/read/10026/chapter/10.

NIH Fact sheet. Iodine (2011). Office of Dietary Supplements. https://ods.od.nih.gov/factsheets/Iodine-HealthProfessional/.

Standard Methods (2017). Standard Methods for the Examination of Water and Wastewater, 23rd Edition. www.techstreet.com/standards/standard-methods-for-the-examination-of-water-and-wastewater-23rd-edition?sid=msn&utm_medium=cpc&utm_source=bing&product_id=1974889.

Trace Elements: Iodine Centers for Disease Control. www.cdc.gov/nutritionreport/99-02/pdf/nr_ch4a.pdf. Accessed February 25, 2018.

WHO (2017). World Health Organization Guidelines for Drinking-water Quality. www.who.int/water_sanitation_health/publications/drinking-water-quality-guidelines-4-including-1st-addendum/en/.

LEAD IN WATER AND FLINT, MICHIGAN

Introduction

Lead has been known to have adverse toxic and neurodevelopmental effects for at least hundreds of years. Lead has many commercial uses including its applications in lead acid batteries, ceramic glazes, ammunition, leaded glass crystal, brass, and solders for electrical equipment. Formerly it was widely used in leaded red and white paint, canned-food container solders, auto radiator solders, production of tetraethyl lead gasoline additive, and in drinking water pipe and solders. Lead acetate was used as a wine sweetener in Roman times. Occupational exposures have been linked to serious and fatal effects. Leaded gasoline and lead paint have been the dominant sources of significant exposures to the general population. Lead service lines and some other plumbing components are known to contribute lead to drinking water if the water is corrosive. Lead has been regulated in drinking water by the US Public Health Service since at least 1946 and by USEPA since 1975, and banned from new US installations since 1986.

Chemistry

Lead is a naturally occurring malleable, dense, and blue-gray metal. Its atomic number (number of protons in the nucleus) is 82 and its atomic weight (average number of protons plus neutrons) is 207.19 Da. The chemical symbol for lead is Pb from the Latin *plumbum*, from which the word plumber was derived. As long ago as Roman times, it was used in water pipes and conduits because of its ease of manufacture and long-term stability.

Lead is widely distributed and occurs as both the metal and many lead salts, for example, lead carbonate and numerous oxides. The principal oxidation states are +2 (PbO) and+4 (PbO_2). Galena is a common lead sulfide ore. There are four stable isotopes of lead that result from decay of radioactive uranium and thorium. It is possible to determine the geological age of rocks from the relative concentrations of the various radionuclides in the decay series and lead. Typical lead concentrations in natural water and treated drinking water at the treatment plant are in the low ppb to below detection range. In the National Inorganics and Radonuclides Survey, 24 of 982 groundwater drinking water supplies exceeded 0.010 mg/L, 16 exceeded 0.015 mg/L.

Organically bound lead (i.e., tetraethyl lead) at one time was widely used as an octane booster additive for automobile gasoline. Most leaded paint use has been banned in the United States since 1978, but road paints may still contain it. Some aviation gasolines may also contain lead. US houses built before 1978 might have lead paint indoors or outdoors, and mitigation is required when it is detected in commercial or residential rental properties.

Health Concerns

Lead is a toxic heavy metal with a half-life in blood of about 30 days. What is not excreted is ultimately deposited in bone, where it can be re-mobilized during pregnancy or aging, or due to calcium dietary deficiency. The principal environmental exposure risk concern is neurotoxicity especially in infants and young children. Consumption of lead paint, often due to pica, and inhalation of lead paint dust are high-dose routes of exposure and major lead toxicity concerns for young children especially in old housing.

The US CDC recommends that lead poisoning requiring chelation therapy be considered if blood lead levels exceed 45 μg/dL (μg per 100 cc (deciliter) of blood. Developmental mental deficits can occur at considerably lower concentrations.

Average lead blood levels in US children have drastically declined in the past 30–40 years, primarily from the elimination of leaded automobile gasoline. Lead has also been eliminated from lead can and water pipe solders, and only low lead brass is now permitted in water fixtures. According to the Second National Health and Nutrition Examination Survey (NHANES II), between 1976 and 1980, average blood lead levels in children from ages 6 months to 5 years in the United States were about 16 μg/dL; 63.3 percent were in the 10–19 μg/dL range, and 0.1 percent was in the 50–59 μg/dL range. Older persons in the 1976–1980 NHANES II study were found to have mean blood lead levels as follows: 6–17 years—12.5 μg/dL and

18–74 years—14.2 μg/dL. The national mean values had declined to 2.7 μg/dL by 1991, and 1.9 μg/dL by 2002. The mean in 2018 is close to 1 μg/dL for the young age group. The CDC established "reference level" based upon the 97.5th percentile concentration for children is now 5 μg/dL, in which case of exceeders, follow-up action is recommended to determine and eliminate the cause. As of 2017, about 2.5 percent of 1- to 5-year-olds exceeded 5 μg/dL. Subtle, but potentially reversible IQ losses are suspected to occur at levels about 5–10 μg/dL or perhaps less as indicated by some studies. Some have suggested that subtle effects can be mitigated by providing a more enriched social and educational environment for the child.

Most of the blood lead levels that were found during the earlier time are probably attributed to use of leaded gasoline fuel, because the blood levels declined rapidly as leaded gasoline was phased out due to the introduction of catalytic converters for automobiles. A likely cause of very high blood lead levels was and is probably living in old housing that contain lead painted surfaces and also perhaps unmanaged dust deposition in the homes. Old galvanized iron pipe and old lead service lines might also be contributors. Renovations of older houses can cause significant blood lead increases in resident children through dust inhalation and pica (ingesting dust and dirt particles) from sanding and paint removals without proper air management and mitigation.

Water Lead Issues

The principal sources of exposure to lead from drinking water are due to the effects of corrosive water on leaded brass faucets, old lead service lines, old galvanized iron pipe, and old leaded pipe joint solders. Galvanized water pipe has been shown to accumulate lead, probably on iron oxide sediments, and significant lead water levels are reached when they are mobilized. Studies in Washington, DC, demonstrated a very strong correlation between high stagnant water lead rule compliance measurements and iron concentrations, and the presence of old galvanized iron pipe in older homes.

Lead can be leached into drinking water by dissolution, but lead particulates (probably mostly insoluble salts) may also be released. Corrective actions usually involve pH or alkalinity adjustments and they might use orthophosphates or silicates to reduce the corrosiveness of the water. If that is insufficient, replacement of lead service lines is required by the Lead and Copper Regulation.

There is a debate on the long-term consequences of partial service line replacement, i.e., when the public segment from the meter to the water main is replaced, but not the private segment from the home to the water main, which is usually the responsibility of the property owner. Lead levels rise initially, after a partial replacement probably due to the mechanical displacements of solids from disturbance of the system. The concentrations typically subside after several weeks. Homeowners should be advised on actions to reduce potential exposures in that interim period. Certified POU filters and pitcher filters, or bottled water have sometimes been provided in the interim. The filters and pitcher filters should be certified for both particulate and dissolved lead removal.

Analysis

Standard methods including ICP-MS and Atomic Absorption are commonly used analytical procedures for lead. US EPA Methods include 200.5 Revision 4.2, 200.8 Revision 5.4, and 200.9 Revision 2.2. The Standard Methods are 3500-Pb, and 3120 and 3025.

Field analyses for lead in soil, dust and paint use X-ray fluorescence instruments with detections in the ppm range.

Treatment Technology

Increased lead extraction has sometimes occurred when water suppliers switched from free chlorine residuals to chloramine residuals. Orthophosphates added at a few mg/L have been successful in restoring the passivated surface on leaded materials, including lead service pipes, and reducing the other lead releases.

Corrosion control treatment is essential at the municipal plant to prevent plumbing corrosion. Its correction is not trivial and requires case-by-case study, but reasonable solutions are available. Typical approaches include pH, alkalinity, and hardness adjustments. The addition of a few milligrams per liter of a form of phosphate has been shown to be a successful, low-cost technique for lead control in many circumstances. Apparently, a coating of relatively insoluble salts forms to passivate the lead-containing surfaces.

POU water treatment units are available for lead reduction at the tap, as are pour-through devices. Numerous manufactured products certified to American National Standards Institute (ANSI/NSF) standards that can claim lead reduction are available. They often utilize zeolites as part of the system for removal of dissolved lead. RO and cation exchange are also effective. More recent certifications also require demonstrated lead particulate removal.

Flint, Michigan and Lead

Because of the national impact of the Flint, Michigan lead problem, a case study-type assessment of the Flint lead problem of 2014 *et seq* is provided below as a somewhat updated 2016 analysis of the most likely events that occurred. These were not always clearly described in some press reports.

A change of water source led to the introduction of very aggressive water that caused grossly contaminated water at the tap from its corrosive action on existing piping and plumbing that resulted in suspension of sediments and biofilms. Lead was also being extracted from old lead pipe surfaces and galvanized iron pipe in older homes whose plumbing had not been upgraded. One of Flint's existing problems was that the population had declined substantially, so the distribution system was significantly oversized resulting in long water detention times in some areas of the city.

The water rates for Flint residents using water purchased from Detroit were very high, and Flint was in serious financial trouble. In 2014, the municipality decided to return to producing its own water to reduce costs by making a temporary shift to the Flint River while a pipe was being laid to an intake in Lake Huron, but they did not manage the interim properly. As a result, consumers were receiving water with very poor quality. However, indications of serious water quality problems existed well before the source water change. The piped drinking water was apparently brown or orange and contained mobilized lead in some locations for some time, even though the city switched back to Detroit water in October 2015. A chlorine residual was difficult to maintain during much of the conversion time, probably due to the chlorine demand from suspended organic matter or reactions with released iron. Consumers were advised at some point that the water was safe, which is debatable, but it could not be considered palatable.

A report from the Michigan Department of Health and Human Services indicated that 2.5 percent of 3,351 Flint children whose blood levels were tested between October 1, 2015, and January 22, 2016, were above 5 µg/dL. In the third quarter of 2014, about 7 percent were above 5 µg/dL. In 2013, blood lead testing before the water change, 2.2 percent of children tested in Genesee County, where Flint is located, exceeded 5 µg/dL, and 0.2 percent exceeded 10 µg/dL. It is notable that in the same year in Detroit, that 8 percent of tested children exceeded 5 µg/dL, and 1.4 percent exceeded 10 µg/dL. Both communities have a lot of older housing, but reports did not include whether the pre-1978 lead paint contributions to the Flint statistics have been determined.

The CDC issued a summary review in 2017 of the collected child blood lead data from more than 9000 samples collected before, during the water change, and after the return to the Detroit city water. Data in Table 1.1 were extracted from CDC (2016).

These data indicate a 1.7 percent increase (2.5–4.2 percent) in the number of children with more than 5 µg/dL after the switch to Flint River water, then a decline from 3.4 to 1.1 percent after the change back to Detroit drinking water. The numbers and percentages of 10 µg/dL or greater did not increase after the change to Flint River water with a small decline later that might not be statistically significant. It is likely that a substantial portion of these reductions were from high use of bottled water rather than from consumption of Detroit water, because bottled water was being supplied. The report notes that 53 percent of the blood samples were from venous blood and 46 percent were from capillary (finger stick) blood samples. It was not clear what the sampling and analyses distributions were in each segment. This complicates the interpretations somewhat because due to skin contamination, capillary blood measurements

TABLE 1.1
Number and Percent of >5 µg/dL Children Aged <6 Years

Blood Lead (µg/dL)	Before Switch 4/25/13–4/24/14	After-Early 4/25/14–1/02/15	After-Later 1/03/15–10/15/15	Back to Detroit 10/16/15–3/16/16
Number of tests	2,408	1,694	1,990	3,330
5–9	59 (2.5 percent)	71 (4.2 percent)	68 (3.4 percent)	37 (1.1 percent)
10–40	15 (0.7 percent)	13 (0.8 percent)	10 (0.5 percent)	11 (0.3 percent)

Source: Flint, Michigan (4/2013-3/2016)(CDC, 2016).

can be higher than venous blood and may be less reliable than venous blood samples. The Physicians, Pediatric Environmental Health Specialty Units (PEHSU) recommends that initial capillary blood lead measurements >4 μg/dL should be confirmed by a venous sample. It was not clear whether that had occurred in this data set.

Water measurements in some Flint homes reported lead levels in the hundreds to thousands of μg/L in water, and iron was more than 3.3 mg/L (the secondary standard is 0.3 mg/L). The most likely reason that child blood lead levels were not higher is that the water tasted and looked so bad that most people did not drink it. Actually, the greater health outcome was the possibility that the corrosive water allowed for the mobilization of Legionella bacteria from biofilms and sediments that increased the risk of legionellosis from inhalation of aerosols. At one point, there had been 87 cases of legionellosis and 12 deaths reported during the period.

A linkage between the excessive corrosivity and legionella mobilization is plausible as indicated by the color and sediment problems in the water. Biofilms and sediments most likely colonized with legionella bacteria were being mobilized contributing to aerosol exposures possibly during showering. Legionella propagate in amoebas which can be protected from chlorine in the biofilms. Most of the cases and deaths were associated with a hospital that did not provide supplemental water treatment, whereas fewer were associated with the hospital that did treat. The likelihood was later (2018) validated by microbiological typing studies.

A somewhat similar increase in lead releases happened in Washington, D.C., about 2003–2004, but for different technical reasons. In Washington, the water system changed from free chlorine to combined chlorine residual in late 2000. That caused a change in the water chemistry that solubilized lead salts and resulted in exceeding the Lead and Copper Regulation. The problem was ultimately solved by adding a few mg/L of phosphate to the water and lead levels in the stagnant water monitoring tests dropped rapidly. In the Flint case, at least part of the corrosion problem might have been due to much higher chloride levels and different chloride/sulfate ratios in the Flint River compared to Lake Huron. A water supplier in a part of the Pittsburgh, Pa, area had a similar event when they changed the pH of their water.

Lead's Health History

In the 1920s, an intense search was held for a gasoline additive that would have excellent antiknock properties so that high compression engines with much better fuel economy could be achieved. Many antiknock chemicals were evaluated including iodine, aniline, bromine, ethyl alcohol, benzene, and tetraethyl lead. The toxicity of tetraethyl lead was the cause of major controversy. Numerous production and user workers died or developed mental health problems including insanity because of the mishandling and lack of worker safety provisions at the time. After much debate, tetraethyl lead was chosen despite the acknowledged risks because of its low-cost-to-low-gasoline dosage ratio of about 1 to 1,000. The toxicity of leaded gasoline was known, but it was downplayed because some argued that the population's lead exposure would be small and less than the amount caused by lead paint. The latter unfortunate comparison ultimately proved to be a mute argument when household lead paint was banned in 1978.

The concern levels determined by the CDC for lead in blood have moved downward over time from 60 μg/dL in 1960 to the current 5 μg/dL "reference" level. The basis for the reference level is CDC's estimates that at least 97.5 percent of children, which is their metric for the reference level, are below it, so at some point it will probably be lowered to the new 97.5 percent level.

The National Health and Nutrition Examination Survey II (NHANES II) found that the average childhood blood lead level in the United States from 1976 to 1980 was 16 μg/dL. That means many of us and our children had continuous high lead exposures during the leaded gasoline days that ran for over 50 years. The EPA's required introduction of catalytic converters in 1975 necessitated the phasing out of leaded gasoline, and it was complete by 1996. As leaded gasoline was phasing out, the child blood levels were dropping, and the average is now around 1 μg/dL. The EPA should be applauded for solving most of the lead exposure problem.

Most remaining high exposure potential is from old lead paint that can cause high blood levels when children are exposed to leaded dust such as during renovations of older houses. In addition, some other water suppliers are possibly not following the corrosion control regulation, although the fall-out from the Flint case has made lead control a much higher priority issue. The CDC states that subtle IQ loss can occur at around 5 μg/dL. There are numerous social and economic factors that also contribute to IQ levels in that age group. At the reference level and above, identification and elimination of the lead source is recommended, as well as educational and social enrichment. According to the CDC, medical intervention chelation therapy is considered at 45 μg/dL.

Congressional Hearing

In a House of Representatives Oversight Committee hearing on February 3, 2016, those who testified were the EPA's Joel Beauvais; Virginia Tech professor Marc Edwards, who was critical of the situation and city; those in state and federal roles; and several others. When asked, both stated that the Flint problem would not have occurred if Flint had done what was required to be in compliance with the existing Lead and Copper Rule. However, several congressmen pressed the EPA for unstated revisions.

Lead and Copper Rule

The EPA's Lead and Copper Rule regulation was promulgated in 1991 and updated in 2000 and 2007. It requires water suppliers to regularly test for excessive corrosivity in drinking water at the tap in highest risk distribution system locations. Testing is performed on water that has been stagnant overnight or for at least 6 hours. A 1 L first draw sample is collected, and if more than 10 percent of the samples exceed the lead action level of 15 μg/L or the copper action level of 1.3 mg/L, the system must introduce corrosion control procedures and public notification. If the corrosion control is not successfully achieving the defined lead action level, then the system must begin a lead service line replacement program of 7 percent every year.

More than 40 percent of the approximately 10.2 million lead service lines have been removed since the Lead and Copper Rule has been in effect, and about 30 percent of community water supplies are estimated to still have some lead service lines. Those communities amount to about 7 percent of the population served by community water supplies, however, only a portion of the services in most of the communities would have remaining lead service lines.

It is important to recognize that the action level is not an MCL. It is a benchmark screening value to indicate excessive corrosion potential for the water as tested under extreme and non-continuous circumstances. Since it is a 1 L stagnant first draw sample, it is intended to be a virtually worst case and it will include water in contact with the usually lead brass tap and some length of plumbing that includes solder joints, which would be high-lead solder if they were installed before 1986 when lead solder was banned by statute.

The WHO's lead in drinking water guideline and the European Union's drinking water lead directive are 10 μg/L. Some have misinterpreted that to mean that they are more protective than the EPA action level, but they actually are not. Those measurements do not require stagnant first draw water as the EPA's corrosivity screening test does, but they would also allow typical running water sampling more typical of most daily use rather than first draw. Therefore, it is possible that routine exposure to drinking water at 10 μg/L or more could occur.

Suggestions for Regulations and Advice to Consumers

The Lead and Copper Rule could be strengthened with limited effort. First, partial lead service line replacements that include the public portion, but not the private segment, are not generally a good idea. In Washington, DC, lead levels peaked and then stabilized within a few weeks of public lead service line replacements. Bottled water or filters should be provided in the interim.

Second, history shows that delegation to the resident to conduct uncontrolled monitoring is difficult and fraught with opportunities for error. A method for controlled sampling must be used, probably on-site by utility or health department personnel with advance approval from residents. Another perhaps better possibility is to use simulated testing of local lead line loops in a laboratory to continuously determine the intrinsic corrosivity of the system's water to a lead line.

Third, the sampling protocol using stagnant first draw water is effective with respect to plumbing lead, but it would only be influenced to some degree by the service line if a leak allowed some continuing flow from the service line. The simplest improvement would be to add a second draw sample when the temperature change indicates that service line water is being accessed. The District of Columbia Water and Sewer Authority (DCWater) also conducted second draw sampling and showed that the phosphate corrosion control process was successful.

Finally, whatever the rule is it must be diligently applied by water suppliers and enforced by the regulatory agencies.

Lead service lines to buildings would not exist because the lead pipe capacity is too small, so first draw stagnant samples would probably be sufficient for determining the effects on plumbing in an apartment building.

Following are some recommendations to consumers and water treatment professionals helping to resolve their clients concerns:

- Check to see if a lead service connection exists. Find where the outside incoming water line connects to the indoor meter if one is present. Ask the water supplier for a water analysis if in doubt.
- Do not drink first draw water regardless of lead-containing plumbing. It will probably be warm and not taste good, and it might have extracted some material from pipe during stagnation. Let the tap water run for at least several seconds, preferably until the temperature has changed, which would indicate in a home that the more distant perhaps service line water has been reached.
- Do not make baby formula, reconstituted juices, rice, pasta, boiled potatoes, or soup from first draw water or water from the hot water tap.
- If the home or building contains galvanized iron pipe, the water should be sampled for lead and iron. Serious consideration should be given to replacement of the old galvanized pipe with currently approved pipe.
- In the United States, read the water supplier's annual Consumer Confidence Report (CCR) and insist that the water supplier is following the law and managing corrosion.

Regulations

Brass with lead content greater than 8 percent and lead solder with greater than 0.2 percent lead content were banned from drinking water applications in 1986 by the US Congress. Lower lead content is now required. Prior to that time the usual pipe solder contained 50 percent lead and 50 percent tin. Replacement solders are now commonly 95 percent tin and 5 percent antimony, or 95 percent tin and 5 percent silver. Reductions of permissible lead in water contact surfaces to 0.25 percent went into effect in January 2014.

The former drinking water MCL for lead was 50 μg/L collected in running tap water. It was the National Interim Primary Drinking Water Standard in 1975, and it goes back to the 1946 Public Health Service Standards. The US EPA Lead and Copper Rule (1991) requires tap water monitoring for lead and copper in a representative number of home taps in the community determined by the population, as indicators of excessive corrosivity, and corrective actions are required if the action levels were exceeded. The "action level" for lead is 15 μg/L (not a health-based MCL) in more than 10 percent of the sampled locations in the water supply. The sample locations are to be selected in the locations of higher potential for lead presence. The action levels apply to the first liter of water drawn from a faucet where the water has been stagnant for at least 6 hours or overnight. Its intent was to identify water supplies where the water was excessively corrosive, resulting in lead leaching above the action level under somewhat extreme conditions.

If the action level is exceeded corrective actions are required to reduce the corrosiveness of the water. This involves pH or alkalinity adjustments and often use of orthophosphates or silicates. If water conditioning treatments are not sufficient then the system will be required to replace any lead service lines, at the rate of 7 percent per year.

The provisional WHO Guideline for Drinking Water Quality is 0.01 mg/L. It recommends measurement at the tap, but does not specify first draw or stagnant water sampling.

Conclusions

EPA's elimination of leaded gasoline, banning of lead paint, requirements for low-lead brass and elimination of lead solders from canned foods, mitigation requirements in residences, and proper implementation of EPA's Lead and Copper Rule have eradicated most of the US population's lead exposure as verified by extensive blood lead measurements. They are much lower now in US cities than since the early 20th century. Lead exposure has risk and no benefit, so less is better, and none is best.

The social, political, and economic consequences of the situation in Flint are real, but they have also been exacerbated by unclear reporting by media. The Flint situation was certainly a breakdown of the water supplier's responsibilities, as well as the state regulator's. If both had carried out their legal and professional responsibilities and followed the 1991 Lead and Copper Rule regulatory requirements from the beginning, the problem would never have happened. So, that problem was caused by a deficiency of enforcement of the Lead and Copper Rule, and not necessarily a deficiency in the content of the regulation, but some minor and logical improvements could be made. The CDC reports of the blood lead data demonstrate that a significant lead adverse health impact in Flint was unlikely; the blood levels probably reflect that the water quality was so poor that few people drank it. However, there are substantial indications that legionella cases and deaths were increased in Flint related to the corrosion consequences.

Sources

Annest JL. et al (1982). Blood lead levels for persons 6 months–74 years of age: United States 1976–1980. Advance Data from Vital and Health Statistics, No. 79. DHHS Pub. No.(PHS) 82:1250. Public Health Service, Hyattsville, Md. May12, 1982.

CDC (2007). Blood Lead, Morbidity and Mortality Weekly Report. Vol. 6/No. RR-8, November 2, 2007.

CDC (2016). Blood Lead Levels Among Children Aged <6 Years—Flint, Michigan, 2013–2016. Morbidity and Mortality Weekly Report. Vol. 65. www.cdc.gov/mmwr/volumes/65/wr/mm6525e1.htm.

Cornwell D. et al (2016). National survey of lead service line occurrence. *Journal American Water Works Association*. 108(4): pp. 182–191.

Cotruvo JA (2013). *Water Technology on Line Contaminant of the Month*. November 1, 2013. www.watertechonline.com/contaminant-of-the-month-lead/

Cotruvo JA (2016). Flint Fact and Fiction. Water Technology on Line. www.watertechonline.com/professor-poupoe-flint-fact-fiction/.

EPA (1991). Lead and Copper Rule 56 FR 26460, June 7, 1991. EPA 816 F-08–018, June, 2008. http://water.epa.gov/lawsregs/sdwa/index.cfm.

EPA (2012). Drinking Water Standards and Health Advisories. www.epa.gov/sites/produciton/files/2015-09/documents/dwstandards2012.pdf.

EPA (2003). Method 200.5, Rev. 4.2. Determination of Trace Elements in Drinking Water by Axially Viewed Inductively Coupled Plasma-Atomic Emission Spectrometry. EPA/600-R-06/115.

EPA (1994). Method 200.8, Rev. 5.4. and Method 200.9 Rev. 2.2. In Methods for Determination of Metals in Environmental Samples, Supplement 1. EPA/600/R-94/111.

Miranda ML. et al (2007). Changes in blood lead levels associated with use of chloramines in water treatment systems. *Environmental Health Perspectives*. 115(2): pp. 221–225.

NIRS (1988). EPA National Inorganics and Radionuclides Survey. In EPA/630/P-03/001B.

PEHSU (2013). Interpreting and Managing Low Blood Lead Levels. Supplemental Information for Physicians. Pediatric Environmental Health Specialty Units. http://deohs.washington.edu/sites/default/files/documents/Interpreting_and_Managing_Low_Blood_Lead_Levels_Suppl_to_Natl_FS_Health_Prof_Factsheet_2013.pdf.

Standard Methods (2017). Standard Methods for the Examination of Water and Wastewater, 23rd Edition. www.techstreet.com/standards/standard-methods-for-the-examination-of-water-and-wastewater-23rd-edition?sid=msn&utm_medium=cpc&utm_source=bing&product_id=1974889.

World Health Organization Guidelines for Drinking-water Quality (2017). www.who.int/water_sanitation_health/publications/drinking-water-quality-guidelines-4-including-1st-addendum/en/4th edition.

Zahran S. et al (2018). Assessment of the legionnaires' disease outbreak in Flint, Michigan. *Proceedings of the National Academy of Sciences*. 115(8): pp. E1730–E1739.

MERCURY

Introduction

Mercury (Hg) is a silvery metal and a liquid under normal conditions. Mercury and its compounds have many commercial and industrial uses. The metal has been used in thermometers and barometers and as a seal in some electrical switches. The salts have been used as biocides. Mercurochrome (merbromin), a former topical antiseptic was determined to be ineffective and removed from the US market in 1998, but it is still used in many other countries. Until 1991, interior latex paints commonly contained mercuric fungicides. Amalgams are alloys of mercury with other metals and different formulations have uses in silvering mirrors and for dental fillings. Unfortunately, mercury is also used in some ethnic folk remedies that can be toxic.

Physical and Chemical Properties

Metallic mercury has a melting point of –39°C (–38°F), so it is a liquid at ambient temperatures. The boiling point is 356.7°C (674°F). Mercury's atomic number is 80 and its atomic weight is 200.59 Da. The specific gravity is 13.59 times water's. It is found in cinnabar ore as mercuric sulfide primarily on the Iberian Peninsula. Heating the oxide to 500°C produces metallic mercury that is distilled out.

Mercury forms a variety of organic and inorganic compounds, including inorganic Hg^{+1} and Hg^{+2} salts, oxides and sulfides, as well as organometallic compounds like dimethylmercury and methylmercuric chloride, and it complexes with amines. Mercury and its compounds are mobile, and they enter the environment from combustion of fossil fuels and some commercial and biological processes. The latter bacteria in surface water sediments produce organomercury compounds from inorganic forms that are much more toxic than the salts and elemental mercury.

Occurrence

Mercury is present in only about 6.7×10^{-6} percent in the Earth's crust. Commercial uses have been decreasing due to toxicity and environmental persistence concerns. It has been used in the electrolysis of sodium chloride for large-scale production of chlorine and caustic soda. Both methylation and demethylation occur in the environment. Inorganic mercury can be converted to organic forms (e.g., methylation) by some aerobic bacteria and also anaerobic bacteria in sediments, and when suspended, the methylated mercury can accumulate in fish flesh.

Food is the principal source of human exposure primarily from fish and fish products. About 8 percent of mercury ingested in food is absorbed verses about 15 percent from water. Dietary exposure estimates are approximately 2–20 µg/day but can be greater depending upon dietary preferences (e.g., certain fish) and locations. Larger fish, e.g., tuna and swordfish, have higher quantities since they feed on smaller fish and bioaccumulate mercury.

Mercury forms are also produced in combustion processes so inhalation can occur in some areas in the vicinity of large emitters, such as coal burning power plants, and deposition adds mercury to the terrestrial and water environment. Typical concentrations in air range from 2 to 10 ng/m^3. Rain water concentrations have been reported to be in the range of 5–100 ng/L with mean levels around 1 ng/L.

Measurements of mercury in hair and red blood cells are biomarkers of mercury exposure/ingestion. The no-observed-adverse-health-effect level (NOAEL) set by the WHO is 10 ng/g in hair. The USEPA blood mercury concern value is 5.8 µg/L.

Drinking water is generally a minor source of exposure. Mercury was found in only 42 of 989 groundwaters used for drinking water in the 1988 National Inorganics Reconnaissance Survey: 26 were detected below 0.2 µg/L, and one exceeded 2 µg/L (the MCLG and MCL). Typical surface waters contain less than 0.5 µg/L.

Health Effects

The biological half-life of mercury is measured in years with elimination in urine and feces. About 8 percent of ingested mercury in food is absorbed; absorption from drinking water is about 15 percent or less depending upon the chemical form, and it may be affected by the solubility, dissociation in the GI tract, and intestinal pH, as well as presence of divalent cations like Cu^{++} and Zn^{++}.The kidney is the primary organ where mercury accumulates and causes toxicity. Organomercurials are much more toxic than inorganic forms. Inhaled mercury is neurotoxic. The Mad Hatter in "Alice in Wonderland" was probably suffering from mercury exposure in his leather-processing occupation.

The FAO/WHO Joint Expert Committee on Food Additives (JECFA) provisional tolerable weekly intake (PTWI) of inorganic mercury (Hg^{++}) from food is 4 μg/kg bw after application of a 100-fold uncertainty factor to a NOAEL from rat study in drinking water. This was considered applicable to dietary exposure to total mercury from foods other than fish and shellfish. Organomercurials like dimethyl mercury are much more toxic than inorganic mercury compounds. The primary exposure is from bioaccumulation in the aquatic environment food chain, such as large predator fish like tuna and swordfish.

Analysis

Analytical methods include EPA 245.1 Cold Vapor Atomic Absorption Spectrometry, and EPA 200.8 ICP-MS which can achieve at least 0.6 μg/L, and atomic absorption is also capable to achieve less than 1 μg/L. The Standard Methods procedure is 3500-Hg and several others.

Water Treatment

Conventional coagulation, sedimentation and filtration can remove about 80 percent of inorganic mercury and about 20–40 percent of organic mercury. Ferric sulfate is a more effective coagulant than aluminum sulfate. Powdered-activated carbon (PAC) and GAC carbons are effective for both forms. Cation exchange is also a possible treatment. Certified POU and POE devices can be applied.

Regulations and Guidelines

The EPA drinking water MCL for inorganic mercury is 0.002 mg/L. The 1-day and 10-day health advisories are conservatively also 0.002 mg/L. Although there are some newer toxicology data available EPA decided not to modify the MCLG and MCL for mercury in its six-year review. The WHO drinking water guideline is 0.006 mg/L for inorganic mercury.

The 2001 EPA ambient water quality criteria for methylmercury are 0.77 μg/L (freshwater chronic) and 0.94 μg/L (saltwater chronic), and 0.3 mg/kg in fish flesh, based upon a total fish consumption rate of 0.0175 kg/day.

Conclusion

Mercury generally is not a significant health concern in US drinking water supplies.

Sources

Cotruvo JA (2015). Mercury. Water Technology on Line, Contaminant of the Month. www.watertechonline.com/contaminant-of-the-month-mercury/.

EPA Water Quality Criteria (2001). EPA 823-F-01-001. www.epa.gov/wqc/national-recommended-water-quality-criteria-human-health-criteria-table.

EPA (2012). Drinking Water Health Advisories. www.epa.gov/sites/produciton/files/2015-09/documents/dwstandards2012.pdf.

EPA (2016). Chemical Contaminant Summaries for the Third Six-year Review of Existing National Primary Drinking Water Regulations. EPA 810-R-16-004.

EPA Method 245.1. www.epa.gov/sites/production/files/2015-06/documents/epa-245.1.pdf.

EPA Method 200.8. www.phaseonline.com/assets/Site_18/files/Technical%20Resources/Technical%20Resources/Mercury%20Analysis%20and%20Mercury%20Speciation.pdf.

JECFA (2011). Provisional Tolerable Weekly Uptake (PTWI). http://apps.who.int/food-additives-contaminants-jecfa-database/chemical.aspx?chemID=1806.

Okati N and Esmaili-sari A (2018). Determination of mercury daily intake and hair-to-blood mercury concentration ratio in people resident of the Coast of the Persian Gulf, Iran. *Archives of Environmental Contamination and Toxicology*. 74(1): pp. 140–153. https://link.springer.com/article/10.1007/s00244-017-0456-z.

Standard Methods (2017). Standard Methods for the Examination of Water and Wastewater, 23rd Edition. www.techstreet.com/standards/standard-methods-for-the-examination-of-water-and-wastewater-23rd-edition?sid=msn&utm_medium=cpc&utm_source=bing&product_id=1974889.

WHO (2005). Mercury in Drinking Water. WHO/SDE/WSH/05.08/10 www.who.int/water_sanitation_health/dwq/chemicals/mercuryfinal.pdf

World Health Organization Guidelines for Drinking-water Quality (2017). www.who.int/water_sanitation_health/publications/drinking-water-quality-guidelines-4-including-1st-addendum/en/4th edition.

NITRATE AND NITRITE

Introduction

Nitrates and nitrites have received much attention as drinking water and dietary contaminants with concerns about potential health risks. Nitrate, and sometimes nitrite, are frequently present at low levels in drinking water sources, but they are common problems particularly in smaller public water supplies and probably more so in some home well waters. The principle health concern is for infants in homes that produce drinking water from their own wells because that water is seldom monitored or treated, except perhaps softening, and almost never disinfected. Disinfection will eliminate pathogenic bacteria and oxidize nitrite (the more immediate toxic form) to nitrate. In some water supplies, particularly where chloramine residuals are used, there can be production of small amounts of nitrite at the extremes of the system with long residence times. Generally, the principle source of human exposure to nitrates and nitrites is dietary from consumption of vegetables and cured meats; however, water can become an important source for bottle-fed infants less than 3–6 months old. The risk is significantly increased when the child has a GI infection, which can increase the reductive conversion of nitrate to nitrite in the stomach. Those infections can be induced by consumption of microbially contaminated drinking water that may concurrently contain nitrate/nitrite.

Water Quality and Occurrence

Nitrate and nitrite can occur in surface waters and groundwaters. Surface waters can contain them from runoff of agricultural fertilizers, which could have periodic peaks associated with planting season or rainfall, or from upstream sewage discharges. Groundwaters can be generally contaminated from surface fertilizer uses, as well as locally from residential septic tank outflows, which would also contribute microbial contamination.

The EPA has reported that eight states have more than 10 percent of their areas with groundwater nitrate concentrations that exceed 5 mg/L as N (half of the drinking water standard).

Information is available from community drinking water suppliers on the composition of their drinking waters and compliance with the drinking water regulations. A Consumer Confidence Report (CCR) is usually required annually that includes their status and water quality and violations. Most of them in the United States can be found online by searching CCR with the name of the community.

For water that is not from a public supplier, it is important to understand the nitrate and nitrite composition and microbial status of the water to be treated to determine the challenge as well as to periodically test treated water to be sure that the water does not exceed a drinking water standard. A United States Geological Survey report suggested that 1 million private wells are located in areas where the groundwater exceeds 10 mg/L as N.

Drinking Water Health Issues

The basis for the drinking water standards and the traditional concern about nitrate and nitrite in drinking water is the risk of infant methemoglobinemia (aka, blue baby syndrome). Nitrate is converted to nitrite under reducing conditions—it can oxidize a portion of the ferrous iron in blood hemoglobin to ferric iron. That reduces its ability to release oxygen to tissues and a sufficient percentage level of methemoglobin results in oxygen starvation and possibly death. This is a particular risk in infants below less than about 6 months of age. They are at greater risk if they are also suffering from a GI infection. The infection risk is greater if they are consuming water that does not meet microbial drinking water standards, and has not been disinfected.

Typical background levels of blood methemoglobin are less than 2 percent; levels approaching 10 percent are a significant concern, especially for pregnant women. Fortunately, methemoglobinemia is treatable when recognized and serious illness and deaths are rare in the United States, but more frequent in some other parts of the world. When it is water-related it is due to groundwater contamination, often from residential septic tanks.

The WHO states that 97 percent of cases in clinical epidemiological studies of drinking water nitrate methaemoglobinaemia and subclinical increases in methaemoglobin levels occurred at concentrations in excess of 44.3 mg/L as NO_3^-, with clinical symptoms associated with the higher concentrations. Almost all affected individuals were under 3 months of age. WHO also concluded that nitrate and nitrite were not carcinogenic in rats and mice that have been tested.

A 2006 review by US CDC epidemiologists, concluded: "The current literature does not provide sufficient evidence of a causal relationship between exposure to nitrates in drinking water and adverse reproductive effects."

There are occasional reports in the press of studies associating nitrate/nitrite in drinking water and various health outcomes, including cancer and birth defects. These can create anxieties among the public because they are frequently not balanced by contrary information. The weight of evidence does not seem to support those occasionally reported associations with nitrate. Here are several quotes from the WHO GDWQ Addendum to the fourth edition:

- "The weight of evidence indicates that there is unlikely to be a causal association between gastric cancer and nitrate in drinking water."
- "There have been suggestions that nitrate in drinking water could be associated with congenital malformations, but the overall weight of evidence does not support this."
- "There have been suggestions of an association between nitrate in drinking water and the incidence of childhood diabetes mellitus. However, subsequent studies have not found a significant relationship..."

There was a later published report by another US group that was widely disseminated in the national press that there was a higher incidence of certain birth defects, including spina bifida, limb deficiencies, cleft palate and cleft lip, associated with offspring from mothers who consumed more than 5–5.42 mg as nitrate per day from drinking water in the first trimester compared to controls (<1 mg/day). This surprising "association" was reported in the press as confirming that there were birth defect risks associated with nitrate in drinking water even at very low levels. The above reported breakpoint exposure was about 6 percent of the nitrate intake for someone drinking 2 L/day of water at the current drinking water standard. The lead author stated that there were insufficient numbers of cases to determine a dose response. The authors also stated that the reported association with nitrate could have been caused by some other component in the water.

However, in a study from most of the same authors reported a few months prior, they concluded: "Overall, odds of neural tube defects, oral clefts or limb deficiencies did not appear to be significantly associated with estimated dietary intake of nitrite, nitrite and nitrosamines."

Nitrate from either food or water would behave similarly (probably identically since absorption is on the order of 90 percent for all intakes, and about 25 percent is recirculated in saliva from metabolic processes) in the GI tract after consumption. Thus, this earlier finding for total daily nitrate intake from dietary food and water, a larger amount than from water alone, is inconsistent with the later water association report from the same organization and, therefore, renders it questionable, at best.

Another example is a report that drinking water nitrate might be a contributor to colorectal cancer risk. The study related drinking water concentrations to colorectal cancer outcomes. It concluded that there was a very small 1.16 relative risk for drinking water above 3.87 mg/L as nitrate. The drinking water standard is 45–50 mg/L. The study was cursory. It compared consumers by reported drinking water community concentrations, not total dietary exposure, and not drinking water consumption or nitrate consumption from drinking water. So, it is appropriate to be cautious when interpreting inadequate studies and unbalanced media reports, and to carefully read and critique published literature reports of adverse effects of this sort from drinking water.

Analysis

Nitrate analyses are conducted by ion chromatography, automated cadmium reduction with colorimetry and nitrate electrode. EPA-approved methods include 300.0 Rev.2.1; 300.1, Rev. 1.0; 353.2, Rev. 2.0. The Standard Method is 4500-NO_3^- (nitrate) and 4500-NO_2^- (nitrite) and others.

There are simple to use and inexpensive colorimetric test kits available for quick measurements of nitrate and nitrite. For example, some companies sell suitable test strips and color comparison tests for drinking water that are very low cost. Carefully follow the directions and be sure whether the reading is as nitrate, NO_3^-; nitrite, NO_2^-; or as N. If a more accurate test result is required, water samples can be sent to a certified laboratory for analysis, but those costs can be about $15 or $20 per sample. There are also simple tests for coliform bacteria that can be conducted at commercial or local public health laboratories, or even on-site using a Colilert-type test kit.

Water Treatment

Nitrate and nitrite are difficult to remove from water. However, disinfection alone will oxidize nitrite to nitrate, which is the less hazardous form for intake. Disinfection is especially important because it also reduces the risk of GI infections from microbially contaminated water, which would be a greater concern in home well situations.

Conventional coagulation/sedimentation/filtration water treatment technologies are not effective because nitrate salts are very soluble in water. Municipal water plants have used anion exchange (IX), RO, electrodialysis (EDR) or biological denitrification. None of these are traditional simple technologies or low cost. EPA has published guidance for water treatment technologies.

Properly certified and operated POU and POE technologies are particularly appropriate for home well contamination situations, but they may also be cost-effective in small community environments. A detailed study of a community-wide POU implementation of decentralized treatment for arsenic removal has demonstrated the methodology and success of the concept. However, if there is the possibility of water contamination as well as the presence of an at risk infant, bottled water for formula and drinking water for the child is probably the best course during the at risk age.

Anion exchange, RO, and distillation are available for POU and/or POE applications. Since the health risk for water from drinking and cooking is the concern, POU will be more cost-effective than POE because only a few liters of water will be needed each day for those purposes. Several RO and IX units have been certified to ANSI/NSF 58 or 53 by CSA, IAPMO, NSF, UL, or WQA. Although anion exchange activated alumina or iron-based media are quite effective technologies for removal of anions like fluoride and arsenic, nitrate is less efficiently bound to the media. The New Hampshire Department of Environmental Services (2006) has concluded that RO is the most cost-effective of the three options for a small required water volume considering all factors, although RO has lower water recovery and higher wastage. Disinfection might also be necessary in many cases, although the RO might also remove most microorganisms.

Drinking Water Standards, Guidelines, and Health

The drinking water standards (MCLG and MCL) in the United States are as follows: nitrate, 10 mg/L as N, (about 45 mg/L as nitrate, NO_3^-); nitrite, 1 mg/L as N, and (~3 mg/L as nitrite, NO_2^-). The standard for the combined total is 10 mg/L as N. The Health Canada values are 45 mg/L as nitrate and 3 mg/L as nitrite, so they are essentially identical to the US standards.

The WHO Guidelines for nitrate is 50 mg/L as nitrate ion (11.3 mg/L as N), to be protective against methaemoglobinaemia and thyroid effects in the most sensitive subpopulation, bottlefed infants, and, consequently, other population subgroups. The nitrite guideline is 3 mg/L as nitrite ion, to be protective against methaemoglobinaemia induced by nitrite from both endogenous and exogenous sources in bottlefed infants, the most sensitive subpopulation, and, consequently, the general population. Combined nitrate plus nitrite, which is the sum of the ratios of the concentrations of nitrate and nitrite to each guideline value, should not exceed 1.

Conclusions

Most nitrate and nitrite exposures to the general population is from vegetables and some cured meats in the diet. There are some marketers advocating consumption of high nitrate beet juice and other products as an energy enhancer from NO biological activity. They fail to mention that in addition to being an important signaling molecule, NO also forms endogenous nitrosamines.

Nitrate and nitrite are regulated in drinking water to protect infants less than 6 months old from methemoglobinemia. They are considered to be the most sensitive population so it is considered to be protective of the entire population. This occurs in some locations particularly in association with private wells containing nitrate and nitrite, and especially when the infant has a GI infection which might have been associated with untreated microbiologically contaminated well water. So, domestic wells should be tested for coliform/*E. coli* contamination as well as nitrate/nitrite; it is advisable to disinfect such water to reduce both risks. The effects on the infant are noticeable and also reversible by appropriate simple medical treatment, so parents should be diligent. Both central and home treatment systems are available, but the technologies are more complex and expensive than the more conventional technologies.

Sources

Brender JD (2013). Prenatal nitrate intake from drinking water and selected birth defects in offspring of participants in the national birth defects prevention study. *Environmental Health Perspectives*. 121(9): pp. 1083–1089.

Cotruvo JA (2011). Nitrate/nitrite Water Technology on Line. www.watertechonline.com/nitratenitrite/ Accessed March 29, 2018.

Cotruvo JA (2013). Nitrate and Nitrite. Water Technology on Line. www.watertechonline.com/professor-poupoe-september-2013/. Accessed March 1, 2018.

EPA. Estimated Nitrate Concentrations in Groundwater Used for Drinking. www2.epa.gov/nutrient-policy-data/estimated-nitrate-concentrations-groundwater-used-drinking.

EPA (2014). Basic Information about Nitrate in Drinking Water. US Environmental Protection Agency. February 2014. http://water.epa.gov/drink/contaminants/basicinformation/nitrate.cfm. Accessed March 29, 2018.

EPA. Point-of-use or Point-of-entry Treatment Options for Small Drinking Water Systems, EPA 815-R-06–010.

EPA. Feasibility of an Economically Sustainable Point-of-Use/Point-of-Entry Decentralized Public Water System. EPA Grant X82952301.

EPA (1993). Method 353.2, Revision 2.0: Determination of Nitrate-Nitrite Nitrogen by Automated Colorimetry www.epa.gov/sites/production/files/2015-08/documents/method_353-2_1993.pdf EPA/600/R-93/100.

EPA (1993). Method 300.0, Rev. 2.1: Methods for Determination of Inorganic Substances in Environmental Samples. EPA/600/R-93/100.

EPA (2000). Method 300.1, Rev. 1.0: Methods for Determination of Organic and Inorganic Compounds in Drinking Water, Vol 1. EPA 815-R-00–014.

Health Canada (2013). Guidelines for Canadian Drinking Water Quality: Guideline Technical DocumentNitrate and nitrite. http://healthycanadians.gc.ca/publications/healthy-living-vie-saine/water-nitrate-nitrite-eau/alt/water-nitrate-nitrite-eau-eng.pdf.

EPA (2016). Analytical Methods Approved for Drinking Water Compliance. Inorganic Contaminants. EPA 815-B-16-014. https://nepis.epa.gov/Exe/ZyPDF.cgi?Dockey=P100PHGZ.txt

Manassaram DM. et al (2006). A review of nitrates in drinking water: Maternal exposure and adverse reproductive and developmental outcomes. *Environmental Health Perspectives.* 114(3): pp. 320–327.
Schullehner J, Hansen B, Thygesen M, Pedersen CB, Sigsgaard T (2018). Nitrate in drinking water and colorectal cancer risk: A nationwide population-based cohort study. *International Journal of Cancer.* 143(1): pp. 73–79. doi:10.1002/ijc.31306.
Standard Methods (2017). Standard Methods for the Examination of Water and Wastewater, 23rd Edition. 4500-NO_3^- (nitrate) and 4500-NO_2^- (nitrite). www.techstreet.com/standards/standard-methods-for-the-examination-of-water-and-wastewater-23rd-edition?sid=msn&utm_medium=cpc&utm_source=bing&product_id=1974889.
UC Davis (2012). Technical Report 6: Drinking Water Treatment for Nitrate. groundwaternitrate.ucdavis.edu/files/139107.pdf.
USGS (2006). Vulnerability of Shallow Groundwater and Drinking-Water Wells to Nitrate in the United States. *Environmental Science and Technology.* 40(24): pp. 7834–7840.
WHO (2017). World Health Organization Guidelines for Drinking-water Quality. www.who.int/water_sanitation_health/publications/drinking-water-quality-guidelines-4-including-1st-addendum/en/.

PERCHLORATE IN DRINKING WATER

INTRODUCTION

Perchlorate (ClO_4^-) is both a natural product and a synthetic chemical with numerous uses including in rocket fuel, fireworks, flares, and explosives. It is also present in some fertilizers depending upon their geographic origin. Perchlorate has been found in some surface and groundwaters around military operations, defense manufacturing facilities, and areas where blasting agents have been used. It is found naturally in subsurface soil, especially in the southwest United States and in deposits in Chile, and it has also been found at low levels in some groundwaters where no anthropogenic source is apparent. Perchlorate is highly mobile in water and can persist for many decades under typical ground and surface water conditions.

Perchlorate is probably the most potent of several anions that compete with iodide transport in blood that can cause thyroid and indirect neurological problems in high risk persons at sustained, high enough doses, and insufficient iodine intake. It has been used as a pharmaceutical to treat Graves' disease (hyperthyroidism) because it depresses thyroid activity. Perchloric acid ($HClO_4$) forms soluble salts with many cations.

In 2008, EPA had proposed not to regulate perchlorate in drinking water and issued an interim Drinking Water Health Advisory (DWHA) of 15 ppb based upon a review, recommended assessment, and RfD provided by the National Research Council (NRC). EPA reversed itself in 2011, issuing a determination to regulate perchlorate with a different interpretation of the requirements in the Safe Drinking Water Act that must be met to arrive at a decision to regulate.

Chemistry

Perchlorate, with the chemical formula ClO_4^-, is an anion and a strong oxidizing agent because chlorine is in its highest oxidation state of +7. In water, it is always associated with a cation, such as hydrogen, sodium, or potassium. Perchloric acid is a strong acid and its salts such as potassium perchlorate ($KClO_4$), ammonium perchlorate (NH_4ClO_4), and sodium perchlorate ($NaClO_4$), are ionized and stable in water. It is stable in its pure state if not in contact with reducing agents and if kept below approximately 150°C, when it becomes thermodynamically unstable. Perchlorate is a natural product of solar irradiation of chlorine species, found in minerals, and a commercial strong oxidizing agent used in explosives, flares, fireworks, and as a rocket fuel component. It is also present in small amounts in aged hypochlorite solutions as a secondary product after chlorate accumulates from disproportionation reactions from storage at warm temperatures for extended periods. It is not formed from chlorine gas.

Occurrence and Human Exposure

Perchlorate can be present in ppb amounts in dairy products and produce and is also in some fertilizers. It is very slightly metabolized after ingestion and is excreted unchanged with a half-life of 8 to 12 hours.

The FDA has estimated dietary exposures in the United States to be age dependent from 0.11 to 0.39 µg/kg/day, with younger individuals having the higher exposures on a per kilogram body weight basis.

In 2011, the WHO/FAO JECFA calculated a provisional TDI of 10 µg/kg/day. It estimated total perchlorate daily exposures of 0.7 µg/kg/day body weight (highest) and 0.1 µg/kg/day body weight (mean) from food and water and concluded they were well below the provisional maximum TDI. The JECFA committee concluded that those estimated dietary exposures were not of health concern. Mendez (2010) utilized UCMR1 and NHANES and other perchlorate data and calculated that the 95th percentile of perchlorate intake for women of childbearing age in the US was 0.15 µg/kg/day.

Detailed US drinking water occurrence data were generated by the UCMR1, which included analyses in 2001–2005 from about 2,800 public water systems larger than 10,000 plus 800 out of about 50,000 small systems. Of 3,865 reporting systems, only 160 (4.1 percent) had one or more measurements at or above 4 ppb—the then reporting limit. The average of the positives was 9.85 ppb, the median was 6.4 ppb and 15 systems exceeded 15 ppb. EPA estimated that between 5.1 million and 16.6 million people were served in the systems exceeding >4 ppb, and between 0.4 million and one million in those exceeding 23 ppb.

Human Health

Perchlorate can interfere with iodide uptake by the thyroid gland, reducing thyroid hormone production and interfering with normal prenatal and post-natal growth and neurological development. Perchlorate and other anions in the diet (nitrate, chlorate, bromide, thiocyanate), smoking (thiocyanate), and sometimes in drinking waters also compete with iodide transport to the thyroid, which can reduce production of thyroid hormones, increasing the risk of hypothyroidism if iodine intake is not adequate. Perchlorate is more potent on a unit weight basis than the other anions, but they are present in much greater quantities than perchlorate in the total diet.

Iodine is an essential micronutrient: >150 μg/day is recommended for neurological development of fetuses and infants. If deficient in the diet, there is increased risk of goiter (hypothyroidism). Iodized table salt was introduced in the United States in 1924 to provide additional iodine in regions with low iodine dietary intake; about 70 percent of household salt is fortified with iodine. According to the Institute of Medicine, iodine intake in the US population is generally sufficient, but with some exceptions. Urinary measurement of less than 150 ppb iodine is considered insufficient. Less than 50 ppb is considered moderately deficient in the general population.

The human thyroid has significant hormone stores. It is estimated that iodide uptake would have to be reduced at least 75 percent for months or more for adverse health effects to occur from abnormal thyroid hormone production.

Perchlorate was used to treat Graves' disease, hyperthyroidism, at doses of up to 1,000 mg/day. Health risks from excess perchlorate exposure are of particular concern to pregnant women and infants with inadequate iodine intake. Perchlorate dosages used in treatment of Graves' disease are typically in the 400–700 mg/day (about 6–10 mg/kg/day) range taken in four or five doses for 3–8 weeks. Minimal side effects were noted.

The NRC IOM provided recommendations for a no observed effect level (NOEL) and a NOAEL. They chose a NOAEL of 0.4 mg/kg bw/day (400 μg/kg bw/day) for adverse thyroid effects, and a NOEL of 0.007 mg/kg bw/day (7 μg/kg bw/day) and the RfD of 0.7 μg/kg bw/day for non-adverse effects by including a factor of 10 to protect the most sensitive populations, fetuses of pregnant women who might have hypothyroidism or iodine deficiency. Neurodevelopmental effects in those newborns are the most sensitive adverse health effects as potentially indicated by slight IQ loss or much more serious developmental effects. The recommendation was based upon reduced uptake of radioactive iodine, which is not an adverse effect per se (serum hormone levels were not significantly altered at the NOEL).

Several human studies are consistent with the NRC recommendation and demonstrate its conservatism. For example, no adverse thyroid effects were observed at 0.2 mg/kg bw/day (one half of the NOAEL); measurable hypothyroid effects occurred at 1 mg/kg bw/day (1,000 μg/kg bw/day) regardless of iodine status; benchmark doses of 0.21–0.56 mg/kg bw/day based upon free thyroxin index and 0.36–0.92 mg/kg bw/day based upon TSH (thyroid-stimulating hormone) changes; no differences were observed in thyroid status in pregnant women with median urinary iodine levels of 269 μg/L in a Chilean city with drinking water at 110–115 μg/L plus 20–30 μg/day of dietary perchlorate, compared to two other cities with none or 6 μg/L perchlorate in the drinking water.

The WHO Guideline for Drinking Water Quality (2017) is 0.070 mg/L based upon the JECFA assessment, which is clearly less conservative than the EPA or state assessments.

Analysis

There are several approved EPA analytical methods for perchlorate analyses, including Method 314.0 Revision 1.0, 331.0, and 332.0. They are described in the EPA (2014) Technical Fact Sheet. ISO 3771:2011 and ISO 19340:2017 are also published.

Water Treatment

Perchlorate is a large anion and very water soluble so treatment technologies include RO, anion exchange, and possibly GAC and catalytic reduction. These are all higher cost technologies for public water supplies and not readily implemented in the small water systems where most of the impact of a regulation would be felt. In-home POU RO systems meeting ANSI/NSF 58 would achieve a low ppb standard, but with very high reject water ratios. ANSI/NSF Standard 58 requires a RO unit to be able to reduce water containing 130 ppb of perchlorate to 4 ppb or less. Additional industry standards for other devices are under consideration.

Cost and Benefits

Benefits versus costs of a national regulation are being debated and questionable. From one of the impact analyses, about 4 percent of all systems would exceed an MCL of 0.002 mg/L, 3 percent at 0.004 mg/L, about 0.5 percent at 0.015 mg/L and 0.2–0.3 percent at an MCL of 0.024 mg/L.

Recent cost benefit estimates of potential MCLs from 0.002 to 0.024 mg/L yield capital costs ranging from $1.1 billion to $36 million, and annualized costs of $151 million to $5 million. These costs exclude California and Massachusetts that have conservative state MCLs of 0.006 and 0.002 mg/L, respectively. Incremental costs were above $3 per 1,000 gallons in small systems. A separate analysis of national upper bound benefits using all conservative assumptions arrived at $2.9 million for an MCL of 0.004 mg/L and $134,000 annually for an MCL above 0.020 mg/L, so, benefits do not exceed costs in any of the regulatory scenarios.

EPA's Regulatory Determinations

In 2008, EPA developed an interim Drinking Water Health Advisory (DWHA) of 15 ppb based upon the NRC recommendation. There is considerable disagreement between the EPA Health Advisory, WHO/FAO JECFA assessment, the WHO Guideline (0.070 mg/L), and the California and Massachusetts assessments.

As of EPA's 2011 determination to regulate perchlorate in drinking water, it is working on a proposed regulation that was originally expected in 2013. That has been delayed with additional studies that were recommended by the EPA Science Advisory Board in 2013. A biologically based dose response model has been developed in 2016 and was peer reviewed in 2017. SAB recommendations are expected in 2018. The more recent studies are calculating neurodevelopmental effects (IQ) at maternal iodine daily intakes of 75 μg/day versus perchlorate intakes at several different perchlorate μg/kg/day levels.

Once the SAB review is completed, a regulatory determination requires that: (1) the contaminant may have an adverse effect on health of persons; (2) it occurs in public water systems with a frequency and at levels of public health concern; and (3) in the judgment of the Administrator regulation presents a meaningful opportunity for health risk reduction. The first criterion could be met for perchlorate at doses well beyond typical dietary and drinking water exposures; the second is questionable except perhaps for very few water systems; and the third seems to be improbable.

Conclusion

The issue is whether controlling low ppb levels of perchlorate in drinking water, in the relatively small number of supplies where it is found, is the most appropriate and effective way of protecting certain pregnant women and very young children, who have insufficient dietary iodine intake. Smoking is a major contributor of thiocyanate that is also a potent competitor of iodide transport to the thyroid by the NIS protein. Although EPA has stated its decision to regulate perchlorate in drinking water and discussed potential Health Reference Levels in the range of 2–47 ppb, it has not indicated a likely MCL as of early 2018. The WHO Guideline for Drinking Water Quality for perchlorate is 0.070 mg/L.

EPA's inspector general concluded that EPA's previous interim DWHA of 0.015 mg/L based upon the 2005 NRC recommendation is conservative, and that increasing maternal total dietary intake of iodine would be the most effective approach for reducing risk.

In its 2017 Q&A information, FDA concludes that, in general, most Americans consume adequate amounts of iodine in their diets, and taking iodine supplements is not necessary for protection from perchlorate in water and foods. Pregnant women are advised to take supplements and to be sure that they have sufficient iodine (and they should not smoke) and FDA does not recommend altering diet or drinking water for the general population, but recommends using water lower than 0.015 mg/L for reconstituted infant formula. The JECFA estimated 0.7 μg/kg bw/day as the high, and 0.1 μg/kg bw/day as the mean from food and water. It concluded that environmental exposures to perchlorate were not a health concern.

The American Thyroid Association reported that there were no effects on thyroid function for women in early pregnancy at typical environmental exposures, even for mildly iodine deficient individuals.

So, it is doubtful whether a national regulation for perchlorate in drinking water would provide significant measurable benefits versus the costs of compliance. Individual states can develop a drinking water MCL if they happen to have some supplies with high concentrations, and they deem it appropriate for their circumstances.

As the EPA Office of the Inspector General stated in their report, it would probably be more beneficial and less costly if programs were initiated assuring that pregnant women received sufficient iodine supplementation, as well as examining opportunities for increasing iodine dietary consumption for the general population. One common counter-productive misdirection for the general public from many TV chefs is their recommendation to routinely use kosher salt or varieties of sea salt.

Those are not usually iodized so that results in a net reduction of iodine intake for those who mistakenly follow that advice.

So the EPA regulatory issues are as follows: Will the new risk analyses be more conservative than the former? If a regulation is proposed, what concentration will it be and what impact will it have on water systems? Will it be supportable by cost and risk benefit analysis, and will it be challenged? Given the multiyear delays, one could assume that there was not a sense of urgency with regard to any current drinking water related risks. EPA's Science Advisory Board will review an assessment that may lead to a new decision.

Sources

Cotruvo JA (2013). Perchlorate. Water Technology on Line. www.watertechonline.com/contaminant-of-the-month-perchlorate/.

Cotruvo JA (2014). Perchlorate. Water Technology on Line. www.watertechonline.com/professor-poupoe-december-2014/.

Cotruvo JA (2015). Perchlorate in US drinking water: Is a federal regulation needed to protect public health? *Journal American Water Works Association*. 107(6):pp. 66–71. www.researchgate.net/publication/277888251_Perchlorate_in_US_Drinking_Water_Is_a_Federal_Regulation_Needed_to_Protect_Public_Health.

EPA (2010). Scientific Analysis of Perchlorate Report 10-P-0101. USEPA Office of the Inspector General.

EPA UCMR 1 (2008). Occurrence of Unregulated Contaminants in Public Water Systems. www.epa.gov/safewater/ucmr/data.html#ucmr1.

EPA (2012). Drinking Water Health Advisories. www.epa.gov/sites/produciton/files/2015-09/documents/dwstandards2012.pdf.

EPA (2014). Technical Fact Sheet-Perchlorate. www.epa.gov/sites/production/files/2014-03/documents/ffrrofactsheet_contaminant_perchlorate_january2014_final.pdf.

EPA (2017). September Draft Report: Proposed Approaches to Inform the Derivation of a Maximum Contaminant Level Goal for Perchlorate in Drinking Water www.regulations.gov/document?D=EPA-HQ-OW-2016-0438-0019.

EPA (1999). Method 314.0 Revision 1.0. Determination of Perchlorate in Drinking Water Using Ion Chromatography.

FDA (2008). Survey data on perchlorate in food.-2005/2006. Total Diet Study Results. www.fda.gov/Food/FoodborneillnessContaminants/ChemicalContaminants/ucm077615.

FDA (2017). Perchlorate Questions and Answers. www.fda.gov/Food/FoodborneIllnessContaminants/ChemicalContaminants/ucm077572.htm.

JECFA (2011). Perchlorate. http://apps.who.int/foodadditives-contaminants-jecfa-database/chemical-aspx?chemID=5885.

Lewendowski TA. et al (2015). Iodine Supplementation and Drinking Water Perchlorate Mitigation. *Food and Chemical Toxicology*. 80: p.261.

Mendez W (2010). Drinking water contribution to aggregate perchlorate intake of reproductive- age women in the United States estimated by dietary intake

simulation and analysis of urinary excretion data. *Journal of Exposure Science and Environmental Epidemiology*. 20: pp. 288–297.
NRC (2005). *Health Implications of Perchlorate Ingestion*. National Academies Press, Washington.
NRC (2006). Dietary Reference Intakes: The Essential Guide to Nutrient Requirements. Chapter: Iodine. www.nap.edu/read/11537/chapter/36.
Russell CG. et al (2013). National Perchlorate Cost Update. Water Industry Technical Action Fund report 316. AWWA. Denver.
WHO (2017). World Health Organization Guidelines for Drinking-water Quality. www.who.int/water_sanitation_health/publications/drinking-water-quality-guidelines-4-including-1st-addendum/en/.

SELENIUM IN DRINKING WATER

Introduction

Selenium is an element which is commonly present in soils and some groundwaters at low levels. There are high selenium areas. It is a trace essential nutrient and possible anti-carcinogen, and it also has numerous commercial uses in paints, anti-dandruff shampoos, as a fungicide, in electronics, pigments, some glass, and as a nutritional supplement in animal feed.

Physical and Chemical Properties

Selenium's atomic number is 34 and its atomic weight is 78.98 Da. Selenium is located adjacent to sulfur and arsenic in the Periodic Table of the Elements so it has chemical similarities to both of them. Elemental selenium exists in several forms including Se_8 rings much like sulfur, as well as long chains. In solution, selenium can exist as selenide (Se^{-2}), and various polyanions, as well as selenium dioxide, selenate, and selenite. In alkaline soils, selenium is present as water-soluble selenate and is available to plants; in acid soils, it is more usually found as selenite bound to iron and aluminum oxides in compounds of very low solubility.

Occurrence and Exposure

Most exposure to selenium is from the diet. Average daily intake from food in the United States is 108 µg/day. Soils content can be a cause of either excessive or insufficient dietary intake because selenium is mobile in many growing plants. Selenium from soil can accumulate in grains, vegetables, and animal products. ATSDR reports that 99.5 percent of drinking water samples were less than 10 ppb. Selenium is present in greater amounts in soils in some western states. Compliance monitoring data from 50,568 water systems concluded that 31 exceeded the MCL of 0.050 mg/L.

Human Health Effects

Selenium is an essential nutrient trace element in humans and animals. It is an active part of numerous proteins, particularly enzymes involved in antioxidant defense mechanisms (e.g., glutathione peroxidases), thyroid hormone metabolism (e.g., deiodinase enzymes), and redox control of intracellular reactions (e.g., thioredoxin reductase). It is considered to be anti-carcinogenic, but the anti-carcinogenic effects may be inhibited by co-exposure to other agents such as arsenic.

The primary adverse effects in laboratory animals exposed to inorganic selenium salts or to selenium-containing amino acids are cardiovascular, GI, hematological, hepatic, dermal, immunological, neurological, and reproductive, although doses causing these effects are generally at least 5 times higher than the RDA selenium intake.

Yang et al. studied endemic selenium intoxication; morbidity was 49 percent among 248 persons whose daily intake was about 5 mg of selenium. Symptoms were brittle hair with intact follicles, lack of pigment in new hair, thickened and brittle nails, and skin lesions. Neurological symptoms were observed in 18 of the 22 inhabitants of one heavily affected village. Those affected recovered once diets were changed following evacuation from the areas. In other studies, average dietary intake that was associated with selenosis is in excess of 900 μg/day. The studies by Yang et al. (1983), in China, indicated that areas with elevated selenium intake of 750 μg/day showed no overt signs of selenosis and in those areas in which selenosis was apparent, intake was approximately 3–6 mg/day.

The RDA for selenium, established by the National Academy of Sciences, Food and Nutrition Board, is 55 μg/day for male and female adults (approximately 0.8 μg/kg/day). The current NAS IOM UL for selenium is 400 μg/day for adults (approximately 5.7 μg/kg/day). Selenium deficiency is probably not a health issue in the United States, but it has been associated with two endemic diseases found in selenium-poor regions of China: a cardiovascular condition known as Keshan Disease and an osteoarthropathy called Kashin-Beck Disease.

The IARC concluded in 1987 that selenium compounds were not classifiable as to their ability to cause cancer in humans. Later EPA concluded that selenium disulfide (SeS_2) was a probable human carcinogen based upon studies in rats at very high doses. Selenium disulfide is not found in foods and is chemically different from other organic and inorganic selenium compounds. It is used in anti-dandruff shampoos, but is not absorbed through the skin. Its water solubility is less than 5 ppb, so exposure from contamination of drinking water from waste sources is unlikely. Combs (2001, 2005) concluded that selenium daily intake should be at least 40 μg/day and perhaps 300 μg/day to reduce cancer risks.

Water Treatment Technology

In the unlikely event that water treatment is necessary, coagulation, anion exchange, activated alumina, and RO membrane treatment will control excess selenium concentrations in drinking water.

Analytical Methods

EPA Methods 200.9 Rev. 2.2, and 270. 2 are capable of analyzing selenium in drinking water. Reporting limits are 0.002 mg/L. The Standard Method for selenium is 3500-Se, and 3113 B (Electrochemical Atomic Absorption), 3114 (Manual and Continuous Hydride Generation/Atomic Absorption Methods) as well as several other techniques.

Regulations and Guidelines

The MCLG and MCL for selenium are both 0.050 mg/L. The WHO Guideline is 0.040 mg/L, and the European Union value is 0.010 mg/L, and the Canadian Guideline is also 0.010 mg/L. Given the fact that selenium is an essential nutrient with an RDA of at least 55 μg/day, and the epidemiological evidence that observed selenosis effects occurred at exposures in excess of 900 μg/day, it appears logical that there is actually greater concern of risk from sub-RDA intake of selenium in low selenium areas, rather than selenium intoxication.

Conclusions

Selenium is an essential nutrient, but very excessive exposures can produce visible but reversible adverse effects. Excess exposures tend to occur in high endemic selenium areas where dietary and water exposures can be problematic. Selenium has a role in disease mitigation and is likely anti-carcinogenic. Selenium is not a significant drinking water issue in the United States with a very low frequency of water supplies that exceed the MCL. Even standards of 0.050 mg/L seem to be conservative, let alone the other even lower standards and guidelines. In the majority of situations it appears that it would not be in the best interest of public health to take steps to remove selenium from drinking water in that range or lower.

Sources

ATSDR (2003). Public Health Statement Selenium. www.atsdr.cdc.gov/phs/phs.asp?id=151&tid=28 Accessed March 5, 2018.

ATSDR (2015). Toxicological Profile for Selenium. www.atsdr.cdc.gov/toxprofiles/tp.asp?id=153&tid=28 Accessed March 5, 2018.

Combs GF, Jr (2001). Selenium in global food systems. *British Journal of Nutrition.* 85: pp. 517–547.

Combs GF, Jr (2005). Current Evidence and Research Needs to Support a Health Claim for Selenium and Cancer Prevention. Proceedings of the symposium, Nutrient Disease Relationships: Closing the Scientific Knowledge Gap. *The Journal of Nutrition.* 135(2): pp. 343–347.

EPA (2016). Chemical Contaminant Summaries for the Third Six-year Review of Existing National Primary Drinking Water Regulations. EPA 810-R-16-004.

EPA (2012). Drinking Water Health Advisories. www.epa.gov/sites/produciton/files/2015-09/documents/dwstandards2012.pdf.

Geoffroy N and Demopoulis GP (2011). The elimination of selenium IV from aqueous solution by precipitation with sodium sulfide. *Journal of Hazardous Materials.* 185(1): pp. 148–154.

NAS IOM (2000). Dietary Reference Intakes for Vitamin C, Vitamin E, Selenium, and Carotenoids. www.nationalacademies.org/hmd/Reports/2000/Dietary-Reference-Intakes-for-Vitamin-C-Vitamin-E-Selenium-and-Carotenoids.aspx.
Standard Methods (2017). Standard Methods for the Examination of Water and Wastewater, 23rd Edition. www.techstreet.com/standards/standard-methods-for-the-examination-of-water-and-wastewater-23rd-edition?sid=msn&utm_medium=cpc&utm_source=bing&product_id=1974889.
WHO (2017). World Health Organization Guidelines for Drinking-water Quality. www.who.int/water_sanitation_health/publications/drinking-water-quality-guidelines-4-including-1st-addendum/en/.

SODIUM

Introduction

Sodium's abundance in the earth's crust is about 2.3 percent as ocean salinity and terrestrial salt deposits. It ranks sixth among elements in nature. About 280,000,000 tons of sodium chloride are mined each year. Sodium chloride is common table salt. It is widely used in seasoning foods and also especially in times past as a means for preserving food. Chlorine and sodium hydroxide are major products produced by electrolysis of salt.

Chemistry

Elemental sodium is a soft, silver-gray metal, with the atomic number 11 and atomic weight 22.99 Da. Sodium's elemental symbol, Na, stands for the Latin name *natrium*. The free element is never found in nature because it reacts rapidly with water to produce sodium hydroxide and hydrogen, so it is only found in salts. Typical open ocean sodium ion concentrations are in the range of 10,500 parts per million (ppm), but some confined seas (such as the Persian Gulf) reach almost 16,000 ppm. The Great Salt Lake is about seven times more saline than seawater. Most sodium salts are very soluble in water, for example, sodium chloride's (NaCl) water solubility is 357 g/L at 0°C.

Occurrence in Drinking Water

Typical drinking waters contain less than 20 mg/L of sodium, but some groundwater can be substantially greater, usually reflected in total dissolved solids (TDS) values. The National Inorganics and Radionuclides Survey reported in 1988 that about three-fourths of 989 groundwater drinking water systems had concentrations of sodium less than 50 mg/L. Runoff from road salt use can significantly increase sodium in surface waters, but groundwater in many regions has elevated salt and many are brackish from former seawater geology. Groundwaters near the sea coasts are often saline, which is exacerbated by seawater intrusion caused by excessive withdrawal of fresh water from the aquifers.

Health Effects

Sodium is an essential nutrient and has numerous functions including maintaining ionic balance and interacting with potassium, calcium, and magnesium for cardiovascular function. Sodium is excreted in urine and lost by perspiration along with other salts.

Inadequate sodium intake or excessive losses from perspiration without replacement can result in hyponatremia, which can be fatal. The NRC recommends that most healthy adults consume at least 500 mg/day, but not more than 2,400 mg/day. That level is usually exceeded in the typical American diet.

Excess salinity in water results in undesirable taste. Thresholds are about 150 mg/L for sodium chloride, 220 mg/L for sodium sulfate and 420 mg/L for sodium bicarbonate.

Analyses

Inductively Coupled Plasma Emission Spectrometry, as well as Atomic Absorption Spectrophotometry, and flame photometry measure sodium in water. EPA Methods include 200.5, Revision 4.2, and 200.7, Revision 4.4. Standard Methods are similar and are in 3111B. The Standard Methods TDS method is 2,540. Low-cost per sample test kits are also available.

Sodium imparts a characteristic yellow color in qualitative flame tests and fireworks, as well is in low-pressure sodium vapor lamps.

Water Treatment

Sodium ions and TDS in drinking water are most readily removed by desalination processes such as RO membranes. Distillation can reduce all salts including sodium.

Cationic water softeners replace the calcium or magnesium ions in hard water with sodium, or sometimes potassium if potassium salts are part of the regenerations.

Regulations and Guidelines

Sodium was listed in the US EPA's 2012 Contaminant Candidate List, not with likelihood that it would be regulated, but that the guidance should be reconsidered.

No health- or aesthetics-based drinking water standard for sodium exists in the United States. The taste threshold is cited in the Health Advisory as 30–60 mg/L. The HA guidance of 20 mg/L for persons on a 500 mg/day sodium-restricted diet is essentially a suggestion since the diet is the dominant source of sodium intake, and people on sodium-restricted diets or with hypertension are treated with diuretics. The guidance level could possibly be raised.

The WHO does not have a recommended level for drinking water because it finds no firm conclusion that relates sodium in drinking water to hypertension. The taste-based WHO suggestion is 200 mg/L.

Conclusions

Sodium is an essential nutrient but many people have excess dietary intake. Drinking water is usually a minor source but some waters have high enough salinity to have undesirable tastes. The taste threshold is estimated at 30–60 mg/L. Persons on a sodium restricted diet should know their drinking water's content so they can make appropriate choices with the advice of their physicians. Sodium is not regulated in the United States.

Sources

Cotruvo JA (2015). Sodium. Water Technology on Line. www.watertechon-line.com/contaminant-of-the-month-sodium/.

EPA (2012). Drinking Water Standards and Health Advisories. www.epa.gov/sites/produciton/files/2015-09/documents/dwstandards2012.pdf.

EPA (2003). Determination of Trace Elements in Drinking Water by Axially Viewed Inductively Coupled Plasma-Atomic EmisEsion Spectrometry. October. EPA/600-R-06/115.

EPA (1994). Determination of Metals in Water and Wastewater by Stabilized Temperature Graphite Furnace Atomic Absorption Spectrometry. 200.9, Revision 2.2. EPA/600/R-94/111. May. https://nepis.epa.gov/Exe/tiff2png.cgi/300036HP.PNG?-r+75+-g+7+D%3A%5CZYFILES%5CINDEX%20DATA%5C91THRU94%5CTIFF%5C00001020%5C300036HP.TIF.

Standard Methods (2017). Standard Methods for the Examination of Water and Wastewater, 23rd Edition. www.techstreet.com/standards/standard-methods-for-the-examination-of-water-and-wastewater-23rd-edition?sid=msn&utm_medium=cpc&utm_source=bing&product_id=1974889.

WHO (2011). World Health Organization Guidelines for Drinking-water Quality. www.who.int/water_sanitation_health/publications/2011/dwq_guidelines/en/.

WHO (2003). Sodium in Drinking Water. Background Document for Development of WHO Guidelines for Drinking-Water Quality. WHO/SDE/WSH/03.04/15.

2 Organic Chemicals in Drinking Water

BENZENE

INTRODUCTION

Benzene is a hydrocarbon manufactured from petroleum and also a natural product in the environment including in some foods. It is among the highest volume industrial organic chemicals and has numerous uses as a chemical intermediate for production of styrene and isopropyl benzene (cumene). It is a component of unleaded gasoline on the order of 1 or 2 percent with other BTEX (benzene, toluene, ethyl benzene, xylenes) aromatic hydrocarbons as well as other organics that raise octane ratings and provide antiknock properties. Petroleum refiners convert paraffin hydrocarbons to cyclic forms and aromatize to benzene and other BTEX compounds. Benzene is present in cigarette smoke and a common combustion product. Drinking water contamination can occur from spills, leaking underground gasoline storage tanks, or other releases from improper chemical waste disposal.

PHYSICAL AND CHEMICAL PROPERTIES

Benzene's molecular formula is C_6H_6. It is a planer six-membered ring of carbon atoms with alternate unsaturation with a hydrogen attached to each carbon. It is defined as having aromatic character which means that the electrons in the ring change the chemistry to a more stable form than an isolated double bond. Its primary chemistry involves catalyzed substitution of attached hydrogens by chemical groups; however, it is also subject to oxidation processes by metabolism as well as certain water treatment processes such as ozonation.

Benzene is a stable, clear, colorless liquid; its molecular weight is 78.11 Da; its melting point is 5.5°C (41.9°F); the boiling point is 80.1°C (176.2°F); and water solubility is about 1,800 mg/L at 25°C. It is a volatile organic chemical (VOC) because of its high vapor pressure and low boiling point, and lighter than water with a specific gravity of about 0.88 g/cc. Its octanol-water partition coefficient (Log K_{ow}) is 2.13, which means that it has some small affinity for water as also indicated by its moderate to low water solubility. The taste threshold is between 0.5 and 4.5 mg/L. The odor detection threshold detection is about 0.84–53 ppm.

HUMAN EXPOSURE

Exposure occurs from occupations in processes that use or emit benzene, airborne inhalation, traces in foods and alcoholic beverages, and minimal amounts in some drinking waters. Outdoor airborne levels average about 1 part per billion (ppb) (0.313 μg/m^3) and contribute around 7.5 μg/day to daily exposure. Sources include evaporation from gasoline and unburned tailpipe emissions. Indoor air exposure is often greater, with contributions from secondhand cigarette smoke, gas cooking, wood burning stoves and fireplaces, as well as releases from furnishings and attached garages, with indoor home levels as high as 31 μg/m^3. Cigarette smoking is the single, greatest general human exposure source. An average cigarette smoker can inhale about 1.8 mg/day (1,800 μg) directly from 32 cigarettes. Drinking water is a negligible source for the vast majority of people.

Occurrence in Water

Most surface and groundwaters contain no detectable benzene. Well water contaminated with gasoline from leaking underground storage tanks or a nearby hazardous waste site often contains some benzene. In one 1992–1994 study of 41,742 sites in 11 US states, 0.63 percent had detectable levels of benzene, and 0.11 percent exceeded 0.005 mg/L (5 ppb).

Health Effects

As with most volatile solvents, benzene can cause drowsiness and headaches at high inhalation levels. The International Agency for Research on Cancer (IARC) and the US Environmental Protection Agency (USEPA) have determined that benzene is carcinogenic to humans. As a known human carcinogen it is classified as USEPA Group A, based upon occupational epidemiology, and (IARC) Group 1. Long-term exposure to high levels of benzene in the air can cause leukemia, particularly acute myelogenous leukemia. This is a cancer of the blood-forming organs.

Breathing very high levels of benzene can result in death, while somewhat lower levels can cause drowsiness, dizziness, rapid heart rate, headaches, tremors, confusion, and unconsciousness. Eating or drinking foods containing high levels of benzene can cause vomiting, irritation of the stomach, dizziness, sleepiness, convulsions, rapid heart rate, and death. The major effect of benzene from long-term lower level exposure is on the blood. Benzene causes harmful effects on the bone marrow and a decrease in red blood cells leading to anemia. The other BTEX hydrocarbons are not carcinogens and have much lower chronic risks than benzene.

USEPA's lifetime risk calculation for benzene lifetime inhalation is about 1 in 100,000 to 1 in 1 million for exposure at 1 μg/m^3 based upon occupational epidemiology studies. USEPA's calculated projected risks for lifetime ingestion through drinking water are between 1 and 10 mg/L for 1 in 10,000 risk, and 0.01 mg/L and 0.1 mg/L for 1 in 1 million lifetime risks.

Analytical Methods

Analyses are by purge and trap gas chromatography and gas chromatography/mass spectrometry related procedures. There are numerous USEPA-approved techniques for volatile synthetic organic chemicals, BTEX, and other approved analyses for volatiles including 8,020 A and 8,021 B, 502.2, and 524.2. Standard Methods techniques include 6,200 for volatile organic compounds by purge and trap and 6,232 by liquid–liquid extraction.

Water Treatment

Granular activated carbon and packed tower aeration are available to water treatment plants. Reverse osmosis (RO) is not very effective because a small organic solvent molecule, such as benzene, can dissolve in the membrane and migrate to the treated water.

Point-of-use (POU) and point-of-entry (POE) treatment systems that have been tested and certified and using activated carbon are effective; however, their cartridges must be replaced frequently before exhaustion.

Regulation

The USEPA drinking water maximum contaminant level goal (MCLG) is zero, as an aspirational goal, and the maximum contaminant level (MCL) is 0.005 mg/L (5 μg/L; 5 ppb). Some states, including California and Florida, have MCLs of 001 mg/L (1 ppb). The World Health Organization (WHO) drinking water guideline is 0.010 mg/L (10 ppb). The Canadian Guideline is 0.005 mg/L. The EU Directive value is 0.001 mg/L. The USEPA health advisory is 0.2 mg/L for 1 and 10 days for a 10-kg child; the reference dose is 0.004 mg/kg/day. These are protective conservative values compared to nondrinking water exposures.

Conclusion

Benzene is well regulated and seldom present in public drinking water supplies. All of the regulations are very protective because drinking water is a very minor source of exposure compared to outdoor and indoor air inhalation and smoking.

Sources

Agency for Toxic Substances and Disease Registry (ATSDR) (2007). Toxicological Profile for Benzene *(Update)*. US Department of Health and Human Services, Public Health Service, Atlanta, GA.

California Public Health Goal or Benzene in Drinking Water. https://oehha.ca.gov/media/downloads/water/chemicals/phg/benzenefinphg_0.pdf.

Cotruvo JA (2015). Benzene. Contaminant of the Month. Water Technology on Line. www.watertechonline.com/contaminant-of-the-month-benzene/.

EPA (1995). Method 524.2 Rev4.1 EPA/600/R-95-131, and EPA (2009) Method 524.3 EPA 815-B-09-009 in www.epa.gov/safewater/methods/analyticalmethods/_ogwdw.html.

EPA fact sheet: Benzene. www.epa.gov/sites/production/files/2016-09/documents/benzene.pdf.

EPA (2012). Drinking Water Health Advisories. www.epa.gov/sites/produciton/files/2015-09/documents/dwstandards2012.pdf.

EU Council Directive 98/83/EC of 3 November 1998 on the Quality of Water Intended for Human Consumption. http://ncphp.government.bg/files/DWD%2098-%2083-%20EC.pdf.

Standard Methods (2017). Standard Methods for the Examination of Water and Wastewater, 23rd Edition. www.techstreet.com/standards/standard-methods-for-the-examination-of-water-and-wastewater-23rd-edition?sid=msn&utm_medium=cpc&utm_source=bing&product_id=1974889.

WHO (2017). World Health Organization Guidelines for Drinking-water Quality, 2017. www.who.int/water_sanitation_health/publications/drinking-water-quality-guidelines-4-including-1st-addendum/en/4th edition.

BISPHENOL A AND DRINKING WATER

INTRODUCTION

Bisphenol A (BPA) is a monomer chemical used in the production of plastic resins and in numerous other applications. Its chemical name is 2,2-bis(4-hydroxyphenyl) propane, and its chemical structure is shown in Figure 2.1.

BPA is present in many consumer products, so high potential for low-level exposure exists. Infants who drink formula from polycarbonate baby bottles generally have higher exposures per kilogram body weight than adults.

The molecular structure in Figure 2.1 shows that BPA is a relatively simple chemical—two phenols linked back to back through a propane unit. It is a white crystalline solid that melts at about 158°C (318°F). Its molecular weight is 228.29 Da and water solubility is 120–300 parts per million at 21.5°C (71°F). It is manufactured easily by condensing two molecules of phenol with acetone. It has many uses. The largest is in the production of polycarbonate plastics (a glass substitute) when it is reacted with phosgene in the original process; and for epoxies are another major use by reaction of BPA with epichlorohydrin.

All the reactants are common, inexpensive chemicals, and the world's BPA production was 5.4 million metric tons per year in 2015. Epoxy and polycarbonate plastics are extremely stable products, but 100 percent reaction does not occur when the polymers are formed, so a small amount of the BPA will remain and be leachable to food and water during contact. It is biodegraded during waste treatment and by numerous environmental microorganisms.

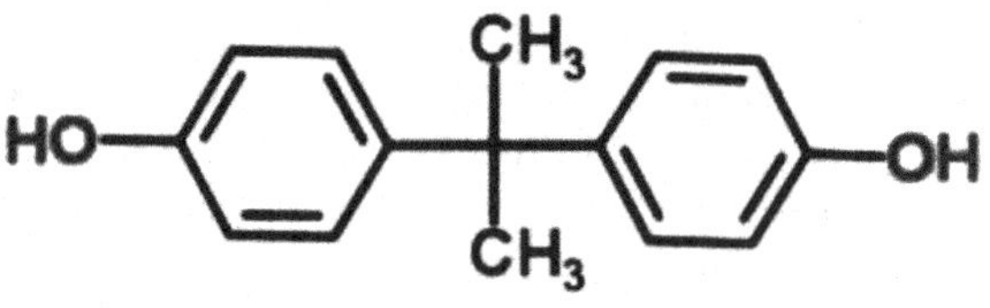

FIGURE 2.1 BPA's molecular chemical structure.

BPA Uses

Apart from plastic product production, BPA has many other applications in its free state as an antioxidant for polyvinyl chloride and a color developer in carbonless copy paper and thermal paper. It is also used in the manufacture of

- Printed circuit boards
- Electronic equipment
- Paints
- Adhesives

Human Exposure to BPA

About 93 percent of tested Americans older than age 6 tested in the National Health and Nutrition Examination Survey (NHANES III 2003–2004) had detectable BPA or BPA metabolites in their urine. Exposure can occur by ingestion from diet, canned foods with epoxy liners, and dermal contact with products such as thermal paper with free BPA. It is efficiently absorbed through the skin. In addition, exposure can occur from extraction to liquids in polycarbonate containers, including baby bottles and water carboys.

Daily adult intake from food, beverage, and environment has been estimated to be about 0.4 μg up to about 1.5 μg/kg bw/day. This is about 28–100 μg/day, or around 1 μg/kg/day for a 70-kg adult based upon urine concentrations. Some occupational exposures can be up to about 100 μg/kg/day, or 7,000 μg/day. Urine measurements are usually calculated relative to the release of creatinine, which is a normal waste product that indicates kidney function and is used as a baseline standard so that variations in urine output can be normalized.

Drinking Water

Public drinking water is a potential source but is a minor contributor (generally less than 1 percent) to total exposure. The USEPA reported that concentrations in US drinking water are typically well below 1 μg/L, or 1 ppb (0.001 mg/L), when it is occasionally detected. Levels in treated wastewater have been reported at up to 0.022 mg/L. Concentrations of BPA in US drinking water had a median range of 0.005 to less than 0.1 ppb and an overall range of less than 0.1–0.42 ppb.

Surface waters ranged from 0.0009 to 12 ppb. Groundwater levels ranged from 0.006 to 2.55 ppb and wastewater from 0.0036 to 50 ppb. If BPA, a phenol, were present in chlorinated drinking water, it would likely be converted to chlorinated forms. BPA and chlorinated BPA would be readily removed from water by activated carbon or RO membranes.

Toxicology

BPA is a hormonally active chemical and a very weak estrogen (17β-estradiol) mimic. It does not bind strongly to the estrogen receptor. The relative estrogenic potency is generally considered to be on the order of one-ten-thousandth of estrogen, and its primary glucuronide metabolite is considered non-estrogenic. Numerous dose-related health effects have been reported in cell culture and *in vivo* animal studies, but human effects at low environmental doses have been more elusive.

BPA has been the subject of thousands of studies over the years, and the interpretations have been controversial. These reports from mostly *in vitro* and animal studies cover its effects on everything including

- Neurological
- Thyroid
- Prostate
- Breast
- Testis
- Mammary gland
- Body size
- Brain structure
- Heart disease
- Diabetes
- Oxidative stress
- The behavior of laboratory animals

Some have since been discounted by later studies. The question becomes: What are the concerns for human exposure at typical and elevated levels?

A few years ago, California's Office of Environmental Health Hazard Assessment (OEHHA) attempted to list BPA for Proposition 65 notification, after its advisory committee declined to identify it as a hazard. OEHHA was litigated, removed it, formed a new advisory committee which voted to list it, which it has now done. The original proposed listing was based on reproductive concerns at an acceptable value of 290 μg/day from several rodent reproductive and developmental toxicity studies with a no-observed-adverse-effect level (NOAEL) of 5 mg/kg/day, and a 1,000 margin of safety for a 58-kg (128-pound) pregnant woman. That value is much higher than the total daily population exposure, thus indicating negligible risk from ambient exposures.

The National Toxicology Program (February 2018) issued a comprehensive draft report for review that evaluated BPA in comparison to ethinyl estradiol (EE). EE is a synthetic estrogen and used in medications including for birth control. Illustrative of the potency differences between the chemicals, BPA doses were 2.5, 25, 250, 2,500, and 25,000 μg/kg bw/day; EE doses were 0.05 and 0.5 μg/kg bw/day.

In the EE reference estrogen dose groups, there were multiple significant treatment-related effects at the 0.5 μg/kg bw/day exposure level in females. BPA produced minimal effects that were distinguishable from background in this study, particularly below 25,000 μg BPA/kg bw/day. In contrast, the high EE dose elicited several strong effects in females. Many of the statistically significant BPA effects were not dose-responsive or occurred in only one dose group. One conclusion was that there was not a clear pattern of consistent responses the two study arms.

Environmental Effects

Because BPA has weak estrogenic properties, concerns about environmental effects in freshwater and marine aquatic organisms should be considered. The European Union computed a predicted no-effect concentration (PNEC) of 7.5 μg/L and included an uncertainty/safety factor of 5 to arrive at a PNEC of 1.5 μg/L.

The PNECs for Canada and Japan are 0.175 and 1.6 μg/L, respectively, demonstrating that all risk assessments contain a substantial element of judgment and use different margins of safety that go beyond the science.

Levels of Concern

Several committees have reviewed the state of the science and often arrived at different conclusions. A 2006 government-sponsored committee concluded that BPA at average concentration levels in the population had caused harm in laboratory animals. On the other hand, a 2008 report from the National Toxicology Program expressed "some" concern for infants, and generally "negligible to minimal" concerns for birth defects. The concern was "minimal" for highly exposed occupational situations.

Numerous calculations of "intake limits" have been reported. The USEPA, US Food and Drug Administration (FDA), and European Food Safety Agency (EFSA) values tended to be in the range of 50 μg/kg/day or higher, and they incorporate safety/uncertainty factors ranging from 100 to 1,000. The EFSA recently lowered its value to 4 μg/kg/day and concluded that it was 3–5 times the highest exposure estimates.

FDA's 2014 perspective, based on its then most recent safety assessment, is that BPA is safe at the current levels occurring in foods. "Based on FDA's ongoing safety review of scientific evidence, the available information continues to support the safety of BPA for the currently approved uses in food containers and packaging."

Metabolism

BPA is rapidly metabolized in the liver and eliminated either as the parent, or conjugated as the glucuronide or sulfate. Researchers from the National Center for Toxicological Research built mathematical models of how it is processed, metabolized and eliminated. They showed that BPA is rapidly metabolized and eliminated through feces and urine. They also did not find evidence of BPA toxicity at low doses in rodent studies, including doses at about human exposure levels.

In addition, the models could not measure BPA being transferred from pregnant rodent mothers to fetuses after being fed amounts that were 100–1,000 times more than people are exposed to from food. The researchers estimated that human infants were exposed from 84 to 92 percent less than previously estimated.

BPA is metabolized differently by humans and other primates than by rodents. Humans produce more of the BPA-glucuronide compared to rodents. Free BPA is weakly estrogenic whereas BPA-glucuronide is not estrogenic. The relative amounts of free BPA and BPA-glucuronide in humans and other primates versus rats indicate that rodents may be more sensitive than humans to BPA. This indication should be considered when attempting to extrapolate data from rodent studies to humans. The USEPA also states that more than 90 percent of the BPA found in the urine of premature infants was in the BPA-glucuronide form, indicating that infants can metabolize BPA to this non-estrogenic form.

Analysis

The ASM test method for water is ASTM D7574-16.

Regulations

Several countries, including the United States and Canada, have banned BPA in baby bottles, usually in the interest of caution, because of the relatively higher intake to body weight ratios for infants versus adults and because alternative materials are available.

The USEPA has produced an action plan for BPA primarily because it is a high-volume chemical and therefore can have substantial releases to the environment (more than 1 million pounds per year) and because alternatives may be available for some uses. Food-related packaging is less than 5 percent of the BPA used in the United States, but it accounts for most of the human population's exposure, except perhaps for dermal contact for some people with high occupational exposure. The USEPA has deferred to the FDA on food-related issues, but it will address environmental releases and nonfood packaging, and whether human environmental exposure is significant, which does not seem to be the case. The USEPA recently did not include BPA as a candidate for the next Contaminant Candidate List (CCL4).

Conclusion

There is a huge published literature on BPA toxicology and risk with reputed adverse effects, but much of that appears to be out of date and not valid with respect to human risk.

The FDA has conducted extensive studies over the years, and it has stated several times (2014) that BPA is not harmful at the current exposure levels. The most recent National Toxicology Program (NTP 2018) draft report concluded that BPA testing produced minimal effects, and that what has been observed in studies were within the range of normal biological variation. USEPA has given it a fairly low priority, indicating low potency compared to estrogen, but chose not to list it in the final Contaminant List CCL4. California's OEHHA relisted it for Proposition 65 notification a few years ago after its replacement reproductive toxicology advisory committee recommended it, although its safe level was much higher than reported human exposures.

Regardless of the scientific and regulatory debates, drinking water is a negligible source of BPA exposure compared to total dietary and environmental exposure. In reality, the case for human risks at normal levels seems extremely weak. Nevertheless, more studies continue to be funded.

Sources

ASTM. Standard Test Method for Determination of Bisphenol A in Environmental Waters by Liquid Chromatography/Tandem Mass Spectrometry. ASTM D7574-16. www.astm.org/Standards/D7574.htm.

Bisphenol A (2002). Analytical Method Criteria for the Determination of Bisphenol A in Various Matrices. www.bisphenol-a.org/pdf/criteria_102002.pdf.

Cotruvo JA (2015). Bisphenol A. Water Technology on Line. www.watertechonline.com/professor-poupoe-bisphenol-a/.

EPA Risk Management for Bisphenol A. www.epa.gov/assessing-and-managing-chemicals-under-tsca/risk-management-bisphenol-bpa.

https://search.epa.gov/epasearch/epasearch?querytext=bisphenol+A&areaname=&areacontacts=&areasearchurl=&typeofsearch=epa&result_template=snapshot.ftl&frontend=snapshot_frontend&site=snapshot.

FDA (2014). Bisphenol A (BPA): Use in Food Contact Application. www.fda.gov/Food/IngredientsPackagingLabeling/FoodAdditivesIngredients/ucm064437.

NIH (2017). Bisphenol A. National Institute of Environmental Health Sciences www.niehs.nih.gov/health/topics/agents/sya-bpa/index.cfm.

NTP (2018). Draft NTP Research Report on the CLARITY-BPA Core Study: A Perinatal and Chronic Extended Dose -Range Study of Bisphenol A in Rats. https://ntp.niehs.nih.gov/ntp/about_ntp/rrprp/2018/april/rr09peerdraft.pdf.

Pub Chem. Bisphenol A. https://pubchem.ncbi.nlm.nih.gov/compound/Bisphenol_A#section=Top.

1,4-DIOXANE

Introduction

para-Dioxane (*p*-dioxane), or 1,4-dioxane, (CAS RN 123-91-1) is a synthetic organic chemical with many commercial uses. It is commonly called dioxane. It is very resistant to biodegradation, a solvent for many chemical processes and virtually completely miscible in water. Dioxane is a high-volume industrial chemical with numerous uses. In 1990 US production was reported as between 10.5 and 18.3 million pounds, but this has declined to about 1 million pounds, because of its reduced use as a stabilizer for trichloroethane. Even though the names are similar, 1,4-dioxane is not related to dioxin (tetrachlorodibenzodioxin).

Physical and Chemical Properties

Dioxane is a clear colorless liquid below its boiling point of 101.2°C (214°F). Its freezing point is 12°C (53.2°F). The molecular formula is $C_4H_8O_2$ and molecular weight is 88.11 Da. The octanol–water partition coefficient (log K_{OW}) is –27 indicating its very high affinity for water. The vapor pressure at 25°C is 38.1 mmHg. Its structure is a six-membered saturated ring of four carbon atoms and two oxygen atoms. The arrangement is two oxygen atoms in the one and four positions in the ring and four CH_2 groups in the two, three, five and six positions. There are three different isomer dioxane molecules; the other two have oxygen atoms in the one and two (1,2-dioxane) and one and three (1,3-dioxane) positions. The isomer 1,3-dioxane has similar physical properties, but it is chemically different because it is an acetal of formaldehyde and 1,3-propane diol and is easily hydrolyzed. 1,2-Dioxane is a cyclic peroxide, so it does not have chemical properties similar to 1,4-dioxane.

Human Exposure

Dioxane is a flammable solvent. It is very stable in the environment and not readily biodegraded or chemically degraded, so it is a persistent contaminant. Among its uses are as a solvent component of varnishes, paint strippers, inks and adhesives, and it is a common contaminant in cosmetics and personal care products, including shampoos, deodorants, toothpaste, and mouthwash. Because dioxane is very stable in the environment and very water soluble it is being found in water sources and drinking water supplies. Trace levels have been found in many foods in Japan with dairy containing the highest levels approaching 15 μg/kg.

Occurrence in Drinking Water

The USEPA reported results from its Third Unregulated Contaminant Monitoring Rule survey in July 2016. 1,4-Dioxane was detected in the highest frequency of any of the 21 listed organic chemicals that were analyzed. It was detected in 1,076 of 4,905 public water supplies above the detection limit of 0.07 ppb. Almost 7 percent exceeded the lowest reference concentration of 0.35 ppb; none exceeded 35 ppb, the higher benchmark.

Health Effects

Dioxane is a skin and inhalation irritant, and rats suffered liver and kidney damage from chronic exposure in drinking water. Dioxane is not genotoxic but is considered a probable human carcinogen by USEPA based upon liver and nasal cavity cancers in rats and mice in chronic tests conducted by the National Cancer Institute at very high concentrations of 0.5 percent and 1 percent in drinking water. The IARC listed dioxane as possibly carcinogenic to humans. The USEPA calculated a projected hypothetical lifetime cancer risks of 1/1,000,000 at 0.35 ppb and 1/10/000 at 35 ppb. Small epidemiological studies of exposed workers did not detect increased cancer incidences attributable to dioxane.

However, more recent data (Dourson et al., 2017) has concluded that the observed rodent liver tumors are caused by a regenerative hyperplasia mode of action (MOA) at levels above metabolic saturation. The observed liver toxicity has a threshold at doses below levels that saturate metabolism, in the range of 9.6–42 mg/kg/day for rats and 57–66 mg/kg/day for mice. Therefore, cancer risk calculations are likely not appropriate, and a safety factor approach should be used.

Analytical Methods

Using USEPA Method 522, the minimum reporting level was 0.07 μg/L (ppb) using solid-phase extraction and GC/MS with selected ion monitoring.

Water Treatment

Due to its high water solubility, solvent properties, and biological and chemical stability, 1,4-dioxane is very difficult to remove from drinking water. Conventional coagulation and filtration, granular-activated carbon (GAC) and aeration and membranes are not effective for treating dioxane. The most effective but high-cost method for treatment of low concentrations is an advanced oxidation process using hydrogen peroxide and ultraviolet (UV) light, or ozone and UV light. These processes produce hydroxyl free radicals that are capable of extracting hydrogen from the molecule leading to its decomposition.

Available POU/POE offerings would be very limited in effectiveness.

Regulations and Guidelines

There are occupational exposure controls, but currently there is no USEPA drinking water standard for dioxane. Dioxane is a likely candidate for future regulation. There is a Drinking Water Health Advisory at 0.035 mg/L for a projected hypothetical cancer risk of 1/10,000. California has a notification level of 1 ppb, and removal of the source from service is required at 0.035 mg/L (35 ppb). The Connecticut action level is 0.003 mg/L (3 ppb), and New York's drinking water standard is 0.050 mg/L (50 ppb). The WHO's Guideline for Drinking Water Quality is 0.050 mg/L (50 μg/L, ppb).

Conclusion

More recent mechanist and MOA information raise questions about the earlier risks attributed to exposure to 1,4-dioxane. All the assessments and guidelines should be reexamined due to the new suggested noncarcinogenic MOA that is described in the text.

Sources

Agency for Toxic Substances and Disease Registry (ATSDR) (2012). Toxicological Profile for 1,4-dioxane. US Department of Health and Human Services, Public Health Service, Atlanta, GA. www.atsdr.cdc.gov/toxprofiles/tpi87.pdf.

Cotruvo JA (2014). 1,4-Dioxane. Contaminant of the Month. Water Technology onLine. www.watertechonline.com/contaminant-of-the-month-14-dioxane/.

Dourson ML. et al (2017). Update: Mode of action (MOA) for liver tumors induced by oral exposure to 1,4-dioxane. *Regulatory Toxicology and Pharmacology*. 88: pp. 45–55.

Eckhardt A (2018). 1,4-Dioxane, *JAWWA*, in press.
EPA (2008). Method 522, EPA/600/R-08/101. www.epa.gov/safewater/methods/analyticalmethods/_ogwdw.html.
EPA (2012). Drinking Water Standards and Health Advisories. www.epa.gov/sites/produciton/files/2015-09/documents/dwstandards2012.pdf.
EPA Technical Fact Sheet-1,4-Dioxane, November 2017. www.epa.gov/sites/production/files/2016-09/documents/benzene.pdf.
Teledyne/Tekmar (2012). Comparing US EPA and FDA Methods for 1,4-Dioxane in Consumer Products. www.teledynetekmar.com/resources/Application%20Notes/14Dioxane.pdf.
World Health Organization Guidelines for Drinking-water Quality (2017). www.who.int/water_sanitation_health/publications/drinking-water-quality-guidelines-4-including-1st-addendum/en/4th edition.

GLYPHOSATE

INTRODUCTION

Glyphosate is probably the most widely used agricultural herbicide for residential lawns, and numerous crop applications, forestry, and aquatic weed control, and it is a registered pesticide in at least 130 countries. Annual world production is more than 720,000 metric tons. Glyphosate, also known as Roundup* and by several other trade names, is a broad-spectrum herbicide that was introduced by the Monsanto corporation in 1974. Its original patents ran out in 1991 and 2000, so today it has many producers.

This post-emergent systemic herbicide kills or suppresses virtually all plant types including weeds, grasses, shrubs, and trees, and also has some aquatic plant control applications.

Its chemical name is *N*-(phosphonomethyl)glycine, and it is a fairly simple phosphonate with the chemical formula $C_3H_8NO_5P$. It is marketed in several salt forms in water solution along with inert ingredients that facilitate plant uptake. Glyphosate is not a persistent chemical and is biodegradable by soil microbes, in water and aquatic sediment. It has low soil mobility. The major metabolites are aminomethylphosphonic acid (AMPA) and carbon dioxide. AMPA is more persistent than glyphosate.

OCCURRENCE AND APPLICATIONS

Glyphosate was detected in 36 percent of the US stream samples, with a maximum of 8.7 μg/L and a median less than 0.1 μg/L, by a 2002 US Geological Survey study in nine Midwestern states. AMPA was detected in 69 percent of the samples with a maximum of 3.6 μg/L. Glyphosate has usually been detected at very low concentrations in a small percentage of cereals, fruit, and vegetable samples.

Glyphosate is a potent herbicide. The weed control application rate is only about 3–4 pounds per hectare (about 2.5 acres or 10,000 m^2). Some weeds are developing resistance to glyphosate, which is nature's way of compensating for a toxic stress. Genetically modified, glyphosate-resistant transgenic corn; cotton; canola; and soybean varieties have been developed and are widely planted, allowing concurrent glyphosate applications for weed control.

Health Effects

Numerous national regulators and advisory panels worldwide have reviewed the toxicology and epidemiology of glyphosate and concluded that it has low toxicity to humans and does not pose a cancer risk. The WHO Guidelines for Drinking Water Quality (GDWQ) indicate that glyphosate and AMPA have similar toxicological profiles and a health-based value of 0.9 mg/L could be derived from the acceptable daily intake (ADI) of 0.3 mg/kg/day for glyphosate and AMPA alone or in combination. It was derived from the NOAEL of 32 mg/kg/day in a 26-month study in rats, with a safety factor of 100.

However, a 2015 late review by the IARC created very great controversy by concluding from essentially the same database that it is probably carcinogenic to humans based on limited evidence of cancer risk in humans and sufficient evidence in experimental animals (mice, not rats). For perspective, other substances listed by IARC include french fries, pickled vegetables, fluorescent lights, using aloe, drinking very hot beverages, and more than 1,000 other products.

A few epidemiological studies provided mixed results primarily in the highest exposure groups, and some were nonstatistically significant for lymphocytic leukemia or non-Hodgkin lymphoma. Several high-dose carcinogenicity studies in mice produced small differences between the zero controls and lower doses, and the highest dose. High-dose rat studies were negative. If it is carcinogenic in mice, the potency is probably very low.

Analysis

Water analyses often involve derivatization and gas chromatography, but the limited occurrence potential and high drinking water MCL and MCLG do not generally warrant analyses in the USEPA's method is 547. The Standard Methods analysis 6651-B-00 is the only online version that Standard Methods has approved.

Water Treatment

Chlorination, ozonation, advanced oxidation processes, nanofiltration, and RO can generally provide good removal of glyphosate. Biodegradation and adsorption processes can be effective for removing glyphosate in bank filtration and slow sand filters. GAC treatment is also effective.

Regulation

The USEPA's MCLG and MCL for glyphosate are the same, i.e., 0.7 mg/L (700 μg/L).

The WHO concluded that drinking water guideline values for glyphosate and AMPA are not necessary because of the low risk from occurrences from drinking water.

Discussion

The IARC conclusion has been controversial. It is not consistent with the many registration decisions made over the years in many countries, nor is it consistent with USEPA and California which had previously concluded that glyphosate is unlikely to pose a cancer risk to humans. The IARC statement of "probably carcinogenic to humans" has resulted in hundreds of lawsuits for damages against Monsanto and others in the United States. A July 7, 2017, listing in California's Proposition 65 requires companies to identify substances in products "known to the State of California to cause cancer," which the State is apparently compelled to do by the 1986 Proposition 65 statute if an IARC listing occurs. Political debates are also underway in the European Union to withdraw registration. That Proposition 65 listing would require notifications on products containing a listed substance and carries fines of $2,500 per violation per day for each unit. However, that listing was challenged, and a federal judge issued a preliminary injunction concluding that California cannot "compel false, misleading and highly controversial statements." That has probably been appealed, but it appears that there is a large body of international disagreement with the IARC conclusion, which IARC has since reiterated.

Sources

Cotruvo JA (2016). Contaminant of the Month: Glyphosate. Water Technology on Line. www.watertechonline.com/contaminant-month-glyphosate/.

EPA (1990). Methods for the Determination of Organic Compounds in Drinking Water, Supplement 1. EPA /600/4-90/020. www.nemi.gov.

EPA (2012). Drinking Water Standards and Health Advisories. www.epa.gov/sites/produciton/files/2015-09/documents/dwstandards2012.pdf.

IARC (2015). IARC Monographs Volume 112: Evaluation of Five Organophosphate Insecticides and Herbicides. www.iarc.fr/en/media-centre/iarcnews/pdf/MonographVolume112.pdf.

Mohan G (2018). Glyphosate Cancer Warning in California Halted. Los Angeles Times. February 27. www.latimes.com/business/la-fi-glyphosate-prop65-story.html.

OEHHA (2017). Glyphosate. https://oehha.ca.gov/proposition-65/chemicals/glyphosate.

Standard Methods (2017). Method 6651B-00. Standard Methods for the Examination of Water and Wastewater, 23rd Edition. www.techstreet.com/standards/standard-methods-for-the-examination-of-water-and-wastewater-23rd-edition?sid=msn&utm_medium=cpc&utm_source=bing&product_id=1974889.

Wall Street Journal (2018). A Cancer Scare Defeat in California. www.wsj.com.

WHO (2011/2017). World Health Organization Guidelines for Drinking-water Quality. www.who.int/water_sanitation_health/publications/drinking-water-quality-guidelines-4-including-1st-addendum/en/4th edition.

MICROCYSTIN ALGAL TOXINS IN DRINKING WATER

Introduction

Algal toxins in drinking water have generated a lot of visibility but they are not a new phenomenon. There are many issues associated with their formation and occurrence, and monitoring, treatment technology, health concerns, and drinking water guidelines.

Numerous algal blooms occur every summer in the United States, including a major one in 2014 that resulted in a probably unnecessary "do not drink" order and major economic consequences at the public water system on Western Lake Erie in Toledo, Ohio. Cyanobacteria are among the most genetically diverse microorganisms and they exist in almost all world locations and environmental niches, including extremes of heat and salinity. They are given credit for converting the earth from an anaerobic to aerobic environment by their ability to convert carbon dioxide into oxygen by photosynthesis. Some of them produce potent toxins. The most common algal toxins are microcystins, anatoxins, cylindrospermopsins, nodularins, and saxitoxins. Microcystins are usually found at the highest concentrations. Each of the toxins has congeners that are very similar chemical structures with differing toxicities.

Some people consume edible cyanobacteria as food or supplements. There are many projects underway attempting to cultivate algae as a source of biofuels including oils and alcohol, and some use sewage as a source of nutrients. The concept is plausible, but the economics have not been successful to date.

Cyanobacteria

There are numerous algae and algal toxins including those that occur in the sea (red tides), and those that are of concern in fresh waters that are drinking water sources and recreational waters. This discussion will concentrate on the fresh waters, particularly those associated with blue-green algae, which are also called cyanobacteria. The name cyanobacteria is misleading because it is related to the blue-green color (cyan) of the algae and has no association with cyanide. Some argue that technically algae (eukaryotes) are not as simple as bacteria (prokaryotes).

Where and How Do Cyanobacteria Grow?

Cyanobacteria are commonly present in surface waters and only some species produce toxins; however, they become a significant problem when they proliferate and produce unsightly biomass (algal blooms) and release toxins, especially when the algae die and decompose. They proliferate under excessive nitrogen and phosphorus nutrient conditions, sunlight and usually in slow moving water. The cells lyse after death and release most of the accumulated toxins into the water; decomposition of the biomass depletes the oxygen in the water and produces eutrophic conditions that are detrimental to the aquatic life. Toxins that may be present can also impact the aquatic organisms.

Drinking water treatment plants drawing from source surface waters prone to summer algal blooms must contend with potential algal blooms and be prepared to respond rapidly. Observable source water conditions could include color, suspended cells and filaments, surface scum and huge masses of aggregated algae. Frequently production of potent taste and odor producing compounds such as geosmin and 2-methylisoborneol occur simultaneously, generating musty off tastes in the drinking water that some people can detect at less than 20 parts per trillion (ppt).

Toxicity of Microcystin-LR

Microcystins have about 250 variants (congeners with similar structures). Microcystin-LR appears to be among the most common, among the most frequently detected and among the most toxic forms. Its molecular weight is approximately 1,000 Da. Concentrations can range from single digits to many hundreds of micrograms per gram dry weight. Raw water samples are usually in single digit micrograms per liter but have been reported in the hundreds in some cases. Elimination mechanisms include biodegradation and photolysis; however, the algae and toxins can be persistent in the water for days.

Human illnesses and some animal deaths have been reported on several continents in recreational exposures—where human exposure can occur by skin contact as well as inadvertent ingestion, and from dialysis where the water treatment system was not functioning properly. Symptoms include nausea, abdominal pain, vomiting, diarrhea, sore throat, and blistering at the mouth. A large outbreak occurred in Brazil in 1988.

Microcystin-LR is a hepatotoxin with reported mouse LD-50 of about 5,000 µg/kg body weight and higher in the rat. Sub-chronic toxicity (90 days) was tested in groups of 15 male and 15 female mice exposed at 0, 40, 200 or 1,000 µg/kg bw/day (Fawell et al, 1999). The NOAEL was 40 µg/kg/day; one male and two females in the 200 µg/kg/day group showed slight liver pathology; all mice at the highest dose showed liver changes. In other studies, young mice were less affected than older mice.

Groups of five pigs were tested for 44 days at several doses with an extract of *Microcystis aeruginosa*. The lowest-observed-adverse-effect-level (LOAEL) was 280 µg/kg/day with one pig showing liver effects. In a longer term study, three velvet monkeys were exposed by gavage three days per week for 46 weeks to increasing doses from 20 to 80 µg/kg/day. No statistically significant changes were observed. No toxicity was observed during an up to 18-month study in female mice consuming drinking water containing 20 µg/L of Microcystin-LR/l.

In a 28-day study in a sensitive rat model with limited history (Heinze, 1999), male rats (10 per group) were dosed for 28 days at 0, 50, and 150 µg/kg bw/day. No NOAEL was observed; the LOAEL was 50 µg/kg/day. A dose-dependent increase in liver weight was observed as well as numerous biochemical alterations.

Analytical Methods

Microcystins can be analyzed by liquid chromatography linked with tandem mass spectrometry (LC/MS/MS). This is USEPA Method 544. It allows analyses of several algal toxins with minimum detection limits in the vicinity of 0.01 µg/L (10 ppt).

The quicker, nonspecific semiquantitative technique is called enzyme-linked immunosorbant assay (ELISA). It uses an antigen–antibody reaction to detect antigen components reactive to the particular antibody that is immobilized on a solid phase. It is less specific than LC/MS/MS and can overcount especially at low concentrations, because it measures a structural feature that is not always associated with toxicity. A mouse bioassay is used in screening, as well as a protein phosphatase assay that is sensitive to sub-microgram levels.

WATER TREATMENT

Water treatment approaches include physical removal of algal cells, chemical conversion, and adsorption.

Conventional treatment that includes coagulation, flocculation, sedimentation, and chlorine disinfection can remove most of the algal cells, but toxin removal is more problematic. It is essential to remove the algal cells by filtration prior to the addition of any oxidant such as chlorine. The oxidant will lyse the cells and release the toxins into the drinking water.

Oxidants/disinfectants such as chlorine, chloramine, chlorine dioxide, ozone, potassium permanganate, and ultraviolet (UV) light are frequently available in a water treatment facility, or can be added, and provide a range of efficacies against the toxins. The following relate to Microcystin-LR, which is a common form and among the most potent:

- Ozone will rapidly lyse the cells; it is effective against the toxin at ozone doses of 5 ppm or less and at very low concentration-time values (CT in mg-min/L). CT means concentration in mg/L × time in minutes, so, for example, a concentration of 1 mg/L for 10 minutes would be approximately the same as 10 mg/L for 1 minute. Elimination of Microcystin-LR is virtually instantaneous.
- Potassium permanganate will lyse the cells and is also a very effective, rapid treatment for the toxin. The CT value for complete elimination is about 25 mg min/L.
- Free chlorine as HOCl will lyse the cells and it is very effective, achieving nearly complete elimination at CT of about 60 mg min/L. Chlorine is present in almost every surface water treatment plant and probably functions as both an oxidizing and a chlorinating agent. However, the most effective form is HOCl, and its concentration and efficacy will be a function of the dosage, contact time, the chlorine demand, and the pH. About 50 percent HOCl and 50 percent OCl^- are present in equilibrium at pH 8; virtually no HOCL is present at pH above 9.5.
- Chlorine dioxide is a good disinfectant and lyses cyanobacteria cells, but it has minimal reactivity toward the toxin.
- Monochloramine has some reactivity against the cells, but not toward the toxin.
- UV light irradiation at fairly high doses has a destructive effect on the cells, but does not affect toxin concentrations.

Membranes such as RO, nanofiltration, ultrafiltration, and microfiltration are all effective for the removal of cells. However, pretreatment and frequent cleaning would be necessary, so cell removal should occur using granular filters. RO and nanofiltration, but not microfiltration, would be effective for toxin removal.

Adsorption using powdered-activated carbon is a short-term technique for the removal of geosmin, 2-methylisoborneol, and toxins. However, the efficacy is variable and is affected by water quality factors. GAC is effective if the filter is of sufficient depth and condition, but it is subject to exhaustion and exceeding its capacity. Only a few GAC systems are in place in the United States that are regularly/frequently reactivated; most applications are in shallow fixed beds for routine taste and odor control and not reactivated for years, so their performance is not generally predictable in a sustained algal bloom. Biologically activated carbon filters would be more likely to have sustained performance without frequent reactivation, because they usually incorporate ozone that would react with the toxins and also provide the opportunity for microbial degradation of chemicals on the GAC surface.

POU and POE Technologies

Because microcystins are large high-molecular-weight molecules, both carbon and RO technology should be effective. The carbon would be subject to exhaustion requiring replacement, and the low pressure RO has a very high water reject ratio.

Guidelines

The WHO GDWQ is 0.001 mg/L (1 μg/L) as a lifetime tolerable daily intake for a 60-kg adult consuming water at 2 L/day. It was based upon the study of Fawell et al.'s 13-week mouse study and incorporated an uncertainty (safety) factor of 1,000. It would be considered conservative.

The USEPA issued 10-day drinking water health advisories that were based upon the Heinze's 28-day study. The health advisory (HA) for infants and preschool age children is 0.3 μg/L; the adult 10-day HA is 1.6 μg/L. Canada has issued a seasonal advisory of 0.015 mg/L (1.5 μg/L) also based upon the Heinze study. All three guidelines applied a safety factor of 1,000 to the NOAEL or LOAEL from animal study. In the Toledo case, which occurred prior to the release of the USEPA and Canadian Guidelines, the no-drink order was issued for exceeding 1 μg/L and lasted for about 2 days. It referred to the WHO Guideline as its basis, but perhaps misinterpreted the meaning of tolerable daily intake to apply for any single day, rather than per day for chronic (70-year lifetime) exposure, which is the basis for the WHO guideline, or it was an example of extreme conservatism.

Comparing the two key studies, the Fawell study was for 90 days, well documented, using a commercial strain of mice with a long history of toxicology testing results with many chemicals and use in risk assessment. The Heinze study was for 28 days and used a very unusual house bred rat which had virtually no published history of toxicology testing results with other chemicals in the published literature. The Heinze rats were much more sensitive than the Fawell mice, but lacking the historical data from testing many other chemicals makes it difficult to provide a context for the appropriateness of those rats for projecting human sensitivity and risk.

There are obvious fundamental differences between the USEPA HA, the Canadian Guideline and the WHO Guideline. USEPA's is for 10 days and it produced concentrations for young children, as well as a higher number for adults. The Canadian Guideline is seasonal and also based upon the Heinze study and recommends that infants could be provided bottled water. The WHO Guideline is for lifetime exposure, although algal blooms in most locations are seasonal and sporadic.

Conclusions

Microcystins are real toxins and they can occur in drinking water when associated with some, but not all algal blooms in source waters. Water treatment is definitely possible but requires care and the appropriate approach. Algal cells should be filtered out prior to exposure to an oxidant/disinfectant. Free chlorine (HOCl) is an essential component in conventional chlorination systems. Monitoring also has its complications. ELISA analyses have applications as screening but are not quantitative at low sub-1 μg/L levels. There are differences between the several drinking water guidelines that have been issued. The WHO is revising its Guideline in 2018/2019 to include short term exposures in addition to lifetime exposures that were in the original GDWQ.

Sources

Cotruvo JA (2014). Algal Toxins in Drinking Water. www.watertechonline.com/professor-poupoe-october-2014/.

Cotruvo JA (2015). EPA Algal Toxin Guidelines. Water Technology on Line. www.watertechonline.com/articles/170097-dr-joe-cotruvo-addresses-epa-algal-toxin-guidelines.

Chorus I and Bartram J (1999). Toxic Cyanobcteria in Water. E and FN Spon on behalf of WHO. ISBN 0-419-23930-8.

Cyanobacterial Toxins in Drinking Water. Health Canada. www.canada.ca/en/health-canada/programs/cyanobacterial-toxins-drinking-water/cyanobacterial-toxins-drinking-water.html Published 2016-02-12.

Cyanobacteria and Cyanotoxins: Information for Drinking Water Systems. EPA-810F11001. July 2012.

Cyanobacterial Toxins—Microcystin-LR. Health Canada. www.hc-sc.gc.ca/ewh-semt/pubs./water-eau, Archived June 24, 2013.

Ding J, Shi H, Timmons T, Adams C (2010). Release and Removal of Microcystins from Microcystis during Oxidative, Physical and UV based Disinfection. *Journal of Environmental Engineering*: pp. 2–11.

EPA Drinking Water Health Advisory for the Cyanobacterial Microcystin Toxins. EPA 820R15100. June 2015.

EPA (2015). Determination of Microcystins and Nodularin in Drinking Water by Solid Phase Extraction and Liquid Chromatography/Tandem/Tandem Mass Spectrometry (LC/MS/MS). Version 1.0. EPA/600/^-14/474. www.epa.gov/nerlcwww/documents/Method 544_Final.pdf.

Fawell JK. et al (1999). The toxicity of cyanobacterial toxins in the mouse. Microcystin-LR. *Human and Experimental Toxicology*. 18(3): pp. 162–167.

Funari E and Testai E (2008). Human health risk assessment related to cyanotoxins exposure. *Critical Reviews in Toxicology*. 38: pp. 97–125.

Heinze R (1999). Toxicity of the cyanobacterial toxin microcystin-LR to rats after 28 days intake with drinking water. *Environmental Toxicology*. 14(1): pp. 57–60.

Kaloudis T, Zervou SK, Avagianos C, Christofhoridis C, Triantis TM, Hiskia A, Fastner J, Cotruvo JA, Isailovic D (2017). Evolution of Analytical Methods for Regulatory Monitoring of Microcystins: Are We There Yet?

Westrick JA and Szlag D (2018). A Cyanotoxin Primer for Drinking Water Professionals. *JAWWA*, in press.

WHO (1998). World Health Organization Cyanobacterial Toxins: Microcystin-LR in Drinking Water. WHO/SDE/WSH/03.04/57, 1998.

WHO (2011). Guidelines for Drinking Water Quality. World Health Organization. 2011, and Addendum to the 4th edition, 2017.

3 Selected Microbial Contaminants

COLIFORMS, *ESCHERICHIA COLI,* AND FECAL BACTERIA IN DRINKING WATER

INTRODUCTION

Coliforms (total coliforms) are diverse bacteria that live (not exclusively) in the intestines of warm-blooded animals, as well as in the general environment. Coliform bacteria are rod-shaped, gram-negative, non-spore-forming bacteria that can ferment lactose with the production of acid and gas when incubated for 24 hours at 35°C–37°C. There are numerous genera included in the group called coliforms: some of them are *Citrobacter*, *Enterobacter*, *Hafnia*, *Klebsiella*, and *Serratia*. Fecal coliforms and *Escherichia coli* are also rod-shaped gram-negative organisms.

Thermotolerant fecal coliforms are a subgroup that can ferment lactose at 44°C–45°C (111.2°F–113°F). *E. coli* are a subgroup of fecal coliforms. They are gram-negative, rod-shaped bacteria named after Theodor Escherich, who discovered them in 1885. There are numerous species and strains of each and most are not harmful, but some can infect humans. *E. coli* constitute about 0.1 percent of gut flora, so they are present in greater numbers than pathogens and are usually beneficial.

E. coli are the most important indicator bacteria for relatively recent fecal contamination, because they are more numerous than fecal pathogens, can survive in the environment and are similarly subject to water treatment. Risks are associated with exposures to sewage/sanitary contaminated milk and food, recreational water and drinking water. Apart from the disease concerns of some strains, *E. coli* have many uses in biotechnology, including recombinant DNA research.

OCCURRENCE

Total coliforms are common environmental organisms in soils and water as well as being found in fecal sources from warm-blooded animals. They are common in surface water, soils, plant materials, and paper mill effluents. For that reason detections of total coliforms alone are not a clear indicator of fecal contamination, whereas the presence of fecal coliforms or *E. coli* is a much more specific marker of fecal contamination. This is especially true for *E. coli*, although even they are not completely unique in that regard, because some have been found in environmental samples in warm climates. *E. coli* detections in food and water are a good indication that relatively recent (perhaps 10–15 days) sewage/sanitary contamination has occurred. They survive longer at lower temperatures.

Health Effects

Total coliforms and bacteria in the genus *E. coli* are usually not pathogens per se. Most strains of *E. coli* are harmless, but some can cause serious illness in humans such as *E.coli* 0157/H7, which can cause fatal disease. Some of its symptoms include bloody diarrhea, stomach cramps, vomiting, and fever. Some *E.coli* can also cause respiratory illnesses and urinary tract infections.

Nonpathogenic *E. coli* begin to colonize an infant's gastrointestinal (GI) tract within 40 hours after birth from food, water, or human contact. They reproduce rapidly under ideal conditions, doubling in 20 minutes.

They are good indicators for potential bacterial and viral contamination in water, but not necessarily protozoan contamination, because they are less likely to survive for long periods in the environment and are much more susceptible to disinfection processes, except perhaps ultraviolet (UV) light.

Certain pathogenic strains can cause diarrhea and illnesses such as gastroenteritis, urinary tract infections, neonatal meningitis, hemolytic-uremic syndrome, peritonitis, septicemia, and some pneumonia. Shiga toxin-producing strains such as *E. coli* 0157:H7 cause hemolytic-uremic syndrome, which has many serious health outcomes and often death.

Analysis

Optimal growth of total coliforms and *E. coli* occurs at 37°C (98.6°F), which is normal body temperature. Traditional analyses involve membrane filtered culture plating and colony counting in a microbiology laboratory. Within the past 30 years, Colilert®-type and some other methods involving detection of activity of the enzymes β-D-galactosidase and β-glucuronidase have greatly simplified the analyses for coliforms and *E. coli*. β-D-Galactosidase acts on lactose which is a sugar consisting of D-glucose and D-galactose. Since most non-coliforms do not have these enzymes, they are unable to grow and interfere. The few non-coliforms that do have these enzymes are selectively suppressed by the test's specifically formulated matrix.

The coliform enzyme β-D-galactosidase metabolizes a marker chemical *O*-nitrophenyl-β-D-galactopyranoside (ONPG) that then produces a yellow color when the nitrophenol is released. OPNG is chemically similar to lactose except that an orthonitrophenyl group has been substituted for glucose. The *E. coli* enzyme β-glucuronidase metabolizes 4-nitrophenyl-β-D-glucopyranosiduronic acid derivative of 4-methylumbelliferyl-beta-D-glucuronide (MUG) also producing a yellow color; however, 4-methylumbelliferyl portion fluoresces blue under UV light indicating the presence of *E. coli*.

Kits costing a few dollars per test allow testing under non-microbiology laboratory conditions. It is essential to have a means of providing up to 24-hour sample storage at approximately 37°C (98.6°F). Quantification can be done using multiple dilutions.

This approach is different from traditional media, which provide a nutrient-rich environment that supports the growth of both target organisms and nontargets. When nontargets grow and mimic target organisms, false positives can occur. Growth of nontargets can also suppress target organisms and give false negatives in traditional media. To suppress nontargets, traditional media often include high levels of salts, detergents, or other selective agents that may inadvertently suppress target organisms and give further false negatives.

The Part 9000 Microbiological Examination section of Standard Methods includes a wide spectrum of methods including for Total Coliforms are 9221 B/E; 9223 B; Total, Fecals and *E. coli* is 9221 F. Numerous other methods are listed in the 9221, 9222, 9223.

Water Treatment

Coliforms, fecal coliforms, and *E. coli* are present in source waters in amounts much greater than specific pathogens, and their analyses are much simpler than for the pathogens. So, since they can be present in drinking water (and certainly wastewater) at least partly from fecal contamination, their detections have been used for many years as usually conservative water quality and treatment performance indicators and as process monitors. The expected minimum log removal performance of a surface water treatment facility is at least 4 logs of virus, and bacteria up to 6 logs, and 2 or 3 logs for giardia and cryptosporidium protozoa.

The drinking water treatment goal in the United States is to achieve no detectable coliform, fecal or *E.coli* bacteria per 100 mL of sample. *E. coli* and total coliforms are effective treatment performance indicators for bacteria and viruses, but not protozoa. Standard disinfection with chlorine, hypochlorite, chlorine dioxide, ozone, and UV are effective in minutes for bacteria and viruses in low turbidity water, as well as chloramines with much larger concentration in mg/L times time in minutes (Ct) values.

The principal conventional water treatment techniques that are effective for controlling pathogens and the indicator organisms are coagulation and filtration and disinfection, and there are numerous variations including choices of disinfectant, dosing levels, and contact times. Slow sand filtration is also effective. In addition, membrane technologies remove particles by size exclusion. Nanofiltration (~0.001 μm pore size) and reverse osmosis (RO) (~0.0001 μm) membranes can directly remove bacteria and viruses. RO membranes can remove at least 6 logs of bacteria, virus or protozoa, but some regulatory agencies will not allow that much credit, because they are concerned about potential mechanical breakthrough; however, daily pressure decay testing provides good assurance of performance, and other barriers in a well-designed system will also compensate in the event of a leakage event. The larger pored membranes, microfiltration (~0.1–1 μm) and ultrafiltration (~0.001–0.1 μm) can also remove many microorganisms including bacteria and viruses to a variable degree since the microorganisms are usually aggregated or adsorbed to particulates, or when the membranes are somewhat fouled.

Conventional coagulation alone is expected to remove 1 or 2 logs of microorganisms. Potent disinfectants can inactivate up to 4 or more logs of microorganisms in a few minutes or less depending upon the concentrations, times and water temperatures (Ct values). Disinfection techniques using chlorine, ozone, and chlorine dioxide are not very specific to particular bacteria and viruses so killing or inactivation of the coliform indicator microorganisms is a good indication of the concurrent elimination of any bacterial or viral pathogens that might be present. Coliforms are not good indicators of protozoa because they are more resistant to disinfection than are the bacterial indicators. Because protozoa are much more resistant to disinfection than are *E. coli* and bacterial and viral pathogens, filtration is often necessary for their removal, although UV is very effective at rendering them nonpathogenic. For small quantities of water, the World Health Organization (WHO) recommends bringing questionable water to full boil, followed by cool down to eliminate all pathogens.

Disinfection and water treatment as practiced is not intended to produce sterile water. The purpose of water treatment is to produce safe water that assures that humans will not be exposed to an infectious dose of the pathogen by significantly reducing concentration of the pathogens that might be present.

Common point-of-use (POU) carbon filters do not remove pathogens. If they advertise that they contain silver, it is only to reduce some microbial regrowth on the filter and not to disinfect the water, and they cannot make disinfection claims. There are, however, certified disinfecting home water treatment devices available, and others are capable of removing protozoa by filtration. POU is not permitted in the United States for meeting microbial drinking water standards in public water supplies. Appropriately certified point-of-entry systems can be used for decentralized compliance.

Regulations

Disinfection and filtration drinking water regulations have reduced risks of waterborne diseases. Reports of waterborne disease outbreaks in the United States have been in decline since the implementation of the Safe Drinking Water Act beginning about 1980. Most outbreaks are now due to microbial regrowth (e.g., *legionella*) and deficiencies in distribution rather than inadequate water treatment.

Until April 15, 2013, the maximum contaminant level (MCL) for total coliforms in the United States was 0/100 mL in at least 95 percent of the samples collected by a water supplier each month. No positive samples for fecal coliform or *E.coli* were allowed. The total coliform MCL (but not fecal coliforms or *E. coli*) was rescinded partly because the compiled data do not indicate a good correlation between total coliform detections and waterborne disease. This has been known for many years. The WHO eliminated total coliforms from its guidelines about 20 years ago. Now total coliforms are considered to be most likely indicative of a lack of proper operation and maintenance (O&M) usually in distribution. Follow-up determinations of cause are required if detections occur.

The current drinking water regulations have an MCL of $<$ 1/100 mL only for *E. coli* or fecal coliforms. Analyses for total coliforms are still required, but they are used primarily to indicate whether there are sanitary flaws in the system that should be corrected. If *E. coli* are verified and not corrected immediately, there is the potential for a boil water notice to be issued because of the connection with sewage contamination.

The surface water treatment rules require that drinking water from surface waters maintains turbidity of less than 0.3 ntu at each filter at least 95 percent of the time, and never exceeds 1 ntu. They are designed to control protozoa including cryptosporidia, but in doing so they also control bacteria and viruses.

Conclusions

E.coli and fecal bacteria are the common indicator organisms that are the nexus between sewage contamination and potential human pathogen contamination of drinking water. They are easy and cost little to analyze and they have an excellent track record of detecting significant contamination possibilities leading to corrective actions in the drinking water treatment plant.

Sources

Beactiviahealth. Intestinal Microflora. www.beactiviahealth.com/html_cap/1_3.html.

CDC (1936). National Center for Emerging and Zoonotic Infectious Diseases. Breed RS, Conn HJ (May 1936). *Journal of Bacteriology*. 31(5): pp. 517–518.

CDC (2014). A Guide to Drinking Water Treatment Technologies for Household Use. www.cdc.gov/healthywater/drinking/home-water-treatment/household_water_treatment.html.

Cotruvo JA (2013). Coliform Bacteria. Water Technology on Line.

Cotruvo JA (2015). *E.coli* and other Fecal Bacteria in Drinking Water. www.watertechonline.com/contaminant-of-the-month-e-coli-and-other-fecal-bacteria-in-drinking-water/.

EPA (1979). Evaluation of the Microbiology Standards for Drinking Water. Hendricks C, editor.

EPA 570/9–78-00C. US Government Printing Office: 1979 O275.621. National Technical Information Service, Springfield, Virginia.

EPA (2013). Revisions to the Total Coliforms Rule, FR 78, No.30, Feb. 13, 2013.

EPA (2013). Basic Information about Pathogens and Indicators in Drinking Water_Basic Information about Regulated Contaminants_USEPA.htm (1 of 6) 23/06/2013.

Idexx (2018). www.idexx.com/en/water/water-products-services/colilert/.

Microbeonline (2018). MUG (beta-Glucuronidase) Test for Rapid Identification of *E. coli*. https://microbeonline.com/mug-test-b-glucuronidase-test-for-rapid-identification-of-e-coli/

Standard Methods (2017). Method 6651B-00. Standard Methods for the Examination of Water and Wastewater, 23rd Edition. www.techstreet.com/standards/standard-methods-for-the-examination-of-water-and-wastewater-23rd-edition?sid=msn&utm_medium=cpc&utm_source=bing&product_id=1974889 and www.awwa.org/store/productdetail.aspx?productid=%20 65266295.

WHO (2001). Indicators of Microbial Water Quality. Ashbolt NJ, Grabow WOK, Snozzi M. www.who.int/water_sanitation_health/dwq/iwachap13.pdf.

WHO (2011). Guidelines for Drinking Water Quality. World Health Organization. 4th edition, 2011, and Addendum to the 4th edition, 2017.

LEGIONELLA, LEGIONELLOSIS, AND REGROWTH OF MICROORGANISMS

INTRODUCTION

Legionellosis is clearly the most significant waterborne disease risk in the United States and probably in many world countries with plumbed water systems and effective drinking water regulatory authorities. In the past, the major sources of traditional waterborne diseases were usually surface source waters contaminated by sanitation-associated contamination and inadequate drinking water treatment or treatment breakdowns. Innate distribution and plumbing system deficiencies are now the most significant sources of waterborne disease in the United States and probably in all developed countries.

Since the passage in 1974 and implementation of the Safe Drinking Water Act after about 1975, Environmental Protection Agency (EPA) has issued comprehensive microbial disease management regulations that have been implemented by the states and public water suppliers. These include MCLs for coliform and *E.coli* indicator microorganisms in 1975, surface water, and Ground Water Under the Influence of Surface Water (GWUDI) filtration regulations in 1989 for bacteria, viruses, and *Giardia lamblia*, Interim Enhanced Surface Water Treatment Rule (IESWTR)—December 1998 to include *Cryptosporidium* removal requirements Treatment Techniques and an MCL goal (MCLG) for *Legionella*. Filter Backwash Recycling Rule (FBRR)—June 2001: Long Term 1 Enhanced Surface Water Treatment Rule (LT1ESWTR)—January 2002: Long Term 2 Enhanced Surface Water Treatment Rule (LT2ESWTR)—January 2006. An MCLG of zero and a treatment technique requirement for *Legionella* under the Surface Water Treatment Regulation applies at the water treatment plant. EPA concluded that treatment for Giardia and virus removal would also be expected to remove *Legionella*. This is reasonable, but *Legionella* and other regrowth microorganisms result from conditions in the distribution and the plumbing systems.

As a result of these actions, public water systems have undertaken major improvements in installations and operations of disinfection and filtration treatment technologies and water quality monitoring, and the traditional waterborne diseases incidence have been reduced significantly. However, the types of illnesses have changed to water distribution-related causes that cannot be entirely eliminated at the central municipal water treatment plant. This calls for a radically different approach to protect public health by regulators and the public.

WATERBORNE DISEASE SURVEILLANCE DATA

Legionella, a rod-shaped bacteria, are common in many environments, including soil and water, and at least 50 species and 70 serogroups have been identified. *Legionella* bacteria-related respiratory diseases include legionellosis caused by *Legionella pneumophila*, and Pontiac fever, a less virulent disease caused by *L. longbeachae*. *L. pneumophila* account for about 80–90 percent of legionellosis infections. The reports cited below are undoubtedly understatements of the actual numbers of outbreaks, cases and deaths because of underreporting and difficulties in diagnoses without the genotyping and serotyping of the disease organisms.

The Centers for Disease Control and Prevention (CDC) tracks and periodically reports on the incidence of waterborne disease and cases in the Morbidity and Mortality Weekly Reports (MMWR). There were 851 reported outbreaks from 1971 to 2010. The biennial reports have ranged from lows of about five incidences to a high of 48 in 1980–1981. The incidence trends have been generally continuously downward from 1980. The types of reported waterborne illnesses have included viral, bacterial, parasitic, and chemical. In the early reports most of the etiologic agents causing the diseases were not identifiable, but as the microbiological and surveillance responses have improved, now almost all specific causes are identified. It was assumed that many of the unidentifiable outbreaks were due to viruses, because viruses could not be efficiently isolated and identified. However, with better disinfection, viruses and bacteria are now a smaller component, and filtration has reduced protozoan diseases.

In the CDC MMWR for years 2009–2010 waterborne disease outbreaks totaled 33 and they resulted in 1,040 cases and 85 hospitalizations and eight deaths. In all but one outbreak the etiologic causes were identified. Campylobacter accounted for 12 percent of the outbreaks and 78 percent of the illnesses. Four outbreaks were caused by *Giardia,* one by *Cryptosporidium,* two by *E. coli*, one norovirus, one hepatitis A and one was undetermined. However, 19 of the 33 outbreaks were caused by *Legionella*, resulting in 72 cases and all eight deaths. Six more legionellosis deaths were associated with other drinking water originated exposures such as from fountains or cooling systems, and it was the only waterborne illness that resulted in deaths.

In addition, public health officials from 11 states reported 18 outbreaks associated with environmental or undetermined water exposures, causing 280 cases of illness, 67 hospitalizations (24 percent of all cases) and 10 deaths. These included 15 legionellosis outbreaks that resulted in 254 cases and all 10 deaths. The legionellosis outbreaks occurred in four hotels and motels, three hospitals and health-care facilities, three long-term care facilities, an indoor workplace/office, a factory/industrial setting, a mobile home park, a resort and a multiuse facility. In the 2017 MMWR for 2013–2014, there were 42 outbreaks and 1,006 cases; 24 were *legionella* accounting for 130 cases and all of the 13 deaths.

Legionellosis has been a reportable disease in the United States only since 2001. The disease is not caused by ingestion of the water, but rather by inhalation of aerosols such as during showering or from inhaling blow down vapors from cooling system heat exchangers, or probably even humidifiers. Those at particular risk are the elderly and smokers, especially people with impaired immune systems such as those who are hospitalized and in extended care facilities, but other at risk people are also in the community. CDC has estimated that between 8,000 and 18,000 people are hospitalized with Legionnaires'-related disease each year in the United States. It is not known how many of those are attributable to exposure from the plumbing or cooling systems.

It is well known that *Legionella* are detectable in a high percentage of plumbing systems, including in homes, hotels and other buildings, and cooling towers, and a substantial number of people in the general population are susceptible because of their ages or health or immune status. Several hospital-related outbreaks of *Legionella*-related diseases are reported annually around the world, but undoubtedly most are not identified or attributed to the water system. The significant health outcome of the Flint, Michigan corrosion problem was likely two spikes of legionellosis cases and deaths mostly associated with a hospital that did not have supplemental disinfection.

Legionella and Plumbing Systems

Legionella microorganisms are common environmental and soil bacteria. Regulated water treatment at the central plant is capable of removing them from influent water.

Re-seeding of the plumbing systems might occur in several situations:

- If a few microorganisms survive water treatment
- Presence of and replication in biofilms
- Warm water temperatures
- From soil contamination during water line leaks and breaks
- During plumbing repairs
- New construction in which the plumbing system has not been properly disinfected prior to commissioning and the facility's placement into service
- Hot tubs and spas
- Cooling towers with outdoor air exposure from airborne particulates

They can proliferate at temperatures in the range of about 25°C–55°C (77°F–120/130°F) such as can be found in hot water systems, shower heads, and in cold water systems in interior plumbing, in warm climates, or during warm times of the year. Yet many "authorities" advise homeowners and building managers to maintain hot water temperatures at about 120°F for energy efficiency and to reduce water heating costs. That is an ideal condition for *Legionella* proliferation.

Other Risks from Distributed Water

Numerous pathogenic regrowth microorganisms are known to colonize water distribution and plumbing systems and nosocomial infections have been attributable to exposures from water. In addition to *L. pneumophila*, *P. aeruginosa*, *Stenotrophomonas maltophilia*, Acinetobacter *baumannii*, and *Mycobacterium avium* are among waterborne opportunistic pathogens found in treated water and linked to nosocomial infections in susceptible persons, not necessarily by inhalation.

Five legionellosis outbreaks had a known water source, including three from ornamental fountains, a cooling tower, and a storage tank. The water source was undetermined for 10 legionellosis outbreaks. Among these, one outbreak had multiple implicated sources (drinking water, a spa, and a cooling system), and the remaining nine had insufficient data to determine a particular source. Five of the 10 deaths caused by *Legionella* were associated with a health-care facility, including two long-term care facilities, two with hospitals, and one was an unknown type of health-care facility.

New York City's Legionellosis Outbreak from Cooling Towers

The cooling tower in a recently renovated hotel in the South Bronx seems to have been one of at least five possible sources of *legionella* bacteria contamination from aerosols in the area. Since early July 2015, 113 cases have been reported with 12 deaths and more were detected later. The mist created from the heat exchange process and blowers can be a carrier of the bacteria. Numerous building cooling towers in the area were tested and several contained the same serotype that was present in infected patients. The cooling towers have been disinfected. The city announced on August 20, 2015, that no new cases of legionellosis had been reported and declared the outbreak over. Other legionellosis outbreaks with illnesses and deaths were recently reported in a California prison and a veteran's home in Quincy, Illinois, in late August. Even Disneyland was reported to have had several cases of legionellosis.

International Legionellosis Surveillance and Outbreaks

Of course, legionellosis risk is not unique to the United States. Contracting legionellosis is a risk factor anywhere in the world because of the ubiquitous environmental sources, but it is likely much more dominant in the developed world with its aerosol sources from indoor plumbing, water-based cooling towers, hot tubs and spas, and concentrations of patients in hospitals and nursing homes.

Legionellosis reporting has been underway in the European Union (EU) since 1995. The trending of reported EU/EEA cases began at about 4 per million population in 1995, rose steadily to about 12 per million in 2005, and has been relatively stable from 2005 to 2013. That is possibly surprising, but it might also reflect the limitations of the reporting compliance. Cases were consistently more concentrated in the warmer months between August and October, and that cycle has been repeated each year from 2008 to 2013. Mortality rates increased with age and were greater for cases acquired during the winter months and peaked in February.

The European Center for Disease Prevention and Control (ECDPC) maintains two reporting systems for disease cases, but again, cases are likely to be underreported. Nevertheless, it probably provides the best available data on legionellosis incidence among developed country populations where living and environmental conditions are similar to the United States.

In 2013, 5,851 cases from all causes and not necessarily water related, were reported by the 28 EU states and Norway. Six countries (France, Spain, Italy, Germany, the Netherlands, and the United Kingdom) accounted for 83 percent of the reports, but that might be closely associated with the diligence of reporting compliance. The actual case numbers are likely much greater. About 160 cases reported without specifying the laboratory analysis method were excluded from the statistics.

People older than 50 were accounted for 81 percent of the cases, with a median age of 63, and the male-to-female ratio was 2.4:1, which might reflect higher smoking frequency among males. The death rate was about 10 percent of cases. Most cases were community acquired and 19 percent were associated with travel. Travel-associated cases, which accounted for 787 of the cases, were reported by 30 EU/ European Economic Area (EEA) countries, Canada, Israel, Turkey, Thailand, and the United States.

Another Potential Risk Factor

Another risk factor may be ice machines. The possibility that chewing contaminated ice could lead to aspiration of the microorganisms needs to be examined. Icemaker water reservoirs are often located near compressors, the heat from which could warm the water to temperatures in which *Legionella* growth could occur during low-use periods, and then they could become entrained in the ice.

Treatment Technologies for Managing *Legionella* and Other Regrowth Microorganisms

Treatment is a real challenge and a cookie cutter approach is not likely to be widely successful. A proper HACCP or Water Safety Plan style management plan that includes assessment, treatment, and monitoring should be the systematic approach to follow. The problem of controlling microorganisms colonizing plumbing and distribution systems is not trivial because many of them are associated with biofilms or protozoa in the biofilms such as amoebas where they can replicate. Thus, even though the *Legionella* bacteria may be susceptible to disinfection when in suspension, the disinfectants may not have ready access to them in biofilms. Disinfectants that have been employed have had successes. They include chlorine, chloramine, chlorine dioxide, ozone, UV light, copper/silver ionization, and shock thermal and steam treatments. Each of them has its benefits and weaknesses, and often a combination of treatments must be applied on a regular basis supported by monitoring to indicate the conditions of the system and the time to re-treat.

Chlorine is a powerful disinfectant for bacteria, but even when applied in a temporary hyperchlorination mode (e.g., 50 ppm for several hours) total eradication may not be achieved. Chloramines, which are far less potent biocides than free chlorine, have demonstrated considerable success in reducing *legionella* counts in some water plumbing systems. This could be due to the lower chemical reactivity of chloramine and greater hydrophobicity that allow greater penetration into biofilms. Chlorine dioxide is a potent disinfectant that also has had mixed success. On-site generation and survival of a residual in far plumbing reaches, dead ends, and in hot water systems can be a problem. Ozone and UV might have some efficacy in recirculating systems, but they will be primarily effective against organisms in the water column. Copper/silver in combination and individually have shown successes when they are properly managed and maintained. Shock thermal treatment for several hours at temperatures above 70°C has shown temporary success, but a complete strategy would require a combination of initial biofilm cleanout with a disinfectant system that will retard regeneration of the biofilm.

The concept of final barrier protection has value in situations where sufficient risk exists. For example, instant hot water delivery systems leave a smaller volume of water to stagnate and provide a growth environment. Temperature control valves at faucets and showerheads may allow maintaining hot water lines at temperatures above the ~55°C upper *legionella* growth temperature, and then blending with cold water at the POU to prevent scalding risk.

Analyses

There are several analytic techniques in development and available for *legionella* analyses, including several commercial methods, as well as analyses supplied by commercial laboratories. Some are culture based, some kits are available, some are polymerase chain reaction, and rapid microarray analyses using antibodies on a measuring chip, and some are DNA and RNA sequencing techniques that will determine and identify all of the microorganisms in the water or biofilm.

Regulatory Issues and Regulatory Impediments

The current US federal and state regulatory environment can be an impediment to many facilities installing supplemental disinfection in the drinking water systems, because drinking water regulations require that if any facility with more than 25 users adds water treatment to the public water entering the facility, it becomes a public water system. Therefore, an apartment building or nursing home with permanent residents would become a community water system, and a hospital with 25 employees would become a nontransient, noncommunity water system. Monitoring and other associated requirements would be commensurate with their regulatory status. States have taken different positions on those situations. Anecdotal information from several state authorities is that they range from not wanting reporting if a hospital were adding supplemental disinfection, to placing minimal requirements, to imposing substantial requirements on the facilities. These requirements could range from monitoring for specific components, such as disinfectant residuals and coliform bacteria, to corrosion indicators and some other MCLs, to broader monitoring, requiring certified operators, formal reporting including public notifications, to preventing the use of some disinfectants such as copper and silver, which are used successfully in numerous locations.

If a building such as a hospital wishes to install treatment to manage *legionella* and other regrowth bacteria, the current interpretations of drinking water regulations actually makes it more difficult for them to do so. The rationale for the NTNCWS designation is that if the water supply is modified by a user, there is the possibility that contamination could be introduced and also that some drinking water standards could be exceeded. That is possible, however, the risk benefit balance is not very reasonable for a case such as a hospital adding a disinfectant to its water.

If, for example, chlorine was being added, the chlorine maximum residual disinfection level, and trihalomethane or haloacetic acid disinfection by-product standards might be exceeded if not properly managed, but they are not significant short term risks. However, additional microbial MCL monitoring is not justified, because the supplemental disinfection treatment is intended to reduce microbial contamination. So, it should be possible to devise a special category exemption for hospital facilities, or utilize a separate oversight process, such as part of the normal accreditation requirements to which health-care facilities are subjected. Hot water is not really regulated as drinking water so treatment of the hot water system, only, could be exempted. In the interest of public health protection, States have the opportunity to devise approaches that would not be as much of a disincentive.

States are asking for EPA guidance, and there is a diversity of state consecutive system requirements, and some are not making decisions while awaiting a formal statement from the EPA. Apparently, historical discretion has been allotted to states on their interpretations of the regulations. Some state officials have said that they had not required formal drinking water system status for introducing some technologies, such as central water softening. If that is the case, then allowing supplemental disinfection would certainly be appropriate, where a clear public health benefit is the purpose.

EPA (2016) has published an "uncritical" information document entitled "Technologies for *Legionella* Control in Premise Plumbing Systems: Scientific Literature Review (PDF)." It provides an overview of the published literature on treatment technology experiences. I wrote a comprehensive paper on the topic with specific recommendations titled "Facilitating Supplemental Disinfection for *Legionella* Control in Plumbing Systems" in Journal American Water Works Association 106:8, 74–83, August 2014. The choices and consequences are clear. There was a comprehensive symposium entitled: Managing Legionella in Building Water Systems, whose proceedings and follow-up webinars provide specific information and recommendations. In general, recommendations include system management plans that include surveillance analyses of water and biofilms for *legionella*, and appropriately demonstrated and managed effective technologies.

Conclusion

Pathogenic microorganisms such as *legionella* frequently colonize water plumbing systems, and they now are the most significant public health risk associated with drinking water. Many illnesses and deaths are attributable to that problem and drinking water standards are not designed to deal with them. Indeed, the existing standards may actually result in increased public health risks because they provide a disincentive for some health-care facilities to take corrective actions. The risk benefit balance is clearly in favor of minimizing the burdens that are imposed upon those facilities, so that they will be more likely to take actions to reduce risks to their patients.

EPA's opportunities to regulate *legionella* in plumbing systems are likely limited since its authority under the Safe Drinking Water Act for private facilities is limited that was tested and restricted by the appellate court from a challenge to the Lead and Copper Rule for corrosion control. However, EPA is not restricted from providing authoritative guidance or in modifying and reducing some of the barriers to implementation of *legionella* control technologies in buildings.

Perhaps the EPA's best choice in the interest of public health would be to propose and promulgate a simple modification of the existing implementation regulations under the Safe Drinking Water Act to allow supplemental disinfection without unnecessary stipulations. The original regulation was issued more than 30 years ago when *legionella* and other regrowth issues were not as explicit. In the interim, the American Society of Heating, Refrigerating and Air-Conditioning Engineers has issued DWA Standard 188–2015, Legionellosis: Risk Management for Building Water Systems. This standard's implementation should provide some level of risk reduction.

The CDC historically had emphasized follow-up after outbreaks rather than prevention that would include aggressive monitoring to identify system contamination and applying cleaning and disinfection to reduce the potential for illnesses to occur. The quantitative relationship between water or biofilm *legionella* concentration and risk of infection is not understood, but regular water quality surveillance and maintenance in high-risk facilities would reduce risks. In the August 14, 2015, MMWR, the CDC called for expanded partnerships between public health, regulatory, and industry professionals to develop and use regulatory and non-regulatory approaches to address groundwater and building plumbing system deficiencies to prevent outbreaks. Perhaps, a more explicit recommendation for water quality and system biofilm monitoring at least in high-risk facilities would encourage more preventive activity sooner.

Sources

CDC (2017). MMWR. Surveillance for Waterborne Disease Outbreaks Associated with Drinking Water—United States, 2013–2014. www.cdc.gov/mmwr/volumes/66/wr/mm6644a3.htm.

Cotruvo JA (2014). Facilitating supplemental disinfection for *Legionella* control in plumbing systems. *Journal of the American Water Works Association*. 106(8).

Cotruvo JA. (2014). Professor POU/POE—Waterborne Disease. Water Technology Online. www.watertechonline.com/professor-poupoe-may-2014/.

Cotruvo JA (2015). Legionella Revisited. Water Technology on Line. www.watertechonline.com/professor-poupoe-legionella-revisited/.

Cotruvo JA et al (2018). Proceedings of the conference on Managing Legionella in Building Water Systems, Baltimore. May 9-11, 2018. Legionella2018.org.

Disneyland (2017). www.cbsnews.com/news/legionnaires-disease-outbreak-disneyland-california/.

EPA (archived 2017). Surface Water Treatment Rules. www.epa.gov/dwreginfo/surface-water-treatment-rules.

EPA (1998). Definition of a Public Water System in SDWA Section 140(4). Guidance. FR 63 (150), 41940–41946.

EPA (2016). Technologies for Legionella Control in Premise Plumbing Systems: Scientific Literature Review (PDF) (139 pp, 2 MB, September 21, 2016, EPA 810-R-16-001).

Managing Legionella in Building Water Systems. Legionella2018@nsf.org

New York (2015). 8 dead in NYC Legionnaires' outbreak. USA Today www.usatoday.com/story/news/nation/2015/08/06/legionnaires-death-toll-eight/31200561/.

Zahran S. et al (2018).Assessment of the Legionnaires' disease outbreak in Flint, Michigan. *Proceedings of the National Academy of Sciences*. 115(8): E1730–E1739.

4 Radioactivity in Drinking Water

RADIONUCLIDES IN DRINKING WATER

Introduction

Radionuclides are elements or isotopes whose nuclei spontaneously disintegrate to release alpha particles (helium nuclei = two protons and two neutrons), beta particles (electrons), or high-energy gamma radiation, and they produce other isotopes and elements. Many produce more than one emission, and they produce other radioactive isotopes that further disintegrate. Most radionuclides are natural and there are also radionuclides that can be made by nuclear bombardment of nuclei by sub-atomic particles. The number after the element or isotope name (e.g., for carbon, C-12) is the total number of protons and neutrons in the nucleus. The number of protons (atomic number) defines the element (C = 6), so the number of neutrons (C-12 = 6) can be variable yielding different isotopes of the same element (e.g., C-13 or C-14). Some nuclear configurations are inherently unstable so the nucleus will spontaneously disintegrate with time. This is a fixed value for each radionuclide and is measured as the half-life, i.e., the time required for half of the nuclei to disintegrate. When this occurs, energy is released and one or more different stable or radioactive elements are produced.

Radioactive Decay

Radionuclides are classified into decay series that describe the grouping of families of elements and isotopes each with their own half-lives, beginning with the initial radionuclide passing through the intermediate products which are generated by releases of alpha particles and beta particles, ending with a stable nonradioactive element. There are four series: uranium, thorium, and actinium which are natural, and the neptunium series which is artificially produced. The uranium series begins with uranium-238 (half-life, 4.5 billion years), it passes through 25 intermediate transformation products, including radium-226, several lead, polonium, bismuth and other radionuclides, radon-214, and ends with lead-206. The thorium series begins with thorium-232 (half-life, 14 billion years), passes through 10 transformation products including radium-228, radon-220, and ends with stable lead-208. The actinium series begins with uranium-235 (half-life, 700 million years), passes through 15 transformation products including radium-223, and radon-219, and ends with lead-207. The neptunium series begins with californium-249 (half-life, 351 years), passes through 15 transformation products including neptunium-237, uranium-233 and radium-225, and ends with stable thallium-205.

Many natural elements have radioactive isotopes, e.g., potassium 39 is stable and potassium 40, which is 0.012 percent of natural potassium, is a beta emitter with a half-life of 1.248 million years. Carbon 12 and carbon 13 are stable and carbon 14 (0.0000000001 percent) has a half-life of 5,730 years. Carbon dating is accomplished by determining the amount of remaining C-14 present compared to total C and back calculating decay time based upon the known half-life.

Radionuclides in the diet and water are referred to as radioactive contaminants. All radionuclides are regulated by the Environmental Protection Agency (EPA) in drinking water, as well as being included in World Health Organization (WHO) Guidelines for Drinking Water Quality. Radium-226 (alpha emitter) and -228 (beta emitter) have specific maximum contaminant levels (MCLs) because of their common presence in some waters. The others are collectively grouped as alpha emitters (gross alpha) and gross beta and photon emitters. They are measured for screening and only if their target values are exceeded are the radionuclides causing the exceedance identified and measured.

Uranium is also regulated, but because natural uranium is mostly a very inactive radioactive element (half-life of 4.468×10^9 years), its MCL regulation is based upon its chemical toxicity in the kidney rather than its radiotoxicity.

Occurrence

Most of the radioactivity found in drinking water comes from naturally occurring sources, such as local geology. These rock types hold traces of radioactive elements with radium being the element of greatest concern. All water has some degree of radioactivity that cannot be removed. Natural water has stable H-1 (99.9844 percent hydrogen or protium), stable deuterium (0.0156 percent H-2), and a trace amount of radioactive tritium (H-3). Tritium is a beta emitter with a half-life of 0.32 years.

While most of the United States has low levels of mineral radioactivity, some groundwaters are known to have significantly higher averages of radium levels. The most common radioactive mineral elements found in groundwater are radium-226, radium-228, and uranium-238. All of which are of natural origin.

Some beta and photon emitters can come from nuclear power plants and other facilities that use radioactive material for manufacturing. However, radionuclides releases are tightly regulated and exposures from man-made sources are minimal relative to natural background radiation. There are also radioactive species used in diagnoses and therapy and some releases can occur.

Health Effects of Common Water-Related Radionuclides

Radioactive decay releases high-energy species that can damage DNA or kill cells if the decay occurs in proximity to the cell. Alpha particles are large (helium nuclei) not radioactive and lowest energy and they can travel a few centimeters in air, and are blocked by a sheet of paper, or skin. Beta electron particles can pass through a sheet of paper, but are stopped by aluminum foil, plastic, or glass. Gamma rays are very high-energy electromagnetic radiation with very high penetration requiring thick lead, concrete, or steel barriers.

Radium is chemically similar to calcium so after ingestion, it is transported like calcium. Radium exposure is known to cause bone cancer and historically in watch dial painters, who used radium containing paint to produce numbers that glowed. They would tip their brushes with their lips.

Uranium can accumulate and become toxic to the kidneys, separate from its radioactivity, which is low level.

Radon-222 is a noble gas in the environment (groundwater, soil, and indoor air) with a half-life of 3.8 days. It is produced in the decay series beginning with uranium and thorium. It is found in some groundwaters; however, airborne exposure is the greatest risk. Exposures occur especially in indoor air from gas penetration into basements from the geology. Most non-smoking-related lung cancers are thought to be associated with radon exposure.

Water Analysis

Gross alpha and gross beta screening analyses can be conducted in specialized laboratories by EPA Method 900.0. The Standard Methods for radioactivity in water are in the 7000 series, and radium is 7500-Ra, radon is 7500-Ra, tritium is 7500-T, and uranium is 7500-U. Gross alpha and gross beta are Method 7110.

Water Treatment

There are several methods for treating radionuclides and each case depends on the contaminant's chemical and physical characteristics and the water system's characteristics.

Known technologies used to treat radionuclides include: ion exchange, reverse osmosis, lime softening, greensand filtration, electrodialysis, for ionic radionuclides, and aeration for radon gas. Cation exchange water softening effectively removes radium because it is a cation similar to calcium or magnesium. Uranium exists as the uranyl anion in nature so it can be removed by anion exchange. Lime softening removes radium from drinking water in municipal plants. Reverse osmosis removes all minerals including radium and uranium with high efficiency. If the source water is very highly radioactive, disposal of concentrates and residues may require special management.

Regulations and Guidelines

The EPA has set an MCL for radium-226 and radium-228 in drinking water at 5 pCi/L (picocuries $= 10^{-12}$ curies). The curie is a very large unit and approximately the amount of nuclear disintegration per second from 1 g of radium. So, 5 pCi/L represents a very small mass of radium. The international unit is the bequerel (Bq) = 1 nuclear disintegration/second. One Ci $= 3.7 \times 10^{10}$ Bq, i.e., 37 billion disintegrations per second.

The MCL established in 1976 for alpha emitters (gross alpha) is 15 pCi/L, which does not include radon and uranium.

Beta and photon emitters have an MCL of 4 mrem/year (millirem/year), which is not a concentration, but a term referring to the cumulative absorbed dosage efficacy and risk of the radionuclide. The term mrem means milli roentgen equivalent man. The common term used outside the United States is the sievert. A rem is equal to 0.01 sievert, so a millirem is equivalent to 0.00001 sievert. For perspective, it is estimated that a 25 rem (25,000 mrem) dose will increase the risk of cancer and heritable effects by 0.05 percent in a lifetime.

The WHO Guideline values for radium species except radium-228 are 1 Bq per liter. The guideline for radium-228 is 0.1 Bq/L. Screening values in the WHO Guidelines are 0.5 Bq/L for gross alpha activity, and 1 Bq/L for gross beta activity. WHO provides tables with values for 192 individual radionuclides in the event that a screening level is exceeded but it would be unusual to apply those values since the guidelines are seldom exceeded in natural waters.

The MCL for tritium is now contained within the 4 mrem/year standard for beta and photon emitters and EPA computes it to be equivalent to 20,000 pCi/L. The WHO level computes to 200,000 pCi/L and the Canadian Guideline is 210,000 pCi/L. The Department of Energy (DOE) in 1999 submitted comments to EPA's proposed revision of the radionuclides regulation, suggesting that the MCL should be 80,000–86,000 pCi/L based upon the dose to soft-body tissues. EPA concluded that the "antibacksliding" provisions of the 1996 SDWA amendments precluded a revision that increased the risk from the original regulation. It is not clear whether the DOE's value increased the risk or was a more reliable quantitation of the actual risk.

The EPA MCL and the WHO drinking water guideline levels are 30 μg/L for uranium based upon chemical toxicity in the kidney.

Conclusion

Radionuclides are a health concern because of their potential to increase cancer risks. However, radionuclides in drinking water constitute a very small portion of the terrestrial radioactivity exposures that occur. Operating nuclear power plants are not a significant source of radioactivity releases, except in an unusual emergency release situation. There are treatment technologies to control the very few natural radionuclides that are found in some groundwaters, but not tritium which is a low risk from a very low presence of the natural hydrogen isotope in H_2O and not removable. Anion exchange and cation exchange, as appropriate, are water softening technologies that are generally very effective. Uranium is regulated as a kidney toxin rather than as a radionuclide because of its low activity.

Sources

Cotruvo JA. (2012). Water Technology on Line. www.watertechonline.com/alphaparticles/.

EPA (1980). Method 900.0: Gross Alpha and Gross Beta Radioactivity in Drinking Water.

EPA (2012). Drinking Water Standards and Health Advisories. www.epa.gov/sites/produciton/files/2015-09/documents/dwstandards2012.pdf.

EPA (2015). Radionuclides in Drinking Water. https://cfpub.epa.gov/safewater/radionuclides/radionuclides.cfm?act.

DOE-HDBK-1129–99 (1999). EPA MCL for Tritium. http://nuclearpowerradiation.tpub.com/hdbk1129/Epa-Maximum-Contaminant-Level-For-Tritium-Cont-D-29.htm.

EPA (2002). Facts about Tritium. https://trainex.org/web_courses/tritium/reference_pages/tritium%20EPA.pdf.

Radiation Basics. Greater-Than-Class C Low-Level Radioactive Waste EIS Information Center US Department of Energy. http://gtcceis.anl.gov/guide/rad/index.cfm.

Standard Methods (2017). Standard Methods for the Examination of Water and Wastewater, 23rd Edition. www.techstreet.com/standards/standard-methods-for-the-examination-of-water-and-wastewater-23rd-edition?sid=msn&utm_medium=cpc&utm_source=bing&product_id=1974889.

World Health Organization Guidelines for Drinking-Water Quality (2017). www.who.int/water_sanitation_health/publications/drinking-water-quality-guidelines-4-including-1st-addendum/en/4th edition.

RADIUM-226, RADON, AND ALPHA PARTICLES

Introduction

Alpha particles (α) are high-energy ionizing radiation emitted by some radioactive elements (e.g., radium-226). They are helium nuclei so they consist of two protons and two neutrons (= 4 atomic mass units), and are actually energetic helium ions (He^{+2}). They are much heavier and larger than the other two principal types of radiation: beta (β) and gamma (γ).

Some common examples of radioactive elements that are alpha emitters include radium-226, uranium-238, plutonium-236, polonium-210, and radon-222. When a radioactive element emits an alpha particle, it becomes a different element with two fewer protons and two fewer neutrons (e.g., radium-226 becomes radon-222).

Alpha particles are high-energy particles, but not radioactive in themselves. Because of their size and mass, they have very limited penetration and they lose energy rapidly, even in air. Human skin or a piece of paper is sufficient to block alpha particles. Because they are cations, they rapidly abstract electrons and become neutral helium gas.

Occurrence

Most alpha emitters are naturally occurring elements. The various natural radionuclides are generated spontaneously and occur in a decay chain. The alpha emitters of greatest interest in drinking water are radium-226 and radon-222. They are groundwater contaminants widely distributed in the United States and associated with geological types.

In the U-238 series, uranium-238 (half-life, 4.5 billion years) goes through several steps to become radium-226 (half-life, 1,602 years), which produces radon-222 (half-life 3.8 days), which becomes polonium-210 (half-life, 138 days), which ultimately becomes stable lead-206. So, it is possible to determine geological ages from the composition of the various radionuclides in the decay series and lead.

Radium is found around the United States and commonly at higher levels in some aquifers in the Midwestern states and in the South from Texas to Alabama and especially to South Carolina, then up the Eastern seaboard states. About 4 percent of samples exceed the MCL of 5 pCi/L.

Radon is a noble gas and exposure is predominantly from inhalation of gas that has seeped into homes from their foundations and it is also present at low concentrations in ambient air. It is also widely occurring in groundwater associated with igneous rock with highest concentrations generally found in Western states from Montana to Arizona and along the Eastern seaboard form South Carolina to Maine. Some radon dissolved in groundwater will be transported into homes by drinking water, where it is released when taps are opened and during showering.

Analysis

The drinking water standards include a gross alpha screening and also radium-226, using EPA Method 900.0. The analyses are performed in specialized laboratories and not in typical water laboratories. The gross alpha test has complications for undercounting because it involves counting of a solid sample concentrated from the water. The release of the alpha particles for counting is impeded by the sample matrix because of the low penetration of the alpha particles.

The Standard Methods for radioactivity in water are in the 7000 series, and radium is 7500-Ra, radon is 7500-Ra, and gross alpha and gross beta are Method 7110.

Radon air sampling is accomplished by placing a collector in the room being tested. The half-life of radon is only 3.8 days. Collector kits are available from several sources. The accumulated radionuclides on the collector are analyzed and back calculated to the radon air concentration.

Health Effects

Health risks from alpha emitters occur from the ingestion of the radionuclide and deposition in a sensitive tissue so that when the alpha particle release occurs it is very close to the target cell. Radium is chemically similar to calcium so it will deposit in bone, and bone cancer is a major risk.

Radon is a gas so exposure is predominantly by inhalation. Radon can be dissolved in groundwaters in regions with appropriate geology (e.g., granitic), and released as water pressure is released when water leaves the tap. Some radon will also be ingested. Lung cancer is the dominant risk. Between 14,000 and 20,000 out of about 160,000 deaths from lung cancer per year in the United States are estimated to be radon related from inhalation predominantly in homes. About 80 to 90 percent of the lung cancer deaths are smoking related.

Water Treatment

Radium is chemically similar to calcium and magnesium so water softening by lime precipitation and cation exchange are effective treatment techniques. Uranium usually exists as the uranyl anion so it is readily treated by activated alumina, iron oxides, and other anion exchange processes.

Radon is a gas so if it is present at significant levels in groundwater it is treated by aeration prior to entry into the water distribution system. Granular-activated carbon (GAC) is also effective, but since the half-life of radon is only 3.8 days, nongaseous radioactive decay products will accumulate on the GAC.

Regulations

Gross alpha measurement is the screening technique used for regulation. It measures the alpha activity in the test sample. Gross beta is also measured in the testing. The gross alpha MCL is 15 pCi/L. If the MCL is exceeded, speciation is required. The MCL for combined radium-226 and radium-228 is 5 pCi/L (1 picocurie = 10^{-12} curie). Radium-228 is a beta emitter. The MCL for radon is 300 pCi/L. Natural uranium, mostly U-238, an alpha emitter, is weakly radioactive so it is regulated by its chemical toxicity to the kidney. The uranium MCL is 30 μg/L.

The WHO Guideline values for radium species except radium-228 are 1 Bq/L. The international unit is the bequerel (Bq) = 1 nuclear disintegration/second. The picocurie unit is used in the United States, but not in other countries. A curie is a very large unit and approximately the amount of nuclear disintegration from 1 gram of radium. So, 5 pCi/L represents a very small mass of radium. One Ci = 3.7×10^{10} Bq.

Additional information is provided in Radionuclides in Drinking Water.

Conclusion

Effectively there are drinking water regulations for all radionuclides. The gross alpha and gross beta measurements are indicator screening measurements for radioactivity in drinking water, primarily in groundwaters. If a screening value is exceeded, then individual radionuclides are analyzed to determine the specific risk and whether a regulation is being exceeded.

Sources

Cotruvo JA (2013). Alpha Emitters. Water Technology on Line. www.watertechonline.com/radionuclides/.

EPA (1979). Method EMSL-19: Determination of Radium-226 and Radium-228 in Water, Soil, Air and Biological Tissue. www.epa.gov/homeland-security-research/epa-method-emsl-19-determination-radium-226-and-radium-228-water-soil-air.

EPA (1980). Method 900.0: Gross Alpha and Gross Beta Radioactivity in Drinking Water www.epa.gov/sites/production/files/2015-06/documents/epa-900.0.pdf.

EPA (1980). Method 903.0: Alpha-Emitting Radium Isotopes in Drinking Water www.epa.gov/sites/production/files/2015-08/documents/method_903-0_1980.pdf.

EPA (2012). Drinking Water Standards and Health Advisories. www.epa.gov/sites/produciton/files/2015-09/documents/dwstandards2012.pdf.

EPA. Drinking Water Contaminants—Standards and Regulations. www.epa.gov/dwstandardsregulations.

Radioactive Series. Encyclopedia Britannica. www.britannica.com/science/radioactive-series.

Radiation Basics. Greater-Than-Class C Low-Level Radioactive Waste EIS Information Center US Department of Energy. http://gtcceis.anl.gov/guide/rad/index.cfm.

Standard Methods (2017). Standard Methods for the Examination of Water and Wastewater, 23rd Edition. www.techstreet.com/standards/standard-methods-for-the-examination-of-water-and-wastewater-23rd-edition?sid=msn&utm_medium=cpc&utm_source=bing&product_id=1974889.

WHO (2017). World Health Organization Guidelines for Drinking-Water Quality. www.who.int/water_sanitation_health/publications/drinking-water-quality-guidelines-4-including-1st-addendum/en/4th edition.

5 Disinfection and Chlorine Disinfectants

CHLORINATION AND CHLORINATION DISINFECTION BY-PRODUCTS

INTRODUCTION

Chlorine in some form is the most widely used disinfection medium for drinking water, wastewater, and foods, and is also commonly used in swimming pools, cooling water systems, and surface sanitizing. It is applied as gaseous chlorine, sodium and calcium hypochlorites, monochloramine, and chlorinated isocyanurates or chlorine dioxide. Chlorine was introduced into drinking water treatment in the United States in the first decade of the 20th century and resulted in immediate reductions of waterborne diseases. Drinking water treatment and chlorine chemistry are also important in the food context because chlorinated drinking water or more highly chlorinated water is frequently used as a vehicle for food sanitation. So, we are commonly exposed to a variety of chlorine-related chemicals and the question is: Are there risks, and if so, what is the risk–benefit cost balance?

DRINKING WATER USAGE

The first continuous application of chlorine for drinking water in the United States was in Jersey City, New Jersey, in 1908 as calcium hypochlorite. The city's typhoid fever death rate in 1895 was 80 per 100,000. They had switched to an alternate supply in 1906 and the rate was 21.4 per 100,000. After chlorination was initiated the typhoid fever rates again declined dramatically. A few days prior to the Jersey City initiation, the Chicago stockyards began to chlorinate animal feed water to improve the animals' health and weight gain. Within a decade, basically every large water supplier in the United States was chlorinating its drinking water, and by 1936, typhoid fever was essentially eradicated.

CHLORINE PRODUCT MANUFACTURING

Electrolysis of sodium chloride brine solution gives chlorine gas and sodium hydroxide, so it is inexpensive to produce. Hypochlorite is made by combining the chlorine with sodium hydroxide in solution. It is provided to water plants in about 15 percent solution and as laundry bleach in about 5 percent solution. Chloramines are produced on-site in the water treatment plant by reacting hypochlorite with ammonia or ammonium salts. The usual chlorine-to-ammonia weight ratio is around 5 so that the monochloramine is the dominant product. Chlorine dioxide is a gas that is made by reacting sodium chlorite with chlorine, or sodium chlorate with hydrochloric acid. It is unstable and explosive and it is made on-site for use without storage.

Chlorine Chemistry

Chlorine is a high volume manufactured chemical, but natural chlorination processes also occur, e.g., on the oceans by solar photochemistry at the surface. Chlorine is chemically reactive and it can engage in numerous chemical processes under mild conditions in water. It is both an oxidizing and halogenating agent. Oxidation is probably the predominant chemical process occurring in chlorine's water and food contact applications. Chlorinated organic disinfection by-products (DBPs) being somewhat hydrophobic are more easily detected at lower concentrations, so there is a tendency to focus on them. Some halogenated DBPs have potential theoretical risks from long-term exposures at low concentrations, whereas the oxidized non-halogenated product alcohols, aldehydes, ketones, and carboxylic acid by-products are considered not to be unique in our oxygenated environment. Concentrated hypochlorite also spontaneously produces several inorganic by-products, including chlorite, chlorate and perchlorate, and ultimately chloride when those have been chemically reduced.

Mixed halogenated and brominated/iodinated DBPs are produced indirectly if bromide or iodide is present in the water by chlorine oxidation of bromide to $HOBr/OBr^-$, which is a rapid brominating agent that competes with the chlorination processes.

Bromate is produced during chlorine production electrolysis if bromide is present in the salt. Bromate is also produced in water if ozone is applied when bromide is present. Bromate is typically not produced to a significant extent in chlorinated water in the presence of bromide, possibly because the intermediate $HOBr/OBr^-$ rapidly reacts preferentially with organic carbon to produce brominated DBPs, such as bromodichloromethane or bromoform (tribromomethane). However, there are some circumstances where bromate can be generated in water in the presence of chlorine if appropriate catalysis is available.

Chlorine Disinfection

Chlorine species are generally excellent microbial disinfectants that function by fundamental chemical halogenation and/or oxidation processes at the cell surface or on the cellular DNA, so it is unlikely that many pathogenic microbes can evolve to become resistant to them as they have to many antibiotics. As far as we know, all bacteria and viruses as well as many protozoa are vulnerable to chlorine disinfection. *Cryptosporidium* protozoa are notably highly resistant to chlorine disinfection, but not to chlorine dioxide.

Disinfectant dosages and residuals range from a fraction to several mg/L in finished water depending upon the treatment purpose and the disinfectant demand of the water. Disinfection CT (concentration in mg/L×time in minutes) values for 4 logs (99.99 percent) reduction at 10°C and neutral to slightly basic pH are chlorine, 6; monochloramine, 1,491; and chlorine dioxide, 25. Chlorine's efficacy is reduced as pH becomes more basic because more hypochlorous acid is converted to the hypochlorite, until it is all hypochlorite at about pH 9.5. Chlorine dioxide is not significantly affected by pH in the range of 4–10. Monochloramine is significantly less effective than chlorine as a biocide, but it has applications as a secondary disinfectant to reduce microbial regrowth during water storage and distribution. However, it is very effective for *legionella* control in plumbing because of its persistence, low chemical reactivity and being somewhat hydrophobic, as well as its likely ability to penetrate biofilms better than chlorine.

Bromamines are much more effective disinfectants than chloramines because their equilibrium distribution lies largely toward HOBr, whereas chloramine is virtually all $ClNH_2$ in equilibrium with a small amount of HOCl and NH_3. Bromamine is not a desirable drinking water disinfectant because of organobromine formation, but it could be much more attractive than chlorine for wastewater disinfection in the presence of the ammonia and amines.

Taste and Odor

Taste and odor detection and objection thresholds are somewhat subjective. Average taste thresholds, but not necessarily objectionable concentrations of free residual chlorine, increased from 0.075 to 0.45 mg/L as the pH increased from 5.0 to 9.0 in one taste panel study. The average taste threshold was 0.156 mg/L, with a range of 0.02–0.29 mg/L at pH 7.0. Those data indicate that taste sensitivity is greater for hypochlorous acid than for hypochlorite ion. Chlorine dioxide taste detections are in the range of 0.2–0.4 mg/L. Monochloramine taste detection is reported to range from about 0.4 to 0.6 mg/L, but in some studies, it is not objectionable up to perhaps 3 mg/L.

Drinking Water Regulations

Surface waters and Ground Waters Under the Direct Influence of Surface Water (GWUDI) in the United States are required to be filtered and disinfected, and at-risk groundwaters are at least required to be disinfected. Both chlorine and chloramine have maximum residual disinfection levels (MRDLs) of 4 mg/L. Chlorine dioxide's MRDL is 0.8 mg/L. These are nominally health-based values, but that is doubtful because these substances rapidly decompose in the presence of reducing conditions as in saliva and in stomach acidity. Chlorite is regulated with a maximum contaminant level (MCL) of 1 mg/L, but it is also chemically reactive when acidified; chlorate is not very reactive under gastrointestinal conditions.

Perchlorate is unreactive upon ingestion and excreted virtually unchanged with a half-life of about 8 hours. It currently has a Drinking Water Health Advisory of 15 parts per billion (ppb), based upon its competition with iodide transport to the thyroid. Chlorate and perchlorate are under active regulatory consideration by EPA. Bromate is regulated at 0.010 mg/L. Trihalomethanes (THMs) (0.080 mg/L) and haloacetic acids (HAAs) (0.060 mg/L) have been regulated for 20 to almost 40 years. The THMs and especially chloroform are no longer considered to be direct carcinogenic risks in drinking water, based upon studies over the past 20+ years, but rather indicator chemicals for DBP formation, as was their original regulatory intent. So, quantitative carcinogen risk assessments historically produced for individual THMs should be disregarded as out of date, and inconsistent with current toxicological information. Epidemiological studies that suggest a risk of bladder cancer correlated with total trihalomethanes (TTHMs) have significant uncertainties. HAAs have more toxicological interest than the THMs.

World Health Organization (WHO) Guidelines are chloroform, 0.3 mg/L; bromodichloromethane, 0.06 mg/L; dibromochloromethane, 0.1 mg/L; bromoform, 0.1 mg/L; and chlorine, 5 mg/L; chlorite, 0.7 mg/L; chlorate, 0.7 mg/L; and perchlorate, 0.070 mg/L.

Analysis

Analytical techniques for trihalomethanes include EPA 502.2 and 524.2 Revision 2.1. The EPA Method for HAAs is 552.1. The Standard Method for trihalomethanes and HAAs is 5710C. The Standard Method is 4500-Cl for chlorine and 4500-ClO_2 for chlorine dioxide.

Organic DBPs

Several hundred individual chlorination DBPs have been identified at ppb and at parts per trillion (ppt) levels in various drinking waters. The aggregated total quantity of DBPs range from a few micrograms per liter to a fraction of a milligram per liter and sometimes more in some waters with high levels of natural organic carbon precursors, depending upon the chlorine dosage, quantity of precursors, pH, temperature, and contact time. Chloramines rapidly form from ammonia and chlorine or hypochlorite, and they are poor halogenating and oxidizing agents, so ammonia will suppress the formation of most of the halogenated and oxidized DBPs, but produce some others. Chlorine dioxide does not directly produce halogenated DBPs, but rather oxidized DBPs, e.g., alcohols and aldehydes.

Despite theoretical concerns about DBPs that led to their regulation and/or WHO guidelines, the issue of potential significant health concerns has been controversial. Epidemiology studies have sometimes indicated potential small incremental cancer risks of bladder cancer associated with TTHMs from long-term chlorinated drinking water consumption; however, some other studies have suggested that some apparent risks may actually be associated with inadequate water consumption. Bladder cancers are most suspected to correlate with TTHMs from some studies, however, there are numerous common associations with bladder cancer, including smoking, diabetes, arsenic and occupational exposures, among others, so those confounders cause difficulties in attributing small incremental risks to DBPs in drinking water. There are significant sex and ethnic differences in bladder cancer risk. In addition, it is extremely difficult to develop accurate lifetime exposures to DBPs for quantitative correlations because of their variability in day-to-day water production, as well as changing drinking water consumption patterns. In 2006, EPA concluded that no dose response or causal relationship existed between exposure to chlorinated drinking water or chlorinated DBPs and adverse developmental or reproductive health effects. In the 6 Year Review published in 2016, the reproduction and developmental toxicity of TTHMs was updated. Most animal and human studies were inconclusive or negative, and observed effects often occurred at high doses that were maternally toxic.

The toxicology of numerous DBPs has been studied extensively for more than 30 years; however, the number of by-products is so large and their individual concentrations are so low that it is questionable whether there is value in examining many of them in detail. One study applied structure–activity techniques and genotoxicity data as a prescreening ranking for carcinogenic potential from long-term exposure. Only 20 of 209 DBPs studied were of priority concern with moderate (17) or high-moderate ratings (3). The three high-moderate chemicals are known to be rapidly detoxified, and hypothetical risk calculations were at two per 1,000,000 upper-bound lifetime risk.

Conclusions

Chlorine disinfection has been recognized by health and international agencies as one of the most significant public health benefits of the last century, and it will likely continue to be so. More widespread chlorination of drinking water and better sanitation would be the most effective measure to rapidly reduce waterborne disease risks in developing countries. Reported waterborne diseases have continued to decline in the United States since the Safe Drinking Water Act implementation in about 1980, but most outbreaks are now due to post distribution regrowth issues, e.g., legionellosis from inhalation of contaminated aerosols.

It is almost fortuitous that chlorine disinfection is so effective, so simple to apply and so inexpensive. It has been stated that in addition to huge morbidity reductions, clean water has been responsible for nearly half of the total mortality reduction in major world cities from the late 19th and early 20th centuries, three-quarters of the infant mortality reduction and nearly two-thirds of the child mortality reductions that have occurred. Excess chlorine species can contribute taste to drinking water, but that is readily eliminated by an inexpensive carbon tap filter. Assessment of bladder cancer risk trends versus TTHMs in eight countries over more than 40 years did not indicate a close relationship. Smoking reduction effects seem to have been dominant and perhaps mask any potential small risk from DBPs. Risks of DBPs are still in debate, but are likely very small lifetime exposure elements. The risk–benefit costbalance is strongly in favor of water chlorination. WHO continues to advise that disinfection by-products should never be a reason (or excuse) for reducing disinfection of drinking water.

Sources

Canada (2005). Guidelines for Canadian Drinking Water Quality: Guideline Technical Document—Taste. www.canada.ca/en/health-canada/services/publications/healthy-living/guidelines-canadian-drinking-water-quality-guideline-technical-document-taste.html.

Cotruvo JA (2015). Chlorine. Water Technology on Line. www.watertechonline.com/professor-poupoe-february-2015/.

Cotruvo JA and Amato H (2018). TTHMs and Bladder Cancer: Toxicity and Trends. AWWA Water Quality Technology Conference Nov. 11–15. Toronto.
EPA (2012). Drinking Water Standards and Health Advisories. www.epa.gov/sites/produciton/files/2015-09/documents/dwstandards2012.pdf.
EPA (1999). Alternative Disinfectants and Oxidants Guidance Manual. EPA 815-R-99-014.
EPA (1999). Chlorine Gas. R.E.D. Facts. EPA-738-F-99-001. www3.epa.gov/pesticides/chem_search/reg_actions/reregistration/fs_PC-020501_1-Feb-99.pdf.
EPA (1998). National Primary Drinking Water Regulations: Disinfectants and Disinfection Byproducts. FR Vol. 63, No. 241/ pp. 69390 et seq. Wednesday, December 16, 1998.
EPA (2013). Basic Information about Disinfectants in Drinking Water: Chloramine, Chlorine and Chlorine Dioxide. http://water.epa.gov/drink/contaminants/basicinformation/disinfectants.cfm.
EPA (1995). Trihalomethanes Method 502.2 Revision 2.1. Volatile Organic Compounds in Water by Purge and Trap Capillary Column Gas Chromatography with Photoionization and Electrolytic Conductivity Detectors in Series. www.caslab.com/EPA-Methods/PDF/502_2.pdf.
EPA (1995a). Method 524.2. Revision 4.1. Measurement of Purgeable Organic Compounds in Water by Capillary Column Gas Chromatography/Mass Spectrometry. www.epa.gov/sites/production/files/2015-06/documents/epa-524.2.pdf.
EPA (2003). Method 552.3 Determination of Haloacetic Acids and Dalapon in Drinking Water by Liquid-Liquid Microextraction, Derivatization, and Gas Chromatography with Electron Capture Detection EPA 815-B-03-002 1.0. Also Standard Methods SM5710C.
EPA 6 year review (2016). https://www.epa.gov/sites/production/files/2016-12/documents/810r16012.pdf.
Standard Methods (2017). Standard Methods (2017). Method 6651B-00. Standard Methods for the Examination of Water and Wastewater, 23rd Edition. www.techstreet.com/standards/standard-methods-for-the-examination-of-water-and-wastewater-23rd-edition?sid=msn&utm_medium=cpc&utm_source=bing&product_id=1974889.
World Health Organization Guidelines for Drinking-water Quality (2017). www.who.int/water_sanitation_health/publications/drinking-water-quality-guidelines-4-including-1st-addendum/en/4th edition.

CHLORAMINES

Introduction

Chloramines are a generic chemical family of compounds that consist of chlorine bound to amine/amide nitrogen. Those of interest in water are inorganic chloramines and organic chloramines. They are also chemical intermediates in the production of other chemicals and they are rapidly formed *in situ* in water by reacting some form of ammonia or amine, including ammonium salts, with active chlorine or hypochlorite. Amides and proteins will also *N*-chlorinate. Chloramines can also be preformed and added to the water.

Chloramines are also spontaneously formed during chlorination of drinking water from reactions with ammonia and organic amines that may be in the source water (Table 5.1). They are referred to as combined chlorine. Breakpoint chlorination occurs when sufficient chlorine is added to oxidize the chloramines to nitrogen, some nitrate, and other nitrogen oxides. Additional chlorine then remains as free chlorine. Deliberate use of chloramines in water treatment dates back around 100 years.

Chloramination occurs in drinking water treatment; chloramines are always present in chlorinated wastewater treatment because the ammonia and organic nitrogen are found in greater concentrations than in drinking water source water, and breakpoint is seldom achieved. Chloramines, including trichloramine, are also formed in swimming pools that are chlorinated because of the high levels of organic nitrogen chemicals supplied by the swimmers and the chlorine dosage. Figure 5.1 illustrates chloramine formation chemistry involving organic and inorganic precursors reacting with chlorine.

Chemical product distributions are determined by the ratio of chlorine and ammonia, pH, temperature, and the order of addition. The double arrow in the reactions (shown below left) means that the reactants and products are in equilibrium, so a very small amount of free chlorine will be present depending on the conditions and could be the functioning disinfectant. The predominant product is NH_2Cl

TABLE 5.1
Performance of Disinfection Chemicals from the EPA*(1999)

	CTs for Virus Log Inactivations		
Disinfectant	**2-log**	**3-log**	**4-log**
Chlorine	3	4	6
Chloramine	643	1,067	1,491
Chlorine dioxide	4.2	12.8	25.1
Ozone	0.5	0.8	1.0

CTs are measured in milligrams-minutes/liter.
2-log: 10°C, pH 8; 1-log and 3-log: 10°C, pH range 6–9.

Inorganic $NH_3 + HOCl \leftrightarrow NH_2Cl + NHCl_2 + NCl_3 + H_2O \rightarrow \rightarrow N_2$

Organic $CH_3NH_2 + HOCl \leftrightarrow CH_3NHCl + CH_3NCl_2 \rightarrow \rightarrow$ Other Products

FIGURE 5.1 Reactions of chlorine/hypochlorous acid with ammonia and amines in water.

(monochloramine) at a chlorine-to-ammonia weight ratio up to about 5:1, which is about one molecule of Cl_2 to one molecule of ammonia, and pH of about 7–9. Monochloramine, the desired product, is stable in that range. Di- and trichloramines are undesirable because they are more volatile and irritating and are much poorer disinfectants than monochloramine. Therefore, it is always important to optimize conditions to produce monochloramine.

Organic *N*-chloramines are also undesirable in water because they are less effective disinfectants, and they can produce additional tastes and other DBPs. Source waters usually contain organic nitrogen that reacts with chlorine to produce chloramines and chloramides.

Monochloramine in Water Disinfection

Inorganic monochloramine is increasingly being chosen as the secondary disinfectant treatment for drinking water in municipal water systems because it is less chemically reactive than free chlorine. Chloramine produces fewer and some different disinfection by-products than chlorine, and it survives longer during drinking water distribution to consumers.

Chloramines' primary application as secondary disinfectants comes in drinking water. Primary disinfectants include chlorine, chlorine dioxide, ozone, and ultraviolet (UV) light. Primary disinfectants are potent biocides that can destroy pathogens in the water treatment plant so the water entering the distribution system is microbiologically safe. Secondary disinfectants reduce regrowth of microorganisms during the transit of the treated drinking water to consumers. The objective method of comparing the efficacy of disinfectants is the CT that quantifies the die off as log reductions at a given temperature and pH, by the product of the concentration (C) in milligrams per liter and the time (T) in minutes (Table 5.1). Smaller values indicate greater efficacy for each level of log inactivation.

Compared to monochloramine under these conditions, free chlorine is about 250 times more potent, chlorine dioxide is about 60–150 times more potent, and ozone is 1,300–1,500 times more potent. During water distribution, monochloramine is more persistent than chlorine or chlorine dioxide, and ozone does not provide a residual. Monochloramine is added or generated in the water before it is released from the plant, where it quenches much of the DBP formation chemistry. During long contact and transport times in distribution, a residual disinfectant suppresses the regrowth of mostly heterotrophic microorganisms, which are generally not harmful but can cause aesthetic and system problems.

However, chloramine may have other benefits compared to more potent and chemically active disinfectants by suppressing growth of biofilms that are a likely environment for colonization by pathogens such as *Legionella* bacteria. After San Francisco switched from free chlorine to combined chlorine residuals in 2004, *Legionella* detections in hot water systems were reduced from 60 to 4 percent. Possible explanations include that the free chlorine residual was not able to survive throughout the system or that chloramine was more capable of penetrating biofilms to reach the microorganisms because it was less chemically reactive to the biofilm and more hydrophobic than hypochlorite ion.

Health Issues

Monochloramine produces fewer DBPs than chlorine, but their nature is also different. Some of the same DBPs are produced, but less halogenation and oxidation of organic carbon in the water will occur because of the lower chemical activity (oxidation potential) of monochloramine. Other chemicals such as dimethylnitrosamine and chlorinated quinones may be produced at ppt concentrations, especially from surface waters that have more nitrogenous precursors present. A greater opportunity for nitrate/nitrite to form occurs during water distribution in systems with longer retention times. The potential lifetime risk from chlorinated drinking water has not yet been completely determined after about 38 years since the first TTHM regulation, and less information is available on chloraminated drinking water.

During dialysis, direct transport of some components from water to blood occurs, which is a very different exposure condition than ingestion. Cases of hemolytic anemias and increased methemoglobin have occurred when chloramine was not sufficiently removed from the dialysis water. Medical instrumentation standards exist, and dialysis systems designed with water treatment make the water acceptable usually with reverse osmosis in the treatment train.

Monochloramine becomes unstable at a pH below 3–4. Studies with chloramines in gastric fluids (typical pH 1 or 2) reported disappearance of monochloramine and no detection of dichloramine or trichloramine in less than 30 seconds.

Chloramines, like other usually innocuous drinking water components such as nitrate, are harmful to kidney dialysis patients if the water is not properly pretreated. Fish are particularly sensitive to both chlorine and chloramines, so tank water must be properly pretreated to remove them. Chloramines are more difficult to remove than free chlorine, so effective technology must be applied.

Swimming pool water will purge chloramines, particularly trichloramine, and indoor pools may not be sufficiently ventilated to maintain good air quality. Respiratory and ocular irritations and risks to asthma sufferers are also possible, so proper air quality control of indoor pools is important.

Some people are opposed to drinking water chloramination because of their concerns with potential allergic reactions and skin irritation. If this did occur, it would be in very low incidence.

Water Analyses

Several low cost analyses for total chlorine that aggregate free and combined chlorine forms exist. Using methods that will provide values for each component is important when the identity of the residual is required. EPA-approved methods include amperometric titration method Standard Method 4500-Cl D, and DPD Methods 4500-Cl F (ferrous titration) and 4500-Cl G (colormetric).

Water Treatment

Chloramine is a beneficial treatment technology for providing a residual disinfectant during distribution of treated water. Using drinking water for dialysis, aquariums, and some other applications requires removal of chloramine either for health or taste reasons. If there is need to reduce the presence of chloramine in water the addition of reducing agents or use of activated carbon are effective. UV light will also decompose chloramines. Reducing agents like thiosulfate, sulfite, or sulfur dioxide can be used. Chloramine is more resistant to chemical reduction than chlorine so significantly longer contact times are necessary for activated carbon reduction systems.

Several devices can remove chloramines from drinking water if desired. These include point-of-use and point-of-entry devices with granular-activated carbon or reverse osmosis that have been certified to ANSI/NSF Standard 42 or Standard 60, and also UV systems.

NB. Switching from free chlorine to chloramine residuals has resulted in water chemistry changes that have released more lead from lead service lines and deposits, exceeding the lead and copper rule action level of 15 μg/L in numerous samples. The addition of a few milligrams of phosphate can resolve the problem along with other adjustments by passivating the exposed lead surfaces.

Regulations and Guidelines

The application of chloramines as a secondary disinfectant in treated drinking water has been increasing since EPA updated regulations for DBP TTHMs and HAAs. The original TTHM regulations in 1979 facilitated the activity, which was increased with the addition of HAAs and the new restrictions and lower TTHM MCLs in 1998 and tightened compliance computation requirements in 2006. All of these increased the numbers of water systems likely to be out of compliance with TTHMs or HAAs and led many to change to the chloramine approach. A more expensive alternative treatment would be to reduce the precursor organic carbon content of the water with membranes before application of the disinfectant, or removing the DBPs with granular-activated carbon after formation.

The EPA maximum disinfectant residual level (MDRL, MCL) for chlorine is 4 mg/L and also for chloramine (4 mg/L or 4 ppm as chlorine). The MCL goals (MCLGs) are also 4 mg/L. The WHO Guideline value is 3 mg/L. The Lifetime EPA Drinking Water Health Advisory is 3 mg/L. The logic of having an MCLG greater than the Lifetime Drinking Water Health Advisory is unclear. The logic for the toxicological bases of the MRDLs for human exposure from drinking water at typical levels is also somewhat weak. Those values were based on high longer term dose exposures in test animals, but chloramines are rapidly decomposed in the gastrointestinal tract at the typical pH of 1–2 of gastric fluid.

Conclusion

Applications of chloramine treatment of drinking water as a secondary disinfectant have increased to help water suppliers meet THM and HAA regulations. Monochloramine is low cost and effective because it is less chemically reactive than free chlorine and produces fewer, different DBPs. DBPs and chloramines are present in larger amounts in swimming pools and hot tubs where their volatility and air concentrations in indoor areas can be a respiratory problem. Chloramines must be removed from fish tank water and water used in kidney dialysis by pretreatment. Chloramines seem to be effective at suppressing regrowth of *legionella* microorganisms in biofilms, possibly because their persistence maintains a disinfectant residual, and their lower chemical reactivity allows greater penetration into biofilms. Taste detection levels are lower than for chlorine. They can also be removed in home tap water, if desired, but their long use history belies some of the concerns that have been expressed.

Sources

Cotruvo JA (2016). Chloramines in Water. Water Technology on Line. www.watertechonline.com/professor-poupoe-chloramines-in-water/.

EPA (1999). Alternative Disinfectants and Oxidants Guidance Manual. EPA 815-R-99-014 (April).

EPA. Chloramines in Drinking Water. www.epa.gov/dwreginfo/chloramines-drinking-water.

EPA (2012). Drinking Water Standards and Health Advisories. www.epa.gov/sites/produciton/files/2015-09/documents/dwstandards2012.pdf.

The Free Library (2006). Reducing *Legionella* Colonization of Water Systems with Monochloramine. www.thefreelibrary.com/Reducing+Legionella+colonization+of+water+systems+with+monochloramine-a0144664532.

American Water Works Association/American Public Works Association/Water Environment Federation (2017). Standard Methods for the Examination of Water and Wastewater, 23rd Edition. Amperometric Titration (Standard Method 4500-C1 D and ASTM Method D 1253-86). DPD Ferrous Titrimetric (Standard Method 4500-C1 F). DPD Colorimetric (Standard Method 4500-C1 G).

World Health Organization Guidelines for Drinking-water Quality, 2017. www.who.int/water_sanitation_health/publications/drinking-water-quality-guidelines-4-including-1st-addendum/en/4th edition.

6 Water Quality Parameters

AESTHETIC FACTORS AND DRINKING WATER QUALITY

INTRODUCTION

The aesthetic aspects of drinking water include: taste, odor, color, turbidity, salinity, hardness, softness, and temperature. Aesthetic quality is a very important consideration for providers of drinking water because they are virtually the only identifiable quality characteristics that consumers can observe and detect. They could lead to perceptions that the water is not of acceptable quality and safe, and cause consumers to lose confidence in their water supplier and perhaps be less likely to support improvements to the municipal system, and install home water treatment devices or purchase bottled water.

The aesthetics are generally not health related. However, consumers can easily detect them, so they can have significant effects on perceptions of water quality and acceptability. These attributes are the source of most complaints to water suppliers and frequently lead consumers to choose home treatment or bottled water.

TASTE AND ODOR

Taste and odor detection are intermixed in human senses and are closely related. Some substances can be detected at very low concentrations, and detection varies by individual and other factors such as water temperature. Some tastes, such as certain minerals, are desirable to some people, but tastes also vary by personal preference and experience. Consumers have concerns that water taste will contribute to undesirable tastes in beverages like coffee.

Other tastes, such as high salinity, are undesirable at sufficient levels. The sodium taste threshold is 30–60 mg/L.

Organics, such as geosmin or 2-methylisoborneol are detectable at micrograms or nanograms per liter. They frequently occur during algal blooms in source waters. Chlorophenols are also produced from chlorination of phenols that may be present in source waters, and they also have very low taste and odor detection levels. Chemical tastes, such as gasoline, indicate potentially significant contamination.

Chlorine and chloramine tastes are frequent causes for consumer dissatisfaction and complaints and often lead consumers to choose home treatment or bottled water. Metallic tastes, such as iron, can be caused by iron or manganese or copper in source water or pipe corrosion because of pH effects.

Sulfides and their rotten egg odors are caused by sulfate-reducing bacteria in the aquifer or in storage tanks. They are common problems with home well water.

Color

Natural sources of corrosion can cause metallic colors. For instance, color can be metallic from iron (rust/black), copper (blue/green, brown), or manganese (pink/black). It can also be a result of pipe corrosion and release of metal salts or biofilms. In addition to coloration of the water, precipitates can form on fixtures and during clothes laundering from oxidation of iron or manganese metal salts and settling on the surfaces that they encounter. Natural organics in source waters can also be colored and include or humus from decaying biota.

Turbidity

Turbidity or cloudiness is caused by suspended particulates that diffuse light. The condition becomes noticeable in a glass of water at about 4 ntu. The particulates could be innocuous if they are caused by calcium carbonate precipitation such as from groundwater, but turbidity can be an important indicator of inadequate filtration and disinfection, overdosing of aluminum coagulants, or sloughing of biofilms from pipes.

Salinity

Salts in the water are usually sodium chloride or similar salts, but they can be any dissolved inorganic salts that contribute to total dissolved solids (TDSs). Salinity can also cause pipe corrosion and solids deposition. Assuming no contaminants of health concern, the recommended TDS concentration is below 500 mg/L, but many water supplies in some areas such as those affected by geologic conditions or by seawater intrusion exceed that level.

Hardness and Softness

Water hardness is caused by divalent ions, primarily calcium and magnesium, but barium or strontium could factor in as well. They are usually associated with groundwater geology but many surface waters are also hard, and many are soft.

Excessive hardness causes scale formation and soap precipitation. Hard ions such as from dissolved calcium bicarbonate will convert to insoluble calcium carbonate by changes in carbon dioxide concentrations and in hot water heaters. Accumulations will reduce the useful life and cause failure of hot water heaters and accumulate and clog especially lateral pipes, leading to major expenses for customers. Excessive hardness will also reduce the efficiency and the useful life of commercial heat exchangers.

Excessively soft water can be difficult to rinse soap completely and can also corrode pipes if the alkalinity and pH are not properly balanced. Such corrosion can become a potential health risk issue if lead surfaces are present, such as from lead service connection, leaded solder, and brass faucets. Even old galvanized iron pipes which accumulate iron oxides can be the source of iron and lead contamination. The lead contamination is a common occurrence from accumulation of low concentrations of lead from influent water on the oxides and their suspension perhaps during water hammer shocks. Exceeders of the Lead and Copper corrosion control rule are often caused by old galvanized pipe releases, which are frequently unrecognized as a cause. The primary focus is often limited to lead service lines which may or may not be the most significant source.

Treatment Techniques

Taste and Odor

These problems can lead to unnecessary expenditures by consumers while they are actually fairly simple and inexpensive to manage. For metallic tastes, first determine the cause and suitable treatment. Use carbon treatment and possibly oxidation with chlorine, chlorine dioxide, or ozone if it is caused by organics. A simple inexpensive tap activated carbon filter can easily remove chlorine taste, while aeration purging or chlorine oxidation can remove sulfide taste and odor.

Color

First determine the specific cause. Coagulation and lime softening can remove many color contributors. Powdered or granular-activated carbon can usually treat organic color. Inorganic color from copper, iron or manganese requires identification of the cause and suitable treatment.

Turbidity

Coagulation, sedimentation, and filtration can remove turbidity after determining the cause. Very low turbidity (less than 0.3 ntu) in a treated surface water or groundwater under the direct influence of surface water assures that the water has been sufficiently treated to remove protozoa such as giardia or *Cryptosporidium*. Some have misinterpreted the World Health Organization (WHO) Guidelines for Drinking Water Quality turbidity recommendations to be primarily aesthetic issues.

Salinity

Reverse osmosis (RO) is the usual treatment for excess salinity. It is expensive and so salinity is often left untreated to more optimal levels.

Hardness

Cation exchange is the common home treatment choice, but municipal plants use lime or lime soda softening. RO or nanofiltration (lower cost) is effective at removing divalent ions.

Softness

Calcite filters and likely pH adjustment and added alkalinity can harden water to acceptable levels.

Analytical Methods

There are numerous analytical methods for aesthetic components, some are observation and some are low-cost kit methods, e.g., calcium and magnesium, EPA Methods 200.7, 200.8; chloride, EPA 300.0; chlorine residual, EPA 330.1, EPA

330.4; alkalinity, EPA 310.1; hardness total as calcium carbonate, SM 2320B; copper, EPA 200.9, EPA 220.2; iron, EPA 200.7, 200.8; manganese, EPA 200.7, 200.8; aluminum, EPA 200.7, 200.8; sodium, EPA 200.7; sulfate, EPA 300.0, 375.3; surfactants, EPA 425.1; TDS, EPA 160.1; total suspended solids, EPA 160.2; and pH, EPA 150.1. There are numerous ASTM and Standard Methods for the Examination of Water and Wastewater. The Part 2000 section of Standard Methods contains numerous analytical techniques dealing with aesthetic quality factors.

Regulation

Federal secondary drinking water regulations exist for most aesthetic factors, but they are not mandatory. Secondary maximum contaminant levels (SMCLs) provide numerical goal levels and guidance. States have the option to include them in their drinking water standards and some do. The SMCLs are as follows: aluminum, 0.05–0.2 mg/L; chloride, 250 mg/L; color, 15 color units; copper, 1 mg/L; foaming agents, 0.5 mg/L; iron, 0.3 mg/L; manganese, 0.05 mg/L; odor, 3 threshold odor number; pH, 6.5–8.5; sulfate, 250 mg/L; and TDS, 500 mg/L. The WHO Guidelines include information and advisory values for many aesthetic factors that are usually similar to the EPA SMCLs.

There is also an SMCL for fluoride of 2 mg/L that is intended to reduce the potential for aesthetic dental fluorosis in children. The current CDC and EPA guidance for addition of fluoride to drinking water is 0.7 mg/L, because some very slight dental fluorosis can occur under some conditions even at that low level.

Conclusion

Even though aesthetic components do not usually have direct public health significance, they are important in public perception and satisfaction of the quality of their drinking water as well as in their decisions about using tap water versus bottled water or home treatment. A very large number of consumers have opted to purchase and install sometimes very expensive home water treatment units, or purchase bottled water, either for chlorine taste or other dissatisfaction reasons, or with the impression that their supplied drinking water quality is not up to par. Aesthetic aspects could also indicate more significant water contamination, so understanding the causes and determining appropriate corrective actions are important. The Flint, Michigan lead problem produced colored and undesirable water which caused many to avoid drinking it and thereby reducing what might have been higher blood lead levels in the community. Public water suppliers frequently do not pay sufficient attention to aesthetic considerations and consumer perceptions, but at their own peril for loss of public confidence in the water and the water provider.

Persons on private wells should be more concerned if their water is not aesthetically pleasing because those problems may be indicative of sanitation or natural or synthetic groundwater contamination problems. In those cases, it is essential that the water has been analyzed and they are advised by competent people, including local health officials so that the causes of problems are identified and the appropriate corrective action is taken.

Sources

Cotruvo JA (2015). Drinking Water Aesthetics. Water Technology on Line. www.watertechonline.com/contaminant-of-the-month-drinking-water-aesthetics.

EPA (2012). Drinking Water Standards and Health Advisories. www.epa.gov/sites/produciton/files/2015-09/documents/dwstandards2012.pdf.

EPA Analytical Methods. www.epa.gov/dwanalyticalmethods and https://nepis.epa.gov/Exe/ZyPDF.cgi?Dockey=P100PHGZ.txt.

EPA. Secondary Drinking Water Standards: Guidance for Nuisance Chemicals. www.epa.gov/dwstandardsregulations/secondary-drinking-water-standards-guidance-nuisance-chemicals.

McGowan W (2000). *Water Processing: Residential, Commercial, Light Industrial.* 3rd edition. Joseph Harrison, Technical Editor. Water Quality Association. Lisle, Illinois.

American Water Works Association/American Public Works Association/Water Environment Federation (2017). Standard Methods for the Examination of Water and Wastewater, 23rd Edition.

WHO (2011). World Health Organization Guidelines for Drinking-water Quality. www.who.int/water_sanitation_health/publications/drinking-water-quality-guidelines-4-including-1st-addendum/en/.

HARD AND SOFT WATER

Many people do not understand the meaning of hard water and some believe that it is a contamination of harmful chemicals. The term "hard water" generally refers to water that has high mineral content, but specifically water that is high in calcium and/or magnesium ions. Barium, strontium, copper, lead, zinc, cadmium, and radium can also be minor components. Hard water forms precipitates of metal carbonates that are very insoluble and it causes problems by forming scale deposits, accumulating in pipe and in cooling systems where they reduce the heat transfer capability. When combined with soap the metal components interfere with lathering and rinsing and cause the precipitated "bathtub ring." Hard water is probably the most common and noticeable water quality problem that occurs. It has been said that about 80–85 percent of the United States has hard water as defined. The good news is that hardness is not known to cause any human health concerns, and it may have some health benefits, but it can certainly have negative aesthetic and economic consequences.

Composition and Chemistry

Water hardness is measured as calcium hardness in milligrams of calcium carbonate equivalent as follows:

Soft less than 17 mg/L
Slightly hard 17–60 mg/L
Moderately hard 60–120 mg/L

Hard 120–180 mg/L
Very hard >180 mg/L

The term "grains/gallon" is commonly used in the water softening industry; 17.1 mg/L as calcium carbonate is equivalent to 1 grain/gallon.

Calcium and magnesium are commonly present in water as soluble bicarbonates that are formed when carbonates react with carbon dioxide. The bicarbonate, carbonate, carbon dioxide, and water are in equilibrium. Bicarbonate predominates in the pH range of about 6–10. Calcium bicarbonate is soluble at about 16.5 g/100 mL around room temperature, but calcium carbonate solubility is only about 0.0013 g/100 mL, so it is clear that it will precipitate when conditions favor its presence. Higher pH and heat cause loss of carbon dioxide and conversion of the bicarbonate to carbonate.

The mineral forms of the carbonate precipitates are hard solids that will deposit and continuously build up on pipe, tanks, boilers, and appliances, and they are difficult to remove. Pipes with deposited carbonate scale have reduced water flow and they can eventually clog. Hot water heaters are damaged from the accumulated precipitates; heating coils are coated reducing heat transfer efficiency and increasing energy costs.

The other commonly noticeable effect of calcium and magnesium and related ions in water is that they react with soap that is a large fatty acid molecule (e.g., a stearate) and form the insoluble metal salt (e.g., calcium stearate) that deposits as soap scum or bathtub ring. These various precipitates from water are not easily removed, and may require an acid wash to clean them from showerheads, faucet aerators, and surfaces. Detergents for clothes washing, dishwashing, and shampoos are formulated for specific purposes and are much less affected by hard water because they are structurally and chemically different from soaps. So, water hardness is at least an annoyance, but that can be overcome. It certainly can have major economic consequences in the home and also for industry.

Chemical Analysis

There are numerous analytical procedures for quantifying hardness, alkalinity, and individual ions. One source is Standard Methods for the Examination of Water and Wastewater Part 2000 series including Method 2340. A calculation of metal hardness can be made if the concentrations of the individual ions are known. Calcium, magnesium, and other metals can be determined by atomic absorption spectroscopy or inductively coupled plasma emission spectrometry (ICP/MS). There are also ethylenediaminetetraacetic acid (EDTA) titrimetric methods and colormetric methods. There are also commercial test kits that provide rapid and simple low-cost analyses.

Water Treatment Softening

Soft water can be hardened when appropriate by percolation through calcite filter beds. Water softening is a common practice both in the home and in larger-scale facilities. Precipitative lime softening with calcium hydroxide and lime-soda ash softening are inexpensive unit processes and used by municipal water plants that soften. Those coagulation and filtration processes also clarify the water and remove contaminants such as radium, giardia, and *Cryptosporidium* oocycts that have health concerns. Removal of dissolved ions (desalination) on a large multimillion gallons per day scale is also accomplished with membranes, particularly high pressure RO, as well as by lower pressure thermal distillation processes.

The two most common home water softening techniques are cation exchange and low-pressure RO. Iron and manganese can also be removed by these techniques, but may require pretreatment to reduce membrane fouling. Point-of-entry (POE) home water softening utilizes a polyvinylbenzene sulfonate cation exchange resin that is neutralized with sodium ions. As hard water passes through the resin, calcium displaces sodium ions from the resin into the water and the resin retains the calcium and other "hard" ions. The resin is periodically regenerated by treating with a concentrated sodium chloride solution brine that goes down the drain. Cation exchange softened water is not necessarily corrosive. These types of softeners have raised some controversy due to the discharging of sodium chloride to the groundwater environment. Some recommend softening only the hot water system to protect the hot water heater, and reduce soap consumption, and also as an economy measure.

Point-of-use (POU) RO softening is another option in the home. RO home softeners are not very efficient and they produce only a small portion of product water, because they operate at low line pressures and therefore can reject to waste on the order of 80 percent of the influent water. However, there is no chemical addition required. RO process water is very corrosive due to its very low dissolved solids content and low alkalinity, so nonreactive contact plumbing is necessary. POE RO softening, which is not common, would require plumbing in the entire house that is corrosion resistant. Large-scale RO desalination is much more efficient because it operates at much higher pressure. The permeate water is very corrosive, so it is stabilized by alkalinity and pH adjustment before it is put into distribution.

Some communities have restricted the use of salt-based cation exchange softeners because of the discharges of sodium chloride to the environment. There are nonchemical softener devices on the market that are based upon magnetic, electromagnetic, electrostatic, electrodialysis reversal, electrodeionization reversal, chelation, catalytic, and mechanical processes. Some of these are softening by ion removal and some are scale prevention approaches. There is controversy and mixed results, and performance certifications are not yet generally available for several of them for home applications from organizations such as the Water Quality Association and the International Association of Plumbing and Mechanical Officials (IAPMO). There is a German standard; however, several standards from these organizations are in development or recently released. There are examples of good performance for some in higher volume industrial applications where there is generally more control over changing conditions and water quality restrictions for use.

Health Considerations

Health-based regulations or guidelines for calcium hardness in drinking water do not exist, but many industrial processes require water that has low mineralization or hardness so pretreatment of process water or cooling water is a major component of many facilities.

Many studies have suggested a benefit of reduced cardiovascular mortality from consumption of hard water. However, it has been concluded that if there is a benefit, it is associated specifically with the magnesium content rather than hardness per se. The removal of essential minerals like calcium and magnesium from water by softening can result in lower lifetime intakes of those essential elements. In addition, health concerns have been raised by some with regard to cation exchange water softeners because of increased sodium intake, especially for people who are salt-sensitive hypertensives. Mixtures of sodium and potassium chloride are used for regeneration in some cases: at least one softener product had a cartridge that adds magnesium after the softening stage.

Conclusion

Hard water is an aesthetic and economic problem, so water softening is one of the most widespread water treatments for municipal and home systems. Different levels of hardness require different treatment levels. Over-softening can make the water aggressive/corrosive so a properly designed and maintained system is essential. Normally, only water for indoor use would be softened in a home system, and frequently softening only the hot water side is sufficient and more economical than softening the entire home supply.

Sources

Fawell J, Abdulraheem M, Cotruvo J, Al-Awadhi F, Magara Y, Ong CN (2010). *Chemical Aspects of Desalinated Water, in Desalination Technology: Health and Environmental Impacts*, CRC Press. ISBN 978-1-4398-2890-8.

Cotruvo J and Bartram J (Eds.) (2009). *Calcium and Magnesium in Drinking Water: Public Health Significance.* World Health Organization, Geneva. Also online at whqlibdoc.who.int/publications/2009/9789241563550_eng.pdf. ISBN 978 92 4 156355 0.

Cotruvo JA (2013). Hard Water. Water Technology on Line. www.watertechonline.com/professor-poupoe-july-2013/.

EPA Method 130.1: Hardness, Total (mg/L as $CaCO_3$) (Colorimetric, Automated EDTA) by Spectrophotometer. www.epa.gov/sites/production/files/2015-08/documents/method_130-1_1971.pdf.

Non-Chemical Devices: Thirty Years of Myth Busting. T. Keister, Water Conditioning and Purification. April 2008.

American Water Works Association/American Public Works Association/Water Environment Federation (2017). Standard Methods for the Examination of Water and Wastewater, 23rd Edition.

Undesser P. Physical Water Treatment Devices. WQA. www.wqa.org/pdf/gov-relations/wqamagneticstaskforcereport.pdf.
USGS. Hard Water and Alkalinity. https://water.usgs.gov/owq/hardness-alkalinity.html.
Water Processing: Residential, Commercial, Light-industrial. W. McGowan and JF Harrison, Technical editor. Water Quality Association, 2000.
Water Softening (2013). Guidance for the Use of Water Softening and Onsite Wastewater Systems on Individual Properties. www.wqa.org/Portals/0/Technical/2013_NOWRA_WQA_GuidanceDocument.pdf.
WHO (2017). World Health Organization Guidelines for Drinking-water Quality. www.who.int/water_sanitation_health/publications/drinking-water-quality-guidelines-4-including-1st-addendum/en/.

SALINITY IN DRINKING WATER

Introduction

Salinity (dissolved inorganic solids) is an important aspect of drinking water quality that can be beneficial or harmful, aesthetically pleasing or a cause for rejection of the water. Distilled water, desalinated water, and rainwater have minimal salts content. Seawater and brines have tens of thousands of parts per million (ppm) of salts, and typical drinking waters can have hundreds to well over 1,000 ppm, mostly less than 200 ppm concentration (ppm equals mg/L of water). The questions are as follows: How much is too much salinity? What are the aesthetic issues? Are there any potential health consequences, and can it be managed at a reasonable cost?

Components of Water Salinity

The basic chemistry definition of a salt is the reaction product of an acid and a base. So, for example, sodium hydroxide plus hydrochloric acid yields sodium chloride plus water.

$$NaOH + HCl \rightarrow NaCl + H_2O$$

Most salts encountered in drinking water are inorganic, but there are also organic salts; for example, methyl amine plus acetic acid yields methylammonium acetate. There are also mixed organic and inorganic salts such as sodium acetate.

$$CH_3CO_2H + CH_3NH_2 \rightarrow CH_3NH_3^+ \; C_2H_3O_2^-$$

Salts consist of paired anions and cations. The cation is positively charged because it has lost one or more electrons; the anion is negatively charged because it has gained one or more electrons. Some are individual element/ions, e.g., chloride, Cl^- or sodium, Na^+ ions; some are complex ions, e.g., ammonium ions, NH_4^+; and some have multiple charges, e.g., sulfate, $SO_4^=$. The pairing is necessary so that the net charges are balanced (net neutralized).

Some salts are ionized in water and some are not or partially ionized. Solid salts usually exist as crystals of several possible arrangements, or as amorphous particles. Because water can be polarized, salts in water solution are "solvated," which means each ion is surrounded by a number of water molecules that locally neutralize the positive and negative charges. The oxygen ends of the water molecules surround the positive ions, and the hydrogen ends surround the negative ions. That is why many salts are soluble in water, which is neutral but polarized, but not soluble in nonpolar organic solvents like benzene. If a salt is soluble in water, it means that the net solvation energy of the ions in solution is lower than the binding energy of the ions in the solid crystal.

Seawater and Brackish Water

More than 97 percent of the water on the earth is salt water. Over the millennia, salts on the land have been washed into the sea or accumulated in aquifers by extraction from the local geology. The salinity of natural water ranges from rain at very low levels, to less than 100 mg/L in many fresh waters, to approximately 35,000 mg/L (ppm) in oceans, to more than 50,000 mg/L (ppm) of TDS in some confined and coastal seawaters, e.g., the Arabian Gulf. A typical seawater could contain about 19,000 mg/L chloride, 10,500 mg/L sodium, 2,600 mg/L sulfate, 1,250 mg/L magnesium, 400 mg/L calcium, 400 mg/L potassium, 150 mg/L bicarbonate, and 80 mg/L bromide—plus lesser quantities of assorted ions. A brackish water of about 3,500–10,000 mg/L TDS could contain at least about 900 mg/L chloride, 750 mg/L sodium, 1,000 mg/L sulfate, 90 mg/L magnesium, 250 mg/L calcium, 10 mg/L potassium, 380 mg/L bicarbonate, and lesser ions.

Salinity Standards

Some individual ions, such as lead or borate, have sufficient toxicity, so they have health-based standards or guidelines for drinking water. Fortunately, most of the mass of salinity in water has only aesthetic concerns, but excessive levels are harmful. Sea water cannot be consumed by humans because it is dehydrating *in vivo*. There are recommended values such as TDS or hardness (mostly calcium and magnesium, plus for some other cations such as barium or strontium). Hardness is reported as calcium carbonate and classified in ppm ranges: Soft water, <17; slightly hard, 17.1–60; moderately hard, 60–120; hard, 120–180; and very hard, >180 ppm.

In the United States, there are SMCLs that are not actually enforceable federal standards, but guidelines for numerous ions based upon taste or other aesthetic reasons. Some states have adopted some of them as state standards. For example, the TDS SMCL is 500 ppm, sulfate is 250 ppm, chloride is 250 ppm, copper is 1.0 ppm, iron is 0.3 ppm, and manganese is 0.05 ppm. TDS, sulfate, and chloride values are primarily driven by taste; copper, iron, and manganese have metallic tastes, but also may add color, or result in undesirable precipitates on laundry and fixtures. The WHO recommendations (not formal guidelines which are health related) are similar to the above.

Health Issues

The human gut has regulatory mechanisms providing some screening of incoming ions and some selectivity of uptake. For example, concurrent calcium intake depresses the uptake of lead ions, so drinking water (or milk) with calcium reduces lead uptake in children; bromide is mitigated by chloride because of the chemical similarity of the two halides. Water and dairy are often more efficient sources of minerals uptake from foods, because there are dietary components (e.g., phytates) that reduce mineral uptake from vegetables.

Humans cannot tolerate excess salt intake. However, sodium, potassium, calcium, and magnesium are macronutrients and hundreds of milligrams daily intakes of each are essential to health; numerous other minerals are micronutrients (perhaps micrograms per day in some cases). We lose salts by perspiration and in urine and feces. Consuming small quantities of clean seawater is not harmful, especially if the seawater is taken along with a larger quantity of fresh water. However, drinking seawater to maintain hydration is counterproductive. The gut cannot absorb water if the salt concentration is above about 2 percent, because more water must be excreted to eliminate the excess salt, causing net dehydration.

The human kidney regulates sodium chloride in the blood within a narrow range around 9 g/L (0.9 percent by weight), above that is toxic and can lead to seizures and heart arrhythmia. At that level there is equilibrium between water entering and leaving red blood cells; lower salt concentrations would cause excess water absorption by the cells and bursting; higher concentrations would deplete water in the red blood cells. Excessive sodium loss can lead to hyponatremia, which can be fatal. Mineral imbalances can also have significant health consequences. The potential for kidney stone formation from calcium in drinking water is still being debated.

There are also indications of positive benefits of minerals such as calcium and magnesium in drinking water. The calcium body burden is about 1,200 g, over 2.5 pounds. Calcium is efficiently absorbed from water and dairy at about 50–60 percent versus about 20 percent from nondairy foods, and that contributes to the daily calcium requirement of about 1,000 mg/day for bone and heart health. Magnesium, with a body burden of only about 25 g, is also better absorbed from water and dairy and it has numerous essential enzymatic activities and heart health functions. Low serum magnesium correlates with metabolic syndrome that is a precursor to some diabetes. In addition, there are several water epidemiology studies that associate magnesium levels above about 10 mg/L with reduced cardiac-related mortality. So, it is possible that consumption of soft or softened water for a lifetime may be less desirable than consumption of harder waters, unless the diet provides sufficient available magnesium, especially from dairy.

Natural Mineral Waters

Many people consume mineral waters either because of perceived health benefits or desirable taste. Natural mineral waters are defined by the Codex Alimentarius. Maximum levels of certain potentially harmful minerals are usually similar to WHO guideline values: antimony, 0.005 mg/L; arsenic, 0.01 mg/L; barium, 0.7 mg/L;

borate, 5 mg/L; cadmium, 0.003 mg/L; chromium, 0.05 mg/L; copper, 1 mg/L; cyanide, 0.07 mg/L; fluoride, notify if > 1 mg/L; lead, 0.01 mg/L; manganese, 0.4 mg/L; mercury, 0.001 mg/L; nickel, 0.02 mg/L; nitrate 50 mg/L; nitrite, 0.1 mg/L; and selenium, 0.010 mg/L.

Taste Considerations

Salts contribute tastes that are sometimes desirable and sometimes not, and they affect palatability. Distilled and desalinated waters usually have a "flat" taste. Salts are often added to improve palatability of bottled water and to reduce corrosivity in piped water. The US SMCL for TDS is 500 mg/L. The WHO states that TDS at up to 600 mg/L is generally considered to have good palatability, and water becomes significantly and increasingly unpalatable as TDS exceeds 1,000 mg/L.

The California SMCLs are as follows: TDS with a recommended consumer acceptance contaminant level of 500 mg/L, an upper level of 1,000 mg/L, and a short term of 1,500 mg/L; and chloride's recommended acceptance level of 250 mg/L, an upper level of 500 mg/L, and a short term of 600 mg/L. Sulfate has a recommended acceptance level of 250 mg/L, an upper level of 500 mg/L and a short term of 600 mg/L.

Excess Salinity Problems

Excess salinity in distributed water is economically undesirable and can cause excessive scale formation in pipes, boilers and appliances, as well as interfere with the performance of washers for clothes and leave residues on glassware. Economic impacts include possible corrosion and reduction of the heat-transfer efficiency of boilers, which can cause premature failures of hot water heaters.

Analyses

Salinity and TDS correlate with electrical conductivity, which is often used for tracking the performance of desalination treatment processes. The Standard Method is 2510 for conductivity and 2520 for salinity.

Water Treatment

Calcium and magnesium, and other divalent ions such as barium, strontium, and radium are readily removed by conventional lime and lime soda softening and cation exchange water softening. Anions such as fluoride, arsenate, and nitrate can be removed by anion exchange treatment. Electrodialysis and electrodialysis reversal systems are also used in numerous commercial applications.

The universal maximum treatment for salinity is membrane treatment related to desalination. Nanofiltration membranes are capable of removing multivalent ions more efficiently than monovalent ions, so they can be somewhat effective especially in non-seawaters, because seawater has very high levels of monovalent ions. Reverse osmosis achieves removal in the 98–99 percent range in thousands of high pressure seawater desalination applications that can operate at rates as high as multimillion gallons per day. A rough estimate for production cost is about $3–$4 per thousand gallons. Home POU technologies can reduce the salinity of domestic waters, but their water reject ratios are high (perhaps greater than 70 percent) because they operate at low water line pressure and with different membranes than the large-scale units.

Some treatment processes increase salinity somewhat because of pH adjustments which add either acids such as HCl or bases such as sodium hydroxide or sodium carbonate, and some other chemical treatment additives. Sewage has higher salinity than the source drinking water because of process waste discharges into the sewage system and also human inputs. Potable water reuse projects often include a salt reduction stage, especially if the original drinking water has high TDS salinity.

Conclusion

Salinity is a universal component of natural and treated water to a greater or lesser degree because water is such a good solvent for ions. Fresh waters make up a minute portion of the earth's water—most is saline. Humans can tolerate limited amounts of salts in drinking water for reasons of health and palatability. Treatment technologies used to produce drinking water from saline water and wastewater are widely available, and the numbers of large-scale applications are rapidly expanding. They are technology's answer to the world's need for universal access to fresh and drinkable water, for a price.

Sources

Cotruvo J and Bartram J (Eds.) (2009). Calcium and Magnesium in Drinking Water: Public Health Significance. World Health Organization, Geneva. Also online at whqlibdoc.who.int/publications/2009/9789241563550_eng.pdf ISBN 978 92 4 156355 0.

Cotruvo JA (2015). Salinity in Drinking Water. Water Technology on Line. www.watertechonline.com/professor-poupoe-january-2015/.

Cotruvo JA, Voutchkov N, Fawell J, Payment P, Cunliffe D, Lattemann S (Eds.) (2010). Desalination Technology: Health and Environmental Impacts. CRC Press and IWA Publishing, Taylor and Francis, K11421, ISBN 978-1-4398-2890-8.

EPA (2016). Conductivity. www.epa.gov/national-aquatic-resource-surveys/indicators-conductivity.

EPA (1983). Methods for Chemical Analyses of Water and Waste. EPA/600/4–79/020.

Standard Methods (2017). Standard Methods for the Examination of Water and Wastewater, 23rd Edition. www.techstreet.com/standards/standard-methods-for-the-examination-of-water-and-wastewater-23rd-edition?sid=msn&utm_medium=cpc&utm_source=bing&product_id=1974889.

WHO (2017). World Health Organization Guidelines for Drinking-water Quality. www.who.int/water_sanitation_health/publications/drinking-water-quality-guidelines-4-including-1st-addendum/en/. Also WHO 4th Edition (2011).

SILICA AND SILICATES IN DRINKING WATER

INTRODUCTION

Silicon is the second most abundant element on earth after oxygen. Silicon dioxide (SiO_2), sand, and fused quartz are silicas. Silicate minerals constitute about 90 percent of the Earth's crust. Silicates are components of glass, detergent formulations, and pottery. Silicon is in computer microchips. Silicates are also used for fireproofing paper and wood.

PHYSICAL AND CHEMICAL PROPERTIES

Silicon is a nonmetallic element with atomic number 14 and atomic weight 28.09 Da. Silicates are anions containing silicon and oxygen (e.g., orthosilicate, SiO_4^{-4}), and several others are usually slightly soluble in water so silicate salts are commonly present in natural water. These consist of many metal silicates such as Zn_2SiO_4, as well as hundreds of complex multimetallic mineral silicates, e.g., $Fe_3Al_2\ (SiO_4)_3$. Silicate minerals exist in multiple forms, including several gemstones, asbestos, talc, and mica. Zeolites are complex aluminosilicates with several metals and silicon in many oxygen complexes. Water fluoridation is often accomplished with fluosilicic acid, which rapidly hydrolyses to silicate and fluoride in water.

OCCURRENCE AND EFFECTS OF SILICATES IN WATER

Silicates in water can be beneficial or cause water quality and treatment problems. Natural concentrations of various silicate forms can range from a few parts per million (ppm)(mg/L) in surface water to more than 100 ppm in groundwater. Some silicates will be in solution, and some are present as colloids that are difficult to manage. Silicates can form scale as well as accumulate to foul membrane surfaces.

HEALTH AND ENVIRONMENTAL ASPECTS

Silicon compounds are present in all living organisms. They exist as hydrated amorphous silicates, and are required for structural elements in single-celled organisms, higher plants, and animals. Silicon in assimilatable forms might be considered an essential element. Body levels of silicates tend to decline after birth while calcium increases. There are claims of positive roles of silicate in bone strength, hair and skin quality, and many other claims of which the validity is yet to be determined. Even silicon supplements are available.

In ecosystems, the silicon and phosphorus ratio and the silicon and nitrogen ratio are thought to contribute to the type of algae and other organisms that will dominate in surface waters, for example, diatoms versus cyanobacteria. Algal populations shift after springtime as the silicate is consumed.

WATER TREATMENT APPLICATIONS

Silicates can form scale deposits that coat contact surfaces. If present in excess, silicate removal technologies are a function of the physical form that is present.

Applications include filtration, chemical precipitation, reverse osmosis, and ion exchange. Settling and filtration will remove granular silicates. Chemical precipitation can be used for some dissolved and colloidal silicates. RO will remove dissolved silicates, but removal of silicates prior to RO is desirable to reduce the risk of fouling the membrane.

Silicates have beneficial applications in water treatment technologies. Silicates can suspend metals such as iron II by sequestration and prevent its precipitation as red oxides. However, that may mask corrosive effects rather than mitigate them. Controlled applications of silicates for water stabilization can help manage corrosivity and reduce concentrations of metals like lead in corrosive water environments. When used as a corrosion control treatment, continuous dosages of about 30 mg/L are common initially for stabilization, but the dose is reduced over time as the "silicate demand" is achieved.

Analysis

There is a molybdosilicate colorimetric method and others in Standard Methods 4500-SiO_2. ASTM D859 is a version of the molybdosilicate method for water and wastewater. Test kits are available to help detect dissolved silica levels in water.

Regulation

There are no primary or secondary regulations for general silicates in drinking water although there is a maximum contaminant level of seven million fibers longer than 10 microns for asbestos. The WHO Guidelines for Drinking Water Quality do not address silica and silicates.

Sources

Cotruvo JA (2015). Silica and Silicates. Water Technology on Line. www.watertechonline.com/contaminant-of-the-month-silica-and-silicates/.

FreeDrinkingWater. Silica. https://search.yahoo.com/search?ei=utf-8&fr=tightropetb&p=freedrinkingwater.com%2Fwater_quality%2Fquality2%2Fj-24silica&type=45241_102617.

Lytle DA and Schock MR (2001). The Use of Silicates for Corrosion Control in Building Drinking Water Systems. Presented at National Association of Corrosion Engineers Corrosion/2001, Technical Information Exchange 1556x, Supplemental Treatment of Potable Water in Building Systems, Houston, TX, 3/13/2001. https://search.yahoo.com/search?ei=utf-8&fr=tightropetb&p=freedrinkingwater.com%2Fwater_quality%2Fquality2%2Fj-24silica&type=45241_102617.

Silicate Minerals Structural Styles. www.indiana.edu/%7Egeol105/images/gaia_chapter_5/silicate_mineral_structural_styl.htm.

Standard Methods (2017). Standard Methods for the Examination of Water and Wastewater, 23rd Edition. www.techstreet.com/standards/standard-methods-for-the-examination-of-water-and-wastewater-23rd-

edition?sid=msn&utm_medium=cpc&utm_source=bing&product_id=1974889.
What is Silica. http://whatissilica.com/. Accessed February 22, 2018.
WHO (2017). World Health Organization Guidelines for Drinking-water Quality. www.who.int/water_sanitation_health/publications/drinking-water-quality-guidelines-4-including-1st-addendum/en/. Also WHO 4th Edition (2011).

7 Special Topics

This chapter is a discussion of several diverse topics that go beyond drinking water composition to address broader issues that have major impacts on drinking water availability, consumer perceptions, and more novel and sustainable water sources and processes such as desalination and potable water recycling. It also addresses distribution system risks, which are actually the most dominant, default factors used in drinking water risk assessments, and it also provides perspectives on foodborne versus waterborne disease risks, and fracking. Anyone who is interested in drinking water production, science, technology, policy, and politics should find several topics of value.

BOIL WATER NOTICES

Introduction

Boil water notices are issued when there are reliable indications that the public water supply, or a definable portion of the supply, is likely to be contaminated by microorganisms that could cause disease if the water is consumed without further water treatment provided by consumers. This can be indicated by failure to meet a significant microbial drinking water standard, failure of an important water treatment process like filtration or disinfection, catastrophic events such as floods and earthquakes that can disrupt drinking water systems, broken or leaking water distribution lines, and epidemiological indications of waterborne disease occurrence. Boil water notices are serious measures that can also have significant adverse consequences, so they should only be issued for good cause.

Boil water notices are not unusual. Kelley Reynolds of the University of Arizona has made a partial tabulation of US boil water notices issued in 2012–2014 and preliminarily located almost 15,000 of them, about 3 percent on average per year from more than 150,000 public water supplies. Boiling would also remove some volatiles, but boiling drinking water is definitely not advisable when the contamination is from a nonvolatile chemical such as nitrate. Boiling would concentrate the contaminant in the water as the water volume was being reduced from release of steam.

Water Treatment

Boiling is a very effective way to eliminate waterborne pathogens. Boiling advisories are accompanied by information on how long to carry out the boiling. The drinking water treatment goal is to eliminate the pathogens to below the limit of detection, but at least to get below the infective dose. The boiling instructions range from bringing the water to a rolling boil and allowing it to cool (no ice) by the

World Health Organization (WHO), to boiling for 1 minute or boiling for 3 minutes (US Environmental Protection Agency [EPA] and Centers for Disease Control and Prevention [CDC]), or for 10 or 20 minutes, which is irrational. CDC and some others also recommend boiling for 3 minutes at altitudes above about 5,000 feet because the boiling temperature is reduced by about 0.9°F (0.5°C) per 1,000 feet of altitude. However, this is a precaution that would usually not be essential. If the water is not microbiologically safe, extra care should also be taken for cooking, washing, showering, and bathing uses.

Pathogenic microorganisms are heat sensitive, and virtually all are killed well before water reaches 212°F or 100°C, which is the normal boiling point of water at atmospheric pressure. Boiling for 1 minute is actually more than necessary, but could perhaps be justified by assuring that the water has actually reached boiling and is not merely purging dissolved gasses. The other recommendations range from unnecessary to the point of being absurd as well as wasteful of heat energy—which could also be in limited supply during a catastrophic emergency. Boiling is also appropriate when camping or traveling where the available drinking water is not known to be safe.

Table 7.1 illustrates the effects of heat and time on microbial survival in water. It is temperature dependent, but the efficacy rises almost exponentially as water temperature rises above 60°C (140°F). So, there are virtually no viable microorganisms of concern remaining long before the temperature reaches boiling at 100°C (212°F). Viruses are more heat resistant than bacteria and protozoa but they are also rendered noninfectious with somewhat longer times at comparable temperatures. The standard pasteurization condition (e.g., for milk) is 72°C (162°F) for 15 seconds or 63°C (145°F) for 30 minutes. Table 7.1 illustrates the susceptibilities of numerous microorganisms to temperature as a water purification process. It demonstrates that most pathogenic microorganisms are fragile and eliminated at temperatures well below boiling.

TABLE 7.1
Examples of Published Temperature and Time Dependency of Die Off of Microorganisms in Water (WHO/FWC/WSH/15.02)

Microbe	Temperature (°C/°F)	Seconds	Log reduction
E. coli	60/140	300	1.5
E. coli 0157	65/149	3	per log
Cryptosporidium parvum	60/140	300	3.4
"	72/162	5–15	>3
Poliovirus1	60/140	1,800	5.4
"	95/203	15	>5
Enteroviruses	60/140	1,800	4.3
"	75/176	30	5

Note: 1 log = 90 percent reduction, 2 logs = 99 percent, 3 logs = 99.9 percent, 4 logs = 99.99 percent and 5 logs = 99.999 percent.

Other Beneficial Water Treatments

Travelers are advised to take precautions when the available water is not reliably safe. Numerous organizations, including CDC and WHO, have published advice on readily available methods travelers could use to reduce risks from unsafe water. These range from boiling, addition of chlorine bleach or iodine, and the use of rated disinfecting filters. Reverse osmosis (RO) and one micron filters may be beneficial for removal of many microorganisms. However, it is essential that performance claims for commercial water treatment devices cannot be made beyond those allowed from their certifications. These are identified in the standards ANSI/NSF 53 (health), 55 (ultraviolet [UV]), 58 (RO), and 62 (distillation).

Regulatory Notices

General public health protection tenets are the basis for boiling. In addition, public water systems in the United States are subject to Safe Drinking Water Act (SDWA) regulations that specify conditions where boil water notices are required and even the language that must be used as well as the methods of dissemination of the notice and supporting information. The EPA Public Notification Rule (65 FR 25982, May 4, 2000) identifies conditions when Tier 1, highest level, notifications are required.

These notifications include the following:

- Within 24 hours of an *Escherichia coli* maximum contaminant level (MCL) violation
- Failure to test for *E. coli* after a positive total coliform test
- Exceedance of the maximum turbidity level (0.3 ntu, 95 percent of monthly samples, or 1 ntu) in a surface supply
- Detection of *E. coli*, *Enterococcus*, or coliphage in a sample from an untreated groundwater drinking water source
- Evidence of a waterborne disease outbreak
- Other events, at the discretion of the primacy agency.

Specified language includes, e.g., "fecal coliforms and *E. coli* are bacteria whose presence indicates that the water may be contaminated with human or animal waste. Microbes in this waste can cause diarrhea, cramps, nausea, headaches or other symptoms. They may pose a special health risk for infants, young children and people with severely compromised immune systems."

It could likely also say, do not drink the water without boiling it first. Bring it to a boil for 1 minute or perhaps 3 minutes and let it cool, or use bottled water, boiled or bottled water for drinking, making ice, brushing teeth, washing dishes, and preparing food until further notice. Bathing is usually acceptable.

Those are fairly ominous statements that should attract attention and cause people to take appropriate actions. But note the absence of mention of other home treatment methods such as disinfection (bleach or iodine), UV, or other certified point-of-use (POU)/point-of-entry (POE) devices. Distillation units involve boiling, so they should be acceptable. These may be appropriate especially for larger volumes of water if boiling is not available.

The boil water notice might actually be too late to affect exposures to contaminated water. Smaller water supplies in the US sample for *E. coli* only a few times per month. The analysis requires about 24 hours of incubation of the sample plus reporting time, and a verification repeat sample might be carried out somctimes before the health agency that would issue the notice is alerted of the violation. An unfortunate example of a boil notice by EPA occurred in Washington, DC, in the 1990s on the third day after a brief turbidity violation in one filter at the treatment plant. The retention time of water in the distribution system was about 2 days, so the affected water had already essentially cleared the system. In reality, there was no emergency.

SDWA regulations (40 CFR 141.100) do not allow community-wide use of POU devices for legal compliance with microbial drinking water regulations. However, proven POE devices would be acceptable, at state discretion, for public water system compliance. The distinction is primarily the need to have microbiologically safe water at all of the taps in a home as well as the need to have central management of the decentralized water system technology.

Variances and exemptions are legal processes that allow a delay in achieving compliance with a drinking water regulation, however, they should not be allowed for acute risks without mitigation. It ought to be possible to negotiate community-wide decentralized treatment systems to reduce the risks that could exist during the often multiyear term of the variance or exemption.

Notification Methods

The regulations also contain mandatory and optional notification procedures that include one or more of alerts by means of radio, TV, hand delivery, and posting in prominent locations. Others could include newspaper, hospitals, physicians, schools, and apartments.

Consequences

Boil notices have serious consequences including panic buying of bottled water, adverse publicity, and economic costs in the community. They require rapid correction of the cause and rescission of the notice when the problem is solved. However, experience shows that not everyone receives the message, some probably ignore it and the response is diluted as the time span of the notice lengthens.

Commercial Opportunities

Any indication of a water quality problem creates an immediate demand for rapid response and opportunities for providers of bottled water and treatment devices. It is essential that any of these activities are consistent with the expectations of regulations and the public health authorities. Bottled water should meet Food and Drug

Administration (FDA) or state standards, or International Bottled Water Association (IBWA) standards, and be appropriately certified. Water treatment devices generally would not be acceptable to regulators as substitutes for boiling or bottled water, but some of them might be providing some benefits commensurate with their certifications to appropriate ANSI/NSF standards, if they were in place.

Conclusions

Boil water notices have serious consequences, so they should be issued only for good cause, consumers need to be kept informed of the cause and provided with mitigation information, and the notice should be lifted as soon as the water supply has returned to normal, safe operation, which should be rapidly accomplished. Notices in the United States have specified language requirements and must follow specified notification procedures plus optional information and procedures at state discretion.

Bottled water should meet all federal and state requirements. Water treatment devices can provide water quality benefits, but they should be consistent with the requirements of responsible state public health authorities, and marketing claims should be specific to the appropriate contaminant issue and the ANSI/NSF standards to which they are certified.

Beyond responding to boil water notifications in public water systems because of water supply failures, regulators and providers of water treatment devices should also be aware of the water contamination problems that can exist in homes with unregulated private wells and be capable of providing water testing and disinfection services, if needed, as well as other water treatment services to address specific contamination that is detected. Again, this should be consistent with state authority expectations.

Sources

Boil Water (2015). WHO/FWC/WSH/15.02.

Boil Water. www.health.ny.gov/environmental/water/drinking/boilwater/boil_water_fact_sheet.htm#q6.

CDC (2009). www.cdc.gov/healthywater/drinking/travel/backcountry_water_treatment.html.

Cotruvo JA (2015). Water Technology on Line. www.watertechonline.com/professor-poupoe-june-2015/.

Point-of-Use Water Treatment for Home and Travel, update, in *UNESCO Encyclopedia of Life Support Systems*, Joseph Cotruvo and Mark Sobsey, W. Grabow ed., at www.eolss.net web encyclopedia, and also monograph publication UNESCO, 2006.

Reynolds K (2016). www.wqa.org/Portals/0/Media%20Kit/WQA%20Publications/Boil_Water_Notice_Study_Brochure_Feb16.pdf.

World Health Organization (2011). www.who.int//water_sanitation_health/publications/2011/dwq_guidelines/en/.

BOTTLED WATER

INTRODUCTION

This is a brief discussion on where bottled water comes from, how is it produced and regulated, and how its quality compares to public drinking water. Numerous types of bottled water are available from many sources, and they are regulated by the federal government, states, and the bottled water industry.

Bottled water consumption in the United States has been rising consistently after the passage of the SDWA in 1974, since the media increased its coverage of environmental and drinking water issues, such as disinfection byproducts, emerging contaminants, chemical spills, and droughts. Every report on the detection of chemicals in drinking water at parts per billion (ppb) or parts per trillion (ppt) levels seems to generate more public concern. Commercial bottled water consumption is common in many parts of the world most importantly because of because of actual concerns about local drinking water safety, however, in many other countries, because of perceived contamination risks, taste preferences or as a substitute for soft drinks. Many people occasionally drink bottled water for convenience and taste. Some people claim that they never drink tap water but do drink mineral water or other bottled waters, because of the presumed health benefits.

The public drinking water quality in the United States is generally excellent from a health perspective. However, some water supplies have persistent or periodic taste issues that may arise from the use of chlorine disinfection or high total dissolved solids (TDSs), and that can result in confidence in the local supply being shaken. Waterborne disease rates from ingested drinking water in the United States are low and have been declining since the full implementation of the SDWA around 1980. On the other hand, aged infrastructure can affect high-quality water entering a piped distribution system and quality can be affected by contact time in aged infrastructure and infiltration from pipe leaks.

People use less than 1 percent of their tap water for drinking and cooking. Most is used for sanitation, washing cars, and watering lawns. Many consumers have more discretionary income and more options for drinking water than in the past. Those options range from tap water to POU or POE treated water and bottled water. More people are opting to differentiate between beverage water and commodity water, which could be the predominant nondrinking water uses.

THE BOTTLED WATER BUSINESS

Bottled water is big business. Bottled water sales in the United States exceeded 10 billion gallons and $12.3 billion in 2013, after some small recession-related declines in 2008 and 2009. Worldwide sales were 70.4 billion gallons and growing. Per capita US consumption was 32 gallons. Mexico's per capita consumption was about double that of the United States for reasons associated with tap water inconsistencies. Today's US and worldwide sales are higher. For perspective, the city of Chicago produces more than 1 billion gallons of public drinking water per day.

Consumer choice variables lead to changing rates of bottled water and bottled beverage consumption by age group and over time, at least partly attributable to the continuing press reports of boil water notices, detections of trihalomethanes (THMs) and other trace chemicals in drinking water. Mineral waters are not chlorinated. Processed bottled waters from public drinking water sources are usually retreated by granular-activated carbon (GAC), RO, UV, ozone, or some combinations.

Bottled water consumption in the United States in 2016 was 39.3 gallons/capita/year (almost a half-liter per person per day on average), which was increased more than 9 percent from 2015. That is compared to 16.2 gallons/capita in 1999 and 1.6 gallons/capita in 1976. There are also significant regional differences, with Southwestern US consumption of 61.9 and Pacific 53.5 gal/capita/year versus West Central and East Central regions of 16.7 and 17.1 gallons/capita/year. Bottled water consumption is in addition to bottled carbonated and still beverage consumption of 38.6 gallons in 2016. Refrigerators now often come with carbon filters built into their water dispensers for drinking water and icemakers. Tap, point-of-use or point-of-entry water treatment involving carbon cartridges or RO units has also increased, but most home treatment devices primarily are carbon based and remove chlorine taste, along with some organic chemicals for some period of time.

About two-thirds of bottled water is provided in thin-walled polyethylene terephthalate (PET) bottles that are usually blown at the bottling site. A rapidly growing segment is home and office delivery in 5-gallon polycarbonate carboys, and bottles. More than 90 percent of US bottled water is still water, so only a small portion is carbonated. About 10 percent of the bottled water total was imported, even though plenty of local products is available. Much of the total appears to be from consumers replacing a portion of former fruit juice and carbonated soda consumption, which are steadily declining.

Based upon the above bottled products, the overall average cost is about $1.23 per gallon, but retail costs for small units are well above that. Undoubtedly most of the cost is for advertising, packaging and transport, and seller profit. For comparison, typical tap water costs are approximately $3–$4 per 1,000 gallons delivered.

Types, Sources and Treatment

Several types of bottled water, by source and treatment, are described in the following edited International Bottled Water Association (IBWA) definitions:

- Bottled water—water intended for human consumption and sealed in bottles or other containers with no added ingredients except that it may optionally contain safe and suitable antimicrobial agents.
- Sparkling bottled water—bottled water that, after treatment and possible replacement of carbon dioxide, contains the same amount of carbon dioxide present at the emergence from the source.
- Mineral water—water containing no less than 250 parts per million TDS, originating from a geologically and physically protected underground water source. Mineral water can be distinguished from other types of water by its constant level and relative proportions of minerals and trace elements at the point of emergence from the source, taking into consideration the cycles of natural fluctuations. No minerals may be added to this type.

- Natural water—bottled spring water, mineral water, artesian water, artesian well water, or well water derived from an underground formation or from surface water that only requires minimal processing. It is not derived from a municipal system or public water supply and is unmodified except for limited treatment (e.g., filtration, ozonation, or an equivalent disinfection process).
- Spring water—water derived from an underground formation from which water flows naturally to the surface of the Earth. Spring water must be collected only at the spring or through a borehole tapping the underground formation feeding the spring.
- Well water—water from a hole bored, drilled, or otherwise constructed in the ground that taps the water of an aquifer.

A large portion of commercial bottled water is produced by reprocessing municipal tap water (e.g., Dasani and Aquafina and many others), and some are from spring waters. The source information can be found on the labels. The municipal water may be treated by RO, ozonation, GAC, UV, or combinations with some minerals sometimes added for taste. Therefore, it would have low TDS and low total organic carbon (TOC). Some assume that water in a bottle must be natural spring water, so complaints have been made by some people and organizations who did not read the labels. Properly retreated tap water's quality is at least equivalent to "natural" water's quality.

Bottled Water Quality

The Natural Resources Defense Council (NRDC) and some other organizations have occasionally published exposés of bottled water quality. In 1999, NRDC issued a report of 185 samples of many bottled waters, which tested for heterotrophic plate counts (HPCs), arsenic, THMs and bis(2-ethylhexyl) phthalate (DEHP). Arsenic was detected in some natural mineral waters, THMs were detected in a few brands, mostly from one supplier, and diethylhexylphthalate (DEHP) was detected in two samples. HPCs were commonly found and a few were at high levels.

HPCs regrow in water that does not contain a residual disinfectant, so bottled water on the shelf has the potential to grow HPCs even though it has been disinfected with ozone or UV light, which, however, leave no disinfectant residual. The FDA allows HPC in bottled water at high levels and the WHO has concluded that they are not generally a health concern. The US EPA has a drinking water treatment technique regulation that limits HPC to 500 bacterial colony units per milliliter, as a general water management indicator.

Standards and Regulations

The Codex Alimentarius, a joint activity of the Food and Agricultural Organization (FAO) and the WHO, provides international standards for bottled and mineral waters. In the United States, the FDA establishes drinking water standards for bottled water that is in interstate commerce, so the national brands are federally regulated. By law, FDA standards are derivative of the EPA National Primary Drinking Water Regulation standards and differ in appropriate minor respects. States have the authority to establish standards for bottled water within their borders, and many do.

Bottled waters that exceed FDA quality standards may not be distributed for public consumption or must be recalled from the marketplace. Six reported recalls of bottled water occurred from 1989 to 2011. A 2009 Government Accountability Office survey of state bottled water regulatory authorities reported no outbreaks of foodborne illness from bottled water during a 5-year period.

FDA's current Good Manufacturing Practices regulations include monitoring requirements that are generally more frequent than community water systems, do not allow for averaging of test results, are not related to the number of consumers and are more frequent on a per-gallon basis than tap water requirements.

In addition, IBWA, located in Alexandria, Virginia, has produced a Code of Practice that includes standards, monitoring requirements, and good manufacturing practices for its members, which are also periodically subject to on-site inspections and water analyses. The code is more restrictive than FDA and EPA standards in several respects.

Conclusions

Tap water regulations have been successful in improving the management and quality of the 150,000 public water supplies that include about 50,000 community water supplies. They are regularly tested and required to meet national regulations and report deviations to their consumers. Regulated tap water in the United States is safe with few intermittent exceptions. Bottled water is a large and growing factor in the US drinking water landscape. Although there may be occasional statements in the press that bottled water is not as highly regulated as public drinking water that is generally not the case. Assuming it has been produced and bottled under controlled sanitary conditions, bottled water is actually an ideal, though expensive, method for providing beverage drinking water, because the water is protected from contamination after being bottled. It will, however, often have much larger quantities of measured HPC than tap water as a partial function of storage and shelf time, and lack of a disinfectant residual.

Consumers have many drinking water options; so choices are widely available for those willing to pay the price for the convenience and taste preference and, potentially, additional quality control, depending upon the source water, and size of the community where they reside. The SDWA mandates the quality and safety of public tap water, and drinking water standards are becoming more restrictive and expensive to achieve. FDA bottled water standards are derived from the EPA drinking water standards. Since less than 1 percent is consumed in drinking and cooking, one could imagine a water delivery paradigm that would distinguish between beverage water and commodity water. In fact, it would be logical and cost effective if community-supplied bottled water or community-managed POU or POE would be acceptable and more widely available, especially in small communities that are having problems meeting national standards.

Public water suppliers could also provide bottled water from their facilities to consumers—some have tried but it has not caught on. Singapore does it with their NeWater. Perhaps, someday the local drinking water supplier will be a full-service water provider by several of those methods.

Sources

Codex (2001). General Standard for Bottled/Packaged Drinking Waters. www.fao.org/fao-who-codexalimentarius/sh-proxy/en/?lnk=1&url=https%253A%252F%252Fworkspace.fao.org%252Fsites%252Fcodex%252FStandards%252FCODEX%2BSTAN%2B227–2001%252FCXS_227e.pdf.

Cotruvo JA (2015). Bottled Drinking Water. Water Technology on Line. www.watertechonline.com/professor-poupoe-july-2015/. Accessed February 22, 2018.

Cotruvo JA, Amato H, Smith C (2018). National Trends of Bladder Cancer and Trihalomethanes in Drinking Water. Report to the World Chlorine Council, February 15, 2018. Submitted for publication. Water Research. 2018.

EPA (2012). Drinking Water Standards and Health Advisories. www.epa.gov/sites/produciton/files/2015-09/documents/dwstandards2012.pdf.

FDA. Federal Food, Drug, and Cosmetic Act (FFDCA) (21 U.S.C. §§ 301 et seq.) and (21 C.F.R. § 165.110 (a)).

IBWA (2016). Bottled Water Market. www.bottledwater.org/economics/bottled-water-market. Accessed February 22, 2018.

IBWA (2016). International Bottled Water Association Code of Practice (Model Code). www.bottledwater.org/education/codes-of-practice. Accessed February 22, 2018.

NAS (2006). *Drinking Water Distribution Systems: Assessing and Reducing Risks*. National Research Council. National Academies Press.

NRDC (1999). Bottled Water Report: Pure Fact or Pure Fiction? April 12, 1999. www.bottledwater.org/content/nrdcs-bottled-water-report-pure-fact-or-pure-fiction-arthur-von-wiesenberger-april-12-1999.

Statistica (2018). Per Capita Consumption of Bottled Water in the United States from 1999 to 2016 (in gallons). www.statista.com/statistics/183377/per-capita-consumption-of-bottled-water-in-the-us-since-1999/2015.

World Health Organization (2011). www.who.int//water_sanitation_health/publications/2011/dwq_guidelines/en/.

CONSUMERS' PERCEPTIONS OF DRINKING WATER QUALITY AND SAFETY

Introduction

Public perceptions of drinking water acceptability and safety have been trending negatively since the passage of the US SDWA in the mid-1970s. This indicates more public sensitivity to drinking water issues, but it is counterintuitive because public drinking water quality has consistently improved since then and has probably never been better on a national scale. Studies in the 1960s that led to the passage of the SDWA demonstrated inconsistency in meeting public drinking water quality specifications, especially in small water systems. Most large systems were then in compliance with the existing US Public Health Service drinking water requirements.

The Water Quality Association (WQA) published the results of a 2015 national telephone survey of 1,200 adults living in private households. WQA is the international trade association representing the household, commercial, and industrial water quality improvement industry. Results were reported by the market research firm that conducted the telephone survey to be accurate within 2.8 percent. The results are found in the 2015 Study of Consumers' Opinions and Perceptions Regarding Water Quality. The fifth survey that WQA has conducted during the past 11 years, it shows a continuation of some trends regarding public perceptions about drinking water quality and people's drinking water choices in response to those views.

Survey Content and Findings by Topic

The survey consisted of a series of water-related questions that respondents answered. Several of the key questions and response rates are provided below with some comments and comparisons of results from the 2011 or 2013 surveys.

- **Overall concern with quality of household water.** Fifty-six percent of the respondents (up from 52 percent) were very or extremely concerned about their water quality, while 23 percent (down from 25 percent) were not very concerned. The responses were slightly more concerned or close to the experimental precision range.
- **Concern about health contaminants.** Fifty-nine percent (up from 54 percent) were very or extremely concerned, while 19 percent (down from 24 percent) were not very concerned. These results are more robustly outside the 2.8 percent precision range.
- **Primary responsibility for safe drinking water**. Seventy percent, consistent with earlier studies, said that the responsibility belonged with the municipality. Twenty-two percent said the responsibility was with home water treatment products and 8 percent with a bottled water plant. This result is somewhat inconsistent with later responses relating to the consumption of bottled water or the use of home water treatment devices.
- **Consumption from drinking water sources.** The question was: Do you currently use any of the following? The responses were as follows:
  - 77 percent compared to 65 percent in 2011 indicated that they use bottled water.
  - 43 percent compared to 49 percent in 2013 have a not fully defined home water filtration product.
  - 45 percent compared to 34 percent in 2011 have a refrigerator water filter.
  - 16 percent versus 15 or 16 percent have a water softener.

Bottled water usage increased, but it is likely not exclusive bottled water usage for most respondents, which could not be determined from the question. Home water softener usage did not change from 2011 to 2015. It is clear that significantly more new refrigerators are being sold with installed filters. Apart from refrigerator filters, the home water filter usage rate was about the same as in 2011.

- **Reasons for purchasing bottled water.** The taste of tap water and the convenience of bottled water were consistent in the 40 percent range. Safety and health concerns were consistent at about 23–26 percent of responses. Other tap water quality elements, such as the appearance and odor of tap water, were consistent in the 14–16 percent range. The percentages are not additive because of multiple responses.
- **Reasons for purchasing a filtering system.** Among the approximate 43 percent of the respondents who had purchased a filtration product, 40 percent stated that they were motivated by the taste of the tap water, and 50 percent were concerned about contaminants. These are not additive because of multiple responses. The approximate 25 percent of all respondents who were concerned with health risks is consistent with the bottled water purchasers. The range of filtration product types that consumers used was not fully defined.
- **Impact of the "green" movement.** Apparently, this question was related to concerns about plastic bottles. Seventy-eight percent said they would still buy bottled water and 9 percent had stopped buying bottled water. Another 6 percent switched from bottled water to a home filter. About 15 percent of them had seemingly eliminated their use of bottled water, but this does not appear to be entirely consistent with the increased bottled water consumption noted in other studies.
- **Reasons for purchasing a filtration system.** Forty-eight percent of the respondents stated that published notifications of unsafe water or boil water notices led to the purchase of a filtration system. Seventy-seven percent purchased a pitcher water filter, an end of faucet device, or a refrigerator filter. This response has some ambiguities since on average only about 3 percent of public water systems issue boil water or similar notices in a typical year. Fifty-six to 66 percent of the respondents expressed willingness to pay for a water treatment system if it could remove certain contaminants.
- **Perceived contaminants in tap water.** About 80 percent of the respondents were concerned about chlorine, about 70 percent about lead, 50 percent about microbiologicals, 42 percent about arsenic, 36–39 percent about pharmaceuticals, 24 percent about radium, 20 percent about chloramine, and 12 percent about methyl tertiary butyl ether (MTBE). These do not add up to 100 because of multiple allowed responses. These responses are puzzling because most of the contaminants are regulated and do not pose significant health risks to public drinking water, and are not present in water at the frequencies of the responses. So, the concerns were likely mostly generated from perceptions from national media publications rather than from personal circumstances.

- Chlorine is commonly used in drinking water treatment and free chlorine is often noticeable since the taste threshold of free chlorine is temperature-dependent, but an approximate value of about 0.6 mg/L is frequently reported. The taste threshold for chloramine can be as high as 5 mg/L. The maximum permissible levels in drinking water are 4 mg/L, but most water supplies are well below those values. Numerous public water systems have converted from free chlorine to chloramine residuals during the past 30 years, so the frequency of chlorine taste detection should be declining.
- Lead would be a concern only in homes connected to water systems that still have some lead service lines or galvanized iron pipe and that do not also provide proper corrosion control required by the lead and copper rule.
- Microbiological contamination is under exceptional control in public water systems because of broad filtration requirements for surface waters and disinfection requirements for vulnerable groundwaters. Gastroenteritis microorganisms are readily controlled by water treatment. Waterborne disease outbreak numbers are low and have consistently declined since the implementation of the SDWA in the 1980s. From 2011 to 2012, 11 outbreak incidents of water-related gastrointestinal disease were reported by the CDC in more than 150,000 public water systems, so the risk is slight.
- Arsenic is regulated and primarily a concern in just a few thousand (low percent and small population) small public water systems and an unknown number of private wells that have difficulty providing treatment. So, 42 percent is a hypothetical rather than a likely realistic personal concern.
- Pharmaceuticals have been detected at ppt or very low ppb levels in some surface water supplies. The WHO concluded they were not a public health concern in drinking water.
- Radium is regulated and seldom found in surface waters and infrequently found above the regulated value in groundwater systems except in certain known areas of the country. It is readily treated by water softening methods.
- MTBE is a potential groundwater contaminant formerly used as a gasoline additive that has a noticeable odor at 20 ppb and taste at 40 ppb. It is not toxic below those levels and would be readily detected if present. The frequency of its presence in public water supplies is well below 12 percent.

Conclusions

The WQA survey of consumer opinions and perceptions provides interesting insights into the concerns of consumers regarding the aesthetics, quality, and safety of their tap water as well as their motivations for accessing bottled water or home treatment devices. Several of the 2015 response rates were not statistically different from the 2011–2013 period. The trend of increasing public dissatisfaction with tap water and using alternatives has continued since the 1970s when the visibility of drinking water quality issues increased commensurate with the passage and implementation of the SDWA, the increasing intensity of media articles and reports on drinking water topics, and with the development of increasingly sensitive analytical methods that allowed detections at very low concentrations not previously possible.

Also interesting is that pitcher, carbon tap, and refrigerator filters are the most popular home treatment devices, and their long-term strengths are in the removal of chlorine and other taste-sensitive chemicals that may reduce the desirability of drinking water, but are not public health concerns. Some pitcher filters remove other trace components. Boil water notices do not necessarily lead to purchases of treatment devices that are designed to control pathogenic microorganisms, and health concerns do not necessarily encourage consumers to purchase more expensive devices designed for long-term removal of trace chemicals (e.g., larger carbon filters or RO devices). Water softeners are effective in reducing hard water that improves water characteristics for domestic uses, and they will remove radium, barium, and strontium in addition to calcium and magnesium.

The survey provided much useful information on public perceptions and attitudes about drinking water and the impact of the media on public opinion. Perhaps additional detail is available on the study, such as on the composition and geographic distribution of the respondents, that would refine the interpretations of the results. For example, what was the breakdown between the public water system and private well users, since wells are more likely to have water quality issues?

Many in the public decide to exercise their options, treating drinking water as a beverage choice rather than a commodity, and they are consuming more bottled water and using home treatment devices. This is probably partly because of the greater availability and convenience of bottled water and home treatment devices and more discretionary income, but it is also driven by people's dislike of the taste of some tap water and their reactions to media reports that stimulate concerns about hypothetical risks that may be related to drinking water.

What is clear is that in many cases consumers perceive that their tap water is of lesser quality than it really is, and they often do not make the appropriate technology choices that relate to their concerns. Producers of home water treatment devices should be more informative in connecting the customers water quality needs to the appropriate certified device. It is also clear that water suppliers should be more concerned about the aesthetic quality (e.g., undesirable taste or excessive hardness) of their product beyond just meeting regulatory requirements.

Water for drinking and cooking makes up only about 1 percent of the tap water provided by the public water supplier and consumers have several beverage choices. The water industry and federal and state regulators should do a better job of educating the public about the actual risks and technologies that are appropriate for treating their water to make it more desirable. In addition, private water supplies (home wells) are much more likely to be a quality and health risk concern than public supplies because they are usually not managed or treated for microbial contaminants, nitrates and nitrites, or natural or synthetic chemical contaminants, such as those from septic tanks or pesticide migration.

Sources

Cotruvo JA (2015). Water Technology on Line. Consumers' perceptions of Drinking Water Quality. www.watertechonline.com/professor-poupoe-consumers-perceptions-of-drinking-water/.
WQA (2015). National Study of Consumers' Opinions & Perceptions Regarding Water Quality 2015 Edition. www.wqa.org/Portals/0/Resources/2015_WQA_Consumer_Opinion_Study_Highlights_Public_final.pdf.

DESALINATION

Introduction

Access to sufficient quantities of safe water for domestic, commercial, and industrial applications is essential for public health, quality of life, and economic development. Total world water is constant, but access to sufficient supplies is decreasing in some areas while demand is increasing, and periodic droughts are affecting more people. Not all can be blamed on climate change, which is the current fashion, because the major driver is probably population growth and water demand increases in historically water-limited areas.

Many areas of the world including parts of the United States have inadequate water resources and accessibility. Population growth and population shifts to urban areas and coastal areas, and increased consumption are concurrent with industrialization and improved economies, standards of living, and quality of life. The world has a great amount of water; however, most of it is seawater or brackish water and it is not always located where it is being consumed, so it is essential to reduce waste, but also utilize technology to provide more water where it is needed. Agriculture accounts for two-thirds to three-fourths of freshwater consumption. Per capita consumption of public water supplies varies widely with the mix of industrial and domestic uses, seasons, climate and also because incentives for conservation are often absent due to governmental subsidies providing water much below cost of production—even in wealthy water short countries.

Per capita consumption varies widely. In countries such as Qatar, it is 430L per capita per day; in Germany, it is about 100L and in the United States about 375L. However, drinking and cooking accounts for less than 1 percent of public water supplied to consumers' taps. Demand from municipal supplies in the United States has been decreasing at the rate of about 1 percent per year for a variety of reasons, partly population shifts and industrial demand changes, but probably often due to passive and active conservation.

"New water" is available from just three sources: conservation, wastewater recycling and reuse, and desalination. Conservation is not actually new water and it has its limits; recycling and reuse are "new" sources and they are being more widely practiced for agricultural, industrial, and potable applications, and desalination offers the opportunity to access the world's almost limitless saline waters. This summary will concentrate on desalination.

What Is Saline Water?

The salinity of natural water ranges from <100 mg/L in freshwaters to approximately 35,000 mg/L in oceans to more than 50,000 mg/L of TDS in some seawaters (e.g., the Arabian Gulf). A typical seawater source could contain about 19,000 mg/L chloride, 10,500 mg/L sodium, 2,600 mg/L sulfate, 1,250 mg/L magnesium, 400 mg/L calcium, 400 mg/L potassium, 150 mg/L bicarbonate and 80 mg/L bromide plus assorted lesser ions. A brackish water of about 3,500 mg/L TDS could contain about 900 mg/L chloride, 750 mg/L sodium, 1,000 mg/L sulfate, 90 mg/L magnesium, 250 mg/L calcium, 10 mg/L potassium, 380 mg/L bicarbonate, and other ions.

Brief History of Desalination

Desalination applications on a large scale began in earnest in about the 1960s in the arid Middle East, where increasing oil revenues and increasing population made water essential to development as well as being financially and technologically accessible. Desalination plants were built and ultimately almost all of the water in that region is now supplied by desalination of water from the Arabian/Persian Gulf and other sources.

Introduction of seawater desalination in the United States has been slow because most areas have access to natural freshwater sources at a much lower cost. However, there are some plants in operation, such as in Tampa, Florida. Southern California has had several groundwater desalting plants in operation for many years. A seawater desalination plant has been built in Carlsbad, California, and several others are in operation or in development.

As of late 2017, more than 19,506 desalination plants were built, ranging from 25 m^3/day to more than 1 million m^3/day and most were in operation throughout the world with capacity for producing about 24.8 billion gallons (~94.17 million m^3) per day and capacity continues to grow rapidly. Seawater desalination comprises about 60 percent, 20 percent is brackish water, 10 percent is river water, and wastewater and purified water are about 5 percent each. The Middle East has the largest capacity, with Saudi Arabia and the United Arab Emirates being the leaders. Production in North America, North Africa, Europe, Australia, and other parts of Asia is growing rapidly. The largest plant in the world is in Saudi Arabia at 270 mgd and sizes go down to a few hundred gallons.

Desalination Technology

There are three general types of desalination technologies: Thermal, membrane, and electrodialysis variants. As implied, thermal processes involve some type of a distillation process; whereas membrane processes involve RO or other novel developments like forward osmosis, and different membranes, e.g., ceramic rather than polymer composites; and electrodialysis involves migration of charged ions to oppositely charged electrodes.

Thermal technologies are of several types: multistage flash distillation, multiple effect distillation, and vapor compression distillation. They all involve heat transfers between phases at lower pressures so that vaporization occurs followed by condensation in several stages, with the heat of vaporization being recovered at condensation and transferred to the liquid phase to cause additional vaporization. About 25–50 percent of the flow is recovered as freshwater condensate. These were the earlier desalination processes and are still dominant in the Middle East. They are energy intensive but efficiencies have been improving as the technologies are refined.

Membrane processes usually involve RO although some nanofiltration (NF) processes are used. High pressure (55–70 bars for seawater and 15–35 bars for brackish waters; 1 bar is 14.5 psi) is applied to the saline side of the membrane to force the reversal of the natural osmosis process, so that water flows from the concentrated side of the membrane to the low salinity side. The nominal pore size of an RO membrane is between 0.0001 and 0.001 μm, while an NF membrane is about 0.001 μm.

These are small enough to remove bacteria, protozoa, and viruses in an intact system. In RO, salts and almost all organics as well as microbes are removed at up to approximately 99-plus percent and at least 6 logs for microbes. Organics with molecular weights less than about 100–150 Da and some not completely ionic inorganic species like borates are not well removed. RO is more energy efficient than distillation processes, yet it is still energy intensive, primarily due to the high pressure pumping requirements. Membrane technologies are more commonly used now and increasing even in the Middle East. Water recoveries can be in the 75 percent and higher ranges.

Electrodialysis is much less utilized but does have specialty applications. A direct current is applied to the water and that drives the ions through permeable membranes to electrodes of opposite charge. One of its benefits is that ions are being mobilized but not uncharged species, so membrane fouling is somewhat less of an operational problem.

Pretreatment by disinfection and filtration is required to protect the membranes and extend run times and reduce fouling that can occur from biofilms and particulate and salts accumulation. Many of the membranes are sensitive to chlorine so it must be removed prior to contact with the membrane. Chloramines are effective and peroxyacetic acid seems to be a candidate as well as for cleaning processes because the membranes are more tolerant of those biocides.

Post-treatment is also required to reduce the corrosivity of the depleted water. Alkalinity and pH adjustments are necessary; otherwise the deionized water would be very aggressive to metal and concrete surfaces.

Many municipal wastewater recycling processes utilize a membrane process as part of their multi-barrier water treatment train. The process provides at least 6 log reduction of microbes, including viruses, although some regulatory authorities will not credit that level of reduction, because of concerns for the potential that a seal or other membrane failure might allow some passage. Daily pressure testing and real time electrical conductivity and TDS and turbidity measurements provide a very strong basis to allow greater microbial log reduction credit. Many commercial bottled waters are produced by reprocessing municipal tap waters with membranes to purify them further. Some salts are often added to the treated water to improve the taste.

Environmental Aspects

Desalination at a large scale requires intake of millions of gallons of raw water per day from the sea source. That causes impingement during the high rate of flow conditions, which occurs when aquatic organisms are entrapped against intake screens and entrainment, and also disruptions when smaller organisms pass through the screens and into the process equipment. Co-location with power plants is advantageous by use of a common intake pipe, waste heat transfer from the power plant to the desalination process, and dilution of the brine with cooling water before discharge.

Brine Management

Reject brines from RO and residue concentrates from thermal and membrane processes are at least double or triple concentrated from the source water. Brine disposal is one of the most difficult problems associated with brine management. At seawater plants, the brines are returned to the sea via long pipes often with diffusers to reduce mixing zone problems that can have environmental consequences. Inland plants using brackish groundwaters must either mechanically concentrate the brines to solids for land disposal, or use lined evaporation ponds, or possibly dispose by deep well injection, which is highly regulated.

Costs

The costs for thermal and membrane processes are highly dependent upon the desalination method, initial salt concentration, disposal costs, fuel costs, construction costs, inflation, regulatory burdens, and local conditions. Membrane processes are generally lower in cost than thermal processes, and most newer plants use membranes. The rough back-of-the-envelope production cost-estimate for seawater desalination is in the range of approximately $4–$6 per thousand gallons for membrane plants, but these costs have been declining as technologies and efficiencies have continuously improved.

Water Quality

Desalination produces very high-quality water equivalent to rain water or distilled water. Salts residues in treated water are well below 100 mg/L, and organic chemical residues are in the low ppb or ppt range for those lower molecular weight natural and synthetic chemicals that are not efficiently removed. Thus, TOC levels are fractions of ppm, and disinfection by-product formation will also be very low after subsequent residual disinfection. The water will be corrosive to most transmission pipes so corrosion control processes are essential.

POU and POE Desalination

Home water desalination treatment, usually referred to as "point-of-use" (POU) devices, are also readily available in the United States; however, these are usually very small-scale, low-pressure RO devices applied to public water as a supplemental treatment for TDS reduction or softening. Many bottled waters are tap waters reprocessed by RO membranes and ozone or UV. The low-line pressures of perhaps 40 psi and the required membranes make them very inefficient with very high water rejection rates of perhaps 70–80 percent in some cases. POU membranes have applications for softening and TDS reduction, but POE devices—those that treat all the water entering a building or residence, are not used because of corrosivity to home metal plumbing. There are, however, many industrial applications where very high-quality low TDS water is required and also where scale formation must be controlled, so membranes or ion exchange or softening processes are essential. Water treatment processes at somewhat less than municipal scale are widely applied.

Health

Because desalinated water has most of its minerals removed it is important that other dietary intakes provide all the necessary minerals. Water is an efficient source because of a higher uptake percent of minerals versus food intake. There are also many natural surface waters that are soft and very low in dissolved minerals like calcium and magnesium, so the issue is not unique to desalinated drinking water. Water consumption usually is only a portion of the source of important dietary minerals, such as calcium, magnesium, and potassium, but it might provide an important lifetime baseline increment. Calcium and magnesium are essential elements that can impact chronic diseases such as osteoporosis and diabetes. There are studies indicating that consumption of drinking water with magnesium has shown a beneficial reduction in cardiovascular disease mortality. This is consistent with well-known effects of magnesium on cardiovascular function. Some countries require remineralization with calcium, magnesium, and other ions. This is not only a health issue, but also important if desalinated water is used for irrigation because irrigation may be applied to low quality desert or depleted soils, and plants also require various mineral nutrients for proper growth.

Conclusion

Desalination is a significant and rapidly growing source of new water where the need is sufficient and the costs are acceptable. Costs are considerably greater than drinking water produced from natural freshwaters, but that is partly because natural waters are often free, require much less treatment, and their costs are artificially low because of subsidies. The saline source waters are widely distributed and almost limitless in quantity. There are environmental issues that require management but their control is feasible. Posttreatment for water stabilization is essential to control corrosivity. There are indications that low, specific calcium/magnesium mineral intake from water could be negative to overall health if dietary intakes are not sufficient.

Sources

Cotruvo JA (2014). Desalination. Water Technology on Line. www.watertechonline.com/professor-poupoe-november-2014/.

Cotruvo, Voutchkov, Fawell, Payment, Cunliffe, Latteman (Eds.) (2010). *Desalination Technology Health and Environmental Impacts.* CRC Press, Taylor and Francis Group, LLC. Boca Raton, FL 33487-2742. www.crcpress.com/Desalination-Technology-Health-and-Environmental-Impacts/Cotruvo-Voutchkov-Fawell-Payment-Cunliffe-Lattemann/p/book/9781439828908.

Pankratz T (2018). Global Water Intelligence.

Voutchkov N (2017). *Pretreatment for Reverse Osmosis Desalination*, 1st Edition. Elsevier. www.elsevier.com/books/pretreatment-for-reverse-osmosis-desalination/voutchkov/978-0-12-809953-7.

Voutchkov N (2013). *Desalination Engineering: Planning and Design*, 1st Edition. McGraw Hill. www.mheducation.com/highered/product/desalination-engineering-planning-design-voutchkov/9780071777155.html.

DRINKING WATER CONSUMPTION, REGULATORY DEFAULT ASSUMPTIONS, AND HEALTH

Introduction

The statement, "Water is life," is not an exaggeration. All living plants and animals require regular and sufficient water consumption for survival, as well as for growth and development, as well as for sanitation. Serious and even fatal outcomes can occur under extreme conditions of either seriously inadequate or very excessive water intake, and there might be some health benefits associated with consumption beyond the averages. Water is also a common element in Christian, Muslim, and Jewish religious writings.

Daily water consumption occurs from several sources: Tap water, beverages, and foods made with tap water, foods, bottled water, bottled beverages, and metabolic water that is produced from ingested food and its conversion to energy. The first five are obvious. The sixth, metabolic water, is created by living organisms through metabolism by digesting and oxidizing energy-containing substances in their food. Metabolism produces about 110 g of water per 100 g of fat, 41.3 g of water per 100 g of protein, and 55 g of water per 100 g of starch. So, it adds a few hundred milliliters to our daily water intake.

How Much Water Should We Drink?

How much water should people drink, and how much they actually drink every day is a complex question. The amount of water that is needed for health and homeostasis varies by a person's age and weight, climate, and his/her level of physical activity. Some estimates and recommendations have been generated from several published studies.

Ingested water serves many functions. It is essential for maintaining blood composition, salts balance, and cellular osmotic pressure, and it aids digestion, helps eliminate wastes in urine and feces, provides a solvent/solute load for the kidneys, and helps control body temperature through perspiration. It usually contains salts and some nutrients like calcium, magnesium, chloride, sulfate, sodium, and potassium; and, uptake of essential minerals is often more efficient from water than from foods. Calcium and magnesium uptake from water and milk is in the range of 50–60 percent versus approximately 15–20 percent from foods.

It is important to consume water regularly, especially during physical stress conditions. At one time coaches would not allow athletes to consume water during practice and games, ostensibly to prevent stomach upset and vomiting. Nowadays, we see athletes drinking frequently. Acute dehydration has immediate, measurable and adverse consequences. Fluid loss of 1 percent stimulates thirst and impairs thermoregulation. Vague discomfort and loss of appetite appears at 2 percent. Dry mouth appears at about 3 percent loss. At 4 percent loss, work capacity decreases by 20–30 percent. Headaches and sleepiness occur at about 5 percent loss. Collapse can occur at about 7 percent, and a 10 percent loss is life-threatening.

Water intake is needed at a minimum to replace losses and prevent dehydration. Water is lost through urine, feces, respiration, and perspiration and evaporation. Young children, pregnant and lactating women, the elderly, heavy work and exercisers, and persons with certain diseases have increased fluid requirements compared to the general sedentary population. Numerous studies have attempted to determine water needs, but in 1989 the National Research Council (NRC) concluded that because of the complexities, a Recommended Dietary Allowance for water could not be established, but an Adequate Intake (AI) reference value was provided for healthy Canadian and American populations.

Water needs under conditions of physical stress, high temperature, and humidity are substantial. Physically active individuals might sweat at the rate of 3–4 L/hour under those conditions. Daily fluid requirements have been shown to range from as little as 2 to 16 L/day. Several national military organizations have conducted studies of the water needs of troops under stressed survival and endurance requirements. A study of members of the Zimbabwe National Army doing strenuous work over 12 days showed that consumption of the test group was 11 L/day versus 7 L/day in the control group.

The US Army revised its water replacement guidelines to 0.5 L/hour for an easy work rest cycle at 78°F–81.9°F, to at least 1 L/hour for a hard work/rest cycle of 10/50 minutes at >90°F. The revision occurred after 190 military personnel were hospitalized over several years for hyponatremia (excess, un-replaced sodium loss by perspiration), which can be fatal when excessively large volumes of plain water were consumed in combination with a low sodium chloride diet.

Gender- and age-specific AIs were established by the NRC in 2004 (see Table 7.2).

The values in Table 7.1 are applicable under typical, nonstressed conditions. For higher stress situations (e.g., athletes), the amount of water ingested should equal the amount lost, i.e., 1 kg of lost weight = 1 kg of water consumption. Alcohol (and coffee) has a known transient diuretic effect, but adequate fluid intake immediately

TABLE 7.2
Estimated Water Consumption

Age	AI (L/day)
0–6 months	0.7 assumed from human milk
7–12 months	0.8 milk plus food and beverages
1–3 years	1.3
3–8 years	1.7
9–13 years	2.4 boys, 2.1 girls
14–18 years	3.3 boys, 2.3 girls
19–70+ years	3.7 men, 2.7 women

TABLE 7.3
Recommended Minimum Water Consumption

	Sedentary, Temperate Environment	Physically Active/Increased Temperature
Female adult	2.2	4.5
Male adult	2.9	4.5–11.0

following alcohol consumption will not result in appreciable fluid losses over a 24-hour period.

The WHO's requirements in liters per day for adults are listed in Table 7.3.

How Much Water Is Actually Consumed by US Citizens?

Regulatory agencies establish regulations for contaminants in water partly based upon default assumed values for daily human tap water consumption. Precise determinations of actual consumption vary by individuals and conditions; so to simplify the regulatory decision, the US EPA has historically assumed the default lifetime consumption of 2 L/day for a 70-kg adult, and 1 L/day for a 10-kg child. WHO assumes 2 L/day for a 60-kg adult and 1 L/day for a 10-kg child. Canada assumes 1.5 L/day for a 70-kg adult. More recently EPA has been using 0.15 L/kg/day for the first year of life, and 0.03 L/kg/day for an 80 kg adult (i.e., 2.5 L/day) in health advisories. The latter results in about a 10 percent lowering of the calculated drinking water value vs a default assumption of 2 L/day for a 70 kg adult. That difference seems to be rather irrelevant considering that safety/uncertainty factors of 100–1,000 are commonly used in drinking water maximum contaminant level goals (MCLGs) calculations for the general population.

Several large-scale surveys have produced data on consumption of community water and/or total water by individuals and groups. Results tend to be in similar ranges given the margins of variability in these types of studies. For example, a 1989 report by Ershow and Cantor, using survey data for three consecutive days from 1977–1978, concluded that the mean value for tap water consumption was 1.193 L per person per day, and the 88th percentile consumed 2 L/day or less. A more recent analysis of a survey for two, nonconsecutive days from 1994–1996 (EPA, 2000) of 15,303 persons gave 0.927 L/day as the average per capita ingestion of tap water. The estimated 90th percentile consumption was 2.016 L/day (range 1.991–2.047). Some people reported drinking no tap water, so results for 14,012 "consumers only" were 1.0 L/day (0.976–1.024) as the mean, and the 90th percentile value was 2.069 L/day.

Values for "total water consumption" for "consumers only" were 1.241 L/day (1.208–1.274) as the mean, and the estimated 90th and 95th percentiles were 2.345 and 2.922 L/day, respectively. So, 83 percent of consumers consumed 2 L of water per day or less.

The average reported consumption for bottled water drinkers was 0.737 L/day; the 90th and 95th percentile estimates were 1.568 and 1.971 L/day, respectively.

The total water consumption average for all individuals was 1.232 L/day, and the 90th and 95th percentiles were 2.341 and 2.908 L/day, respectively. In this study, approximately 84 percent of the US population consumed 2 L/day or less. About 13 percent of the US population water consumption in those studies was attributable to bottled water and 10 percent to other sources. Bottled water consumption has been increasing consistently. A more recent study of bottle water consumption resulted in a national average of about 0.5 L/day.

For children between 1 and 10 years old, the mean total water consumption was 0.528 L/day, and the 90th and 95th percentile values for total ingestion were 1.001 and 1.242 L/day. Thus, 90 percent of children consume 1 L of water per day or less.

Are There Health Benefits from Greater Water Consumption?

Although it is difficult to precisely determine desirable and ideal water consumption levels, there are reports that people with greater water consumption may benefit more compared to those with less. Dehydration has been linked to increases in risks of urinary tract infections, dental disease, constipation, kidney stones, and impaired cognitive function. Higher fluid intakes have been associated with reduced risks of urinary tract stones, colon and urinary tract cancer, and mitral valve prolapse in some studies. More research is necessary on this appealing hypothesis.

Conclusions: How Do These Approximate Values Compare to AIs and Regulatory Default Assumptions?

It is clear that the actual water consumption in the United States is below the recommended AI values for almost every age group. Some additional water is provided by metabolism and non-tap water sources, but the AI values would not likely be exceeded in many cases except perhaps for active high consumers, some of whom may have illnesses that increase consumption.

Regarding the default water consumption values of 2 L/day for adults and 1 L/day for a 10-kg child, approximately 90 percent of adults are consuming 2 L/day of tap water or less, and almost all young children are consuming about 1 L of tap water per day or less. So, water consumption levels indicate that drinking water standards are protective of the population and have sufficient margins of safety for essentially all very young children and adults. Additional conservatism is embedded in calculations of drinking water MCLGs by inclusion of relative source contribution factors attributable to drinking water as a source. The usual default value is 20 percent, resulting in an additional safety factor of 5.

Different nations use different default values for water consumption, but the drinking water standards or MCLG calculations are not significantly different with respect to health protection considering the liberal use of conservative safety factors and relative source contributions in the calculations. There are also several studies indicating potential health benefits from long-term consumption of greater amounts of water, which is worth exploring further.

So, the take-home message is: More water and a little more salt is good for people with more strenuous activity, and that community tap water in the United States and is safe almost everywhere, and somewhat exceeding most MCLs for a moderate time or often longer has no significant increased risk to health due to the usually large margins of safety that are imbedded, so negative claims to that effect are unfounded.

Sources

Cotruvo JA (2015). Healthy Drinking Water Intake. Water Technology on Line. www.watertechonline.com/professor-poupoe-may-2015/.

EPA (2000). Estimated Per Capita Water Consumption in the U.S. EPA-822-00-008.

EPA (2011). *Exposure Factors Handbook*, 2011 Edition. EPA/600/R-09/052F.

Grandjean AC (2005). Water Requirements, Impinging Factors and Recommended Intakes. In *Nutrients in Drinking Water*, World Health Organization, Geneva, 2005. ISBN92 4 159398 9.

NRC (2005). Dietary Reference Intakes for Water, Potassium, Sodium, Chloride, and Sulfate. www.nap.edu/read/10925/chapter/6.

Ong CN, Grandjean AC, Heaney RP (2009). The mineral composition of water and its contribution to calcium and magnesium intake. In: Cotruvo JA and Bartram J (Eds.) *Calcium and Magnesium in Drinking Water.* World Health Organization, Geneva, 2009. ISBN 978 92 4 156355 0.

THE DRINKING WATER DISTRIBUTION SYSTEM

Introduction

The water leaving the water treatment plant is not necessarily the same quality when it arrives at the tap. The water distribution system is the most vulnerable element of providing safe public drinking water. Water encounters many hazards along the way to the consumer and after arrival that can significantly alter its quality and safety. Following is a brief overview of several distribution system water quality degradation and risk contributors.

The water distribution system consists of the path that finished drinking water takes after it leaves the treatment plant to the consumers' taps. It can include storage tanks and finished water reservoirs, water mains and laterals, service lines to the home, house plumbing and taps and shower fixtures. Total waterborne disease outbreaks have been in general decline resulting from the changes in regulations and practices that have occurred since the implementation of the SDWA, starting about 1976–1980. Microbial indicator monitoring is enforced, several filtration rules require surface watersand groundwaters under the influence of surface waters to be filtered and disinfected. Vulnerable groundwaters must be disinfected, and lead and copper corrosion potential must be assessed and corrected. Numerous disinfection by-products (DBPs) and chemicals have been regulated via TTHM and HAA surrogates.

While reported waterborne disease outbreaks have been declining, there has been a shift of the origin of disease outbreaks to distribution system deficiencies. In the CDC MMWR for 2009–2010, waterborne disease outbreaks totaled 33 and they resulted in 1,040 cases, 85 hospitalizations and 8 deaths. Most notably, 19 of the 33 outbreaks were caused by *legionella* bacteria, resulting in 72 cases and 8 deaths, and it was the only waterborne illness that resulted in deaths. Six more legionellosis deaths were associated with other drinking water originated aerosol exposures, such as from fountains or cooling systems. Reporting for drinking water-related legionellosis began in 2001.

There are numerous opportunities for water quality degradation to occur during its transit from the plant to the consumer. Here are a few.

Disinfectant Residuals

Some groundwaters are not disinfected, and some countries have curtailed use of disinfectants and minimize residuals. Disinfectant residuals provide some protection from posttreatment contamination and microbial regrowth, and keep the oxidation potential positive (e.g., nitrate, instead of nitrite). Primary disinfectants include chlorine, ozone, chlorine dioxide, and UV light. Chloramines are secondary disinfectants. Chlorine is the most common primary disinfectant with chlorine dioxide, ozone, and UV as distant, but growing methods. Free chlorine and chlorine dioxide (less so) can provide residuals, but ozone and UV do not, so a secondary disinfectant is also necessary in many circumstances. Chloramines are weak disinfectants, but they are chemically more stable and persistent than free chlorine. Chloramines are probably more effective at suppressing *legionella* regrowth than chlorine and chlorine dioxide because they can penetrate biofilms more effectively. Measurement of disinfectant residuals in the distribution system is an important way to assure that the water is protected during that transit period and kept in an oxidative state so that microbial regrowth can be suppressed.

Uncovered Reservoirs

Until recently, there were many uncovered finished water reservoirs in use. Regulations now require coverage. Uncovered reservoirs allowed recontamination by runoff and animals. Even a disinfectant residual might not have been sufficient to provide adequate kill of some microorganisms. There are even examples of production of bromate in an uncovered reservoir from solar reactions with residual chlorine in the presence of bromide. That can be solved by floating opaque plastic balls to eliminate direct solar UV penetration.

Transit Time and Water Age

Transit time and water age can vary from hours to days depending upon the system configuration, size, length, extreme dead ends, and water demand. Low use extremities and dead ends provide opportunities for loss of disinfectant residual, microbial regrowth, and water degradation, including nitrification. Communities with declining populations have problems because of reduced water use and longer detention times.

Distribution Pipes

Distribution pipe ranges from pressurized large pipes, which are several feet in diameter, to laterals, several inches in diameter, to service lines from a few inches to 1 inch. Their composition could be coated or uncoated ductile iron or cast iron, and a few asbestos cement in the large diameters, to copper and polyethylene or polyvinyl chloride plastics and some remaining old lead service lines in the smaller diameters. Tuberculation that reduces flows, biofilm formation, pipe leaks and breaks, and corrosion are common problems. Total investments in distribution systems are in the trillions of dollars, so many are deteriorating and not being maintained and replaced as soon as necessary. Distribution systems are aging with many miles in the United States over 100 years old. Water suppliers often delay replacements. Replacement rates are often much less than 0.5 percent per year, so risks of breaks are high, and hundreds of breaks (hundreds of thousands of total national breaks) occur each year (or even hundreds per month in large systems especially in colder climates where thermal changes further stress buried pipe. Small leaks occur and breaks can cause major disruptions of service and damage to property, but they also provide opportunities for contamination to occur. Lines are disinfected before they are placed back into service, but inflows due to loss of line pressure cannot be readily disinfected.

Maintenance Flushing

Distribution systems accumulate sediment, tuberculation and biofilms, so regular maintenance is essential. This is usually accomplished by unidirectional flushing between fire hydrants. The dislodged material often colors the water reddish brown, and customers are usually notified to anticipate the temporary changes, and also assured that the water is safe to drink. It seems unlikely whether that can be assured, because those sediments often accumulate microbial and chemical contaminants. Building plumbing systems also require maintenance to reduce risks of microbial, e.g., *legionella*, regrowth.

Service Lines

Millions of lead service lines were installed in some cities in the early part of the 20th century because of low cost and very long service lives. About half of the remaining lead service lines have been replaced since the Lead and Copper Regulation of 1991.

However, as lead toxicity concerns grew it was recognized that corrosive waters can leach significant amounts of lead from them. Since that time, lead service lines are being replaced with other materials by attrition and sometimes by directive when the Lead and Copper Corrosion Rule monitoring detects excessive corrosion. A notable example was the increase of lead measurements in Flint, Michigan in 2014 after changing water sources without corrosion adjustments, and Washington, D.C. in the early 2000s, when the system shifted from free chlorine residual to chloramine to reduce disinfection byproduct formation. Insoluble lead salt coatings were dissolving because of the change of water chemistry. However, some studies also show that almost in every case when high lead levels were detected there were also concurrent high iron measurements. This indicated that old galvanized iron pipe in some home plumbing was the source of the lead, and it was verified by plumbing inspections. It is well known that iron oxides are very efficient adsorbers or absorbers of many ions including lead and arsenic, so, focusing entirely on lead service lines is not the most appropriate way to address lead at the tap. The Washington problem was ultimately resolved by addition of a few mg/L of phosphate at the treatment plant.

DBPs and Nitrification

DBP formation continues when there is available organic carbon and active disinfectant residual present. THMs and haloacetic acids (HAAs) that are regulated DBP indicators are monitored and regulated in the distribution system, and treatment processes are adjusted to control them. Chloramines have been an inexpensive way to limit posttreatment plant distribution-related DBP formation.

Nitrification is the conversion of nitrogen species to nitrate and nitrite and possibly nitrosamines during distribution. It occurs especially in long distribution systems when water is derived from surface sources, chloramine is used as the residual disinfectant, and nitrosomonas bacteria are present and capable of converting ammonia or organic amines to nitrite, and nitrite to nitrate. About 25 percent incidence of several ppt levels of nitrosamine has been detected in surveys, especially in surface supplies using chloramine disinfection. However, this is a minute portion of total daily exposure to nitrosamines from endogenous production, and food consumption.

Microbial Regrowth

There is an article in this volume and in *Water Technology on Line* on *legionella* risk from regrowth in plumbing and cooling towers warm water environments and showerheads. There are numerous additional pathogenic or opportunistic microbes such as *Pseudomonas aeruginosa* and *Mycobacterium avium* that can regrow and that have caused disease in high-risk populations, such as in hospital patients.

Backflow

Some plumbing configurations can permit backflow resulting from pressure drops in a system. Contaminated water can enter the drinking water by that route. Pressure drops can occur in an area when water is being pumped for fighting fires or other high demand events in a service area. Many plumbing codes require backflow preventers to be installed, but this is usually observed in the breach; a regular maintenance of the backflow preventers is also required but usually lacking.

Cross-Connections

Cross-connections between potable and non-potable plumbing systems in homes and buildings are not uncommon. They can occur from errors that occur in original installations and during repairs. Loss of a disinfection residual and taste and appearance changes can indicate a cross-connection or intermittent contamination. The disinfection residual is not substantial enough to eliminate this contamination, but at least its loss should be an indication that a significant incident might have occurred.

Terrorism

Distribution systems and plumbing are vulnerable to deliberate contamination. Most toxicants require such large additions to high volume water supplies that source and storage contamination is an unlikely risk. However, contamination in a building system requires only a small amount of material and a small pump for its introduction

What Can a Consumer Do?

Apart from encouraging their water suppliers to do their best and invest in the needed improvements, consumers have the option to add POU or POE treatment as barriers to some of those potential problems. POU for chlorine taste and ion exchange water softening are common treatments for aesthetic water problems, but some have suggested a "Final Barrier" concept, where treatment in the home is intended to remove contaminants of concern that might possibly occur after central treatment. A complete "Final Barrier" approach would be expensive and require microbial filters and chemical removal treatment, probably RO plus activated carbon, or microfiltration, ultrafiltration, and UV. RO is wasteful of water and removes valuable minerals like calcium and magnesium, and carbon will grow heterotrophic bacteria. First, if a homeowner really wishes to become their own drinking water quality manager, it is essential to obtain objective advice from competent officials and qualified service providers and install the appropriate technology for the specific problem. Then regular maintenance is important, since no treatment system will perform without loss of efficacy over time.

Conclusions

Many professionals would say that water quality changes from regrowth in distribution and the need for rehabilitation of distribution systems should be EPA's highest drinking water and health priorities, rather than regulating a few more trace chemicals of marginal concern that get headlines, but are of little public health consequence. Numerous distribution system problem opportunities are itemized here.

In the US regulatory environment, drinking water is almost always well treated and safe when it leaves the plant. However, the distribution process is clearly where more problems can occur and some of them are very difficult and expensive to control. Distribution systems were designed to provide sufficient water during peak demand such as fire events. That results in longer retention times and opportunities for degradation of microbial and chemical quality. Population declines in some cities add to the supply/demand cause of degradation problems.

Other problems occur in the users' plumbing system. Distribution systems and plumbing are expensive fixed investments and continuously aging, and costly to repair, replace, and maintain. Backflow preventers should be installed and maintained. Tuberculation, biofilms that harbor pathogens, leaks and breaks, and corrosion are common. Some people have decided to use POU or POE treatment to give them more control over the quality of their drinking water supply. Of course, that means that they are taking responsibility for controlling some of those problems, so they must be diligent in selecting the appropriate technologies and providing proper maintenance of their system.

Sources

Ainsworth RG (Ed.) (2004). *Safe Piped Water: Managing Microbial Quality in Piped Distribution Systems.* WHO Drinking Water Quality Series. IWA Publishing, London.

CotruvoJA(2014).TheDistributionSystemofDrinkingWater.WaterTechnology on Line. www.watertechonline.com/professor-poupoe-september-2014/.

Cotruvo JA (2006). *Health Aspects of Plumbing.* World Plumbing Council, and World Health Organization.

NAS (2006). *Drinking Water Distribution Systems: Assessing and Reducing Risks.* National Research Council, National Academies Press.

Waterborne Zoonoses (2004). *Identification, Causes and Control.* Emerging Issue sin Infectous Disease Series. Cotruvo JA, Dufour, A, Rees G, Bartram J, Carr R, Craun G, Fayer R, Gannon VPJ (Eds.) WHO, IWA Publishing.

World Health Organization (2011). www.who.int//water_sanitation_health/publications/2011/dwq_guidelines/en/.

FOODBORNE AND WATERBORNE DISEASE

Introduction

What is the extent of the microbial foodborne and waterborne disease risks in the United States, and how do they compare? Considering the diversity of foods sources and handling, and multiple sources and history of water from source to tap, it should not be a surprise that foodborne and waterborne disease risks can be substantial without adequate controls. Comprehensive and detailed statistics are nonexistent, but estimates place food at a significantly higher risk than public drinking water.

We all consume food and water daily, but inherent risks are associated with anything that we ingest (or inhale). We are constantly exposed to microorganisms in our living environment. Fortunately, most microorganisms are beneficial or are not pathogens. Most food- and waterborne diseases in the United States are now not serious or fatal for healthy people, but exceptions exist. Foodborne diseases are being reported with greater frequency, which might or might not mean that they are increasing but they are certainly can affect large populations when they occur. Although sporadic waterborne disease incidence is difficult to quantify, recognized waterborne disease outbreaks occur with very low and declining frequencies.

Many microorganisms cannot survive human stomach acidity, the gastrointestinal tract environment, and the immune system, but many others can. The role of public health authorities is to work with producers, distributors, and sellers to minimize the exposure risks to a feasible extent and reduce the numbers of serious disease incidences and deaths that can result from exposure to contaminated food and water. Additional risks exist in the home from regrowth of microorganisms in plumbing and from food storage and preparation. Public water supplies are regulated and almost always safe, but private wells are not usually tested or treated. We have a huge infrastructure and high number of requirements to ensure safety in water and food production, but they are not perfect.

Food Risks and Safety

Many opportunities exist for bacterial, viral, or protozoan microbial contamination of food, from seed to plant or animal, to processing, distribution, home storage and preparation, restaurant serving, cooking, and plate. Estimating the actual number of cases of foodborne disease, commonly called food poisoning, is very difficult, partly because many are subtle, including brief upset stomach, diarrhea and self-limiting unreported gastrointestinal illnesses where medical treatment is not sought. The CDC estimates that each year about one in six (more than 48 million people) will become ill, 128,000 will be hospitalized, and 3,000 will die by consuming pathogen-contaminated food or beverages.

More than 250 potential foodborne diseases have been identified. The top five microorganisms accounting for many foodborne illnesses and rounded estimated cases are as follows:

Norovirus (5.5 million)
Salmonella non-typhoidal (1 million)
Clostridium perfringens (1 million)
Campylobacter (850,000)
Staphylococcus aureus (250,000)

The top five foodborne illness pathogens resulting in hospitalization are as follows:

Salmonella non-typhoidal (19,336)
Norovirus (14,663)
Campylobacter (8,463)
Toxoplasma gondii, a parasite (4,428)
E. coli O157H7 (2,138)

The top five foodborne pathogens resulting in deaths are as follows:

Salmonella non-typhoidal (378)
T. gondii (327)
Listeria monocytogenes (255)
Norovirus (149)
Campylobacter (76)

Salmonella bacteria are widespread in animals and can spread to humans from foods of animal origin. Salmonellosis symptoms include fever, diarrhea, and abdominal cramps. Norovirus causes gastrointestinal illness with vomiting and usually resolves within 3 days. Infections are readily transmitted by human contact, and food contamination by food service workers is not uncommon. *Campylobacter* is the most commonly identified worldwide cause of diarrheal illness. It is common in poultry and other animals and spread, for example, by the ingestion of undercooked chicken. *C. perfringens* is widespread in the environment, can be present on raw meat and produces a toxin that causes illness. In addition to direct infections, several pathogens, such as *S. aureus* and *Clostridium botulinum*, produce toxins that survive after the infection. The CDC estimates that up to 60 million people in the United States may be infected with *T. gondii* without symptoms because healthy immune systems can suppress it. Handling contaminated animal products and even exposure to cat feces can be a risk, especially to pregnant women.

Changing Foodborne Disease Causes

Typhoid fever, tuberculosis, and cholera were once common foodborne illnesses. Pasteurization of milk, better canning practices, and process water disinfection have virtually eliminated those diseases in developed countries. More recently, foodborne cases of cyclosporiasis have been caused by the contamination of Guatemalan raspberries; *Vibrio parahaemolyticus*, caused infections from eating raw oysters from Galveston Bay, Texas; cryptosporidiosis from unpasteurized apple cider probably caused by apples collected from the ground where they could contact animal feces; and kidney failure from hemolytic anemia caused by *E. coli* O157H7, sometimes from consuming inadequately cooked hamburger meat. Some of these outbreaks have been the result of imported foods that had not been produced under proper sanitary conditions.

Detecting Foodborne Diseases

Most foodborne diseases in the population are undiagnosed unless they are serious enough to require physician care or hospitalization. Even then, the specific microorganism may not be identified because many diseases, such as from norovirus, are not reportable to CDC. The disease surveillance process involves the collection of incidence data at the county health department level, reporting to the state, which reports to the CDC, but not all states participate in the system and reportable diseases are not identical in each state. CDC's FoodNet surveillance system is a collaborative program among the CDC, 10 state health departments, the United States Department of Agriculture Food Safety and Inspection Service, and the FDA. It conducts surveillance for several diseases and covers 15 percent of the US population. Each year it identifies more than 1,000 foodborne outbreaks that are investigated by local and state health departments.

Foods Associated with Foodborne Illness

The CDC lists the following foods that have a higher potential of contamination with pathogens:

- Raw meat, raw eggs, and unpasteurized milk
- Filter-feeding shellfish, such as raw oysters
- Foods produced by combining numerous animal sources, such as bulk raw milk, raw eggs, or hamburger meat
- Fruits and vegetables consumed raw
- Unpasteurized fruit juice

Preventing Foodborne Disease

Some suggestions for reducing foodborne disease risks are as follows:

- To assure that producers and shippers meet US standards, improve and implement more comprehensive controls and inspections on imported fresh and processed foods.
- Take special care to know the source and handling when consuming any raw foods, such as oysters.
- Do not consume unpasteurized milk and eggs without cooking them.
- Wash lettuce, fruits, and vegetables well if they will be consumed raw. However, even chlorinated water washes have limited effectiveness because of the surface properties of many foods. Some products claim to improve surface cleaning of vegetables.
- Do not mingle external fruit surfaces with the fruit or juice. Whole fruit or vegetable smoothies can be a questionable choice.
- Practice good food sanitation in the home. Wash hands frequently when cooking. Do not mix raw and cooked food on cutting boards or plates. Clean utensils and sanitize kitchen surfaces. Cook foods, especially meats, to the recommended temperatures.
- Do not store foods under inappropriate temperature and moisture conditions or for excessive times.
- Be careful with picnic foods, especially those containing eggs and mayonnaise that are susceptible to spoilage at warmer temperatures.
- Taste and smell are good sensors. If it does not seem right, do not eat it.

Waterborne Disease Risks

The CDC has estimated from published projections that from 4 to 32 million annual cases of acute gastrointestinal illness may occur from the approximately 150,000 public drinking water supplies in the United States. Most of the estimates fall in between or toward the lower end, which seems to be much more plausible. The large uncertainties are because of the similar circumstances of self-limiting and untreated mild cases and the limited reporting as described for foodborne disease detection. However, most of the waterborne estimate numbers are significantly smaller than the foodborne numbers, which is quite reasonable. Public water supplies of 25 persons or more that provide piped water consumed regularly by most people are subject to significant federal and state regulatory controls including monitoring, treatment requirements, and finished water quality requirements. Boil water notices are issued to advise the public during a risk situation.

Historically, 1,870 outbreaks were reported in all water types from 1920 to 2002, ranging from 11.1 to 32.4 per year, and averaging 10,648 cases and 14 deaths per year, including both chemical and microbial causes. However, these numbers were limited by the capabilities of the surveillance systems in place and would likely have been much higher; as a result most outbreaks were probably not detected. Also, the most frequently detected outbreaks are now legionellosis. It was not identified before 1976, and legionellosis was not reportable to CDC before 2001.

Since the passage (1974) and significant implementation (1980) of the SDWA, water management and compliance with regulations have significantly improved and reported waterborne disease outbreaks have been in a declining trend. One aberration exception was Milwaukee's cryptosporidiosis outbreak of 1993 because of an unusual systemic problem, the cause of which was corrected, while surveillance and detection have improved. The types and causes of waterborne diseases have also changed, from those associated with inadequate water treatment, to those associated with distribution system problems, especially microbial regrowth in plumbing biofilms.

The more relevant and most up-to-date outbreak information from the last two CDC Morbidity and Mortality Weekly Reports cover 2009–2010 and 2011–2012 and 2013–2014. The 2009–2010 report recorded 33 outbreaks, 1,040 cases, 83 hospitalizations, and nine deaths. *Legionella* accounted for 58 percent of the outbreaks (19), 7 percent of the illnesses (72), and all nine deaths. *Campylobacter* accounted for 12 percent of the outbreaks and 78 percent of illnesses. *Giardia,* norovirus, *E. coli,* and *Cryptosporidium* contributed a smaller number of outbreaks and illnesses.

In the 2011–2012 period, reports recorded 32 outbreaks, 431 cases of illness, 102 hospitalizations, and 14 deaths. *Legionella* accounted for 66 percent of the outbreaks, 26 percent of the illnesses and all 14 deaths. Noroviruses were responsible for 32 percent of cases, and non-*legionella* bacteria caused 21 percent of the cases (90), including *Shigella sonnei*, *E. coli*, and *Pantoea agglomerans*. The latter was unusual and caused hospital-acquired blood infections, probably from using drinking water to produce infusion fluids. The microorganism was identified in the drinking water, an ice machine and sinks. Interestingly, no illnesses from cryptosporidium were reported, and only one *Campylobacter* and two norovirus outbreaks were identified in the 2011–2012 period.

In the 2013–2014 period, there were 42 drinking water associated outbreaks in 19 states, accounting for 1006 cases, 124 hospitalizations, and all 13 deaths. *Legionella* accounted for 24 outbreaks and all 13 deaths. There were 3 giardia and 2 norovirus outbreaks.

Most of the reported cases and outbreaks for all three reporting periods were associated with drinking water plumbing systems (legionellosis), and the next most reported were associated with untreated groundwaters.

Conclusions

Food contamination somewhere in the production-to-consumption sequence appears to be a significantly greater health risk than public drinking water supplies, but drinking water is an important contributor to risks from ingestion or inhalation exposures, especially legionellosis. Room for improvement exists in the prevention and risk reduction in both media. Some improvement would occur from having stricter control over the safety of imported foods and better storage, sanitation, and preparation practices in homes. Swab tests usually find more microorganisms in kitchens than bathrooms. There are no data indicating adverse health outcomes from genetically modified organisms and non "organic" foods.

Drinking water quality and safety have improved, as more universal applications of filtration and disinfection of surface water, and disinfection resulting from SDWA regulations. However, risks are still associated with microbial regrowth in plumbing and the consumption of untreated or inadequately treated water from both public and private water sources. Risks from inhalation of aerosols contaminated by regrowth of microorganisms such as *legionella* in plumbing and cooling towers are likely the greatest concerns. Supplemental water treatment in hospitals and long-term health care facilities, and management of cooling towers would reduce legionellosis risks. Tested and certified POU and POE technologies can further reduce drinking water risks if they are applied to higher risk waters, and properly selected and managed.

Sources

CDC. Surveillance for Waterborne Disease Outbreaks Associated with Drinking Water, United States, 2013–2014. Morbidity and Mortality Weekly Report. November 10, 2017/66(44);1216–1221. www.cdc.gov/mmwr/volumes/66/wr/mm6644a3.htm.

CDC (2014). Foodborne Illness. Foodborne Disease, (sometimes called Food Poisoning). www.cdc.gov/facts.html.

Cotruvo JA (2016). Foodborne and Waterborne Disease. Water Technology on Line. www.watertechonline.com/professor-poupoe-foodborne-waterborne-disease/.

Reynolds KA, Mena KD, Gerba CP (2008). Risk of Waterborne Disease via Drinking Water in the United States. *Reviews of Environmental Contamination and Toxicology*. 192: pp. 117–158.

FRACKING AND DRINKING WATER ISSUES

Introduction

Fracking, or hydraulic fracturing, is a process used by many oil and gas recovery operations. It involves injection of a liquid that is usually a mixture of water, sand, and chemical additives. The injection is under pressure so it causes fissures or cracks in the underground formations, and that allows release and recovery of oil and gas that often would not be recoverable by other means. Fracking could be applied in older spent wells to increase their yields, or in new wells where oil and gas production would not otherwise be feasible.

Fracking was originally introduced in the 1940s, and more than 100,000 individual hydraulic fracturing treatments had been applied by 1955 and many more since. The technology has undergone recent major improvements that have made it much more attractive and productive and much more widely practiced. The numbers have grown rapidly particularly because of the introduction of horizontal drilling techniques, which allow formerly inaccessible rock formations to be reached and tapped for hydrocarbons. This oil and gas recovery method has grown and been successful in the United States and other countries for extracting hydrocarbons for fuel and other uses.

Where Fracking is Occurring

Suitable shale oil and gas locations are identified using seismic exploration methods. Some of the major US shale plays are as follows: Barnett, North Texas; Fayetteville, Arkansas; Haynesville, Louisiana, and East Texas; Marcellus, Northeast United States; and Woodford, Oklahoma.

Since some fracking projects are relatively small-volume producers and costly, the application is sensitive to economic conditions and world oil and gas prices. In 2007, 1,000,000 total oil and gas wells were active in the United States including traditional wells and hydraulically fractured and non-fractured wells.

Due to those more recent technological improvements, which include horizontal drilling and multi-stage hydraulic fracturing within a horizontal well, fracking has been applied in many locations around the United States that were never considered to be energy producing, and US oil and gas production has increased rapidly. Production of shale oil has increased more than five-fold from 39 million barrels in 2007 to 217 million barrels in 2011.

Estimates of technically recoverable shale oil in the United States are as high as 33 billion barrels. Not all deposits are recoverable. The Marcellus shale area holds one of the largest technically recoverable shale gas deposits—up to 227 trillion cubic feet. The Bakken formation in North Dakota has recently become a very productive oil producing area. There are numerous other areas under exploration; however, the recovery potentials differ due to geologic conditions.

Fracking Processes

The overall process consists of clearing and leveling the area and constructing a pad where the drilling rig will be located. Often roads and other infrastructure must be constructed. Then, the drilling and well construction occur; the fluids are produced and pressurized hydraulic fracturing is utilized. Apart from the chemical additives to be managed, the natural water that is surfaced may contain very high levels of dissolved solids (salts), toxic metals, radionuclides, and hydrocarbons. TDS values may range from less than 1,000 mg/L to hundreds of thousands of mg/L (seawater typically contains about 35,000–40,000 mg/L).

Potential Health and Environmental Effects

Fracking involves injection of large volumes of the hydraulic fluid. Much of that is recovered along with deep, often saline, groundwater that surfaces and must be processed and safely disposed or reused. By law, wells must be drilled below freshwater aquifers and cased to prevent contamination of those aquifers by the fluids and additives as well as by water from the deeper aquifers. That groundwater sometimes contains contaminants like radionuclides or bromide.

Apart from standard on-site operations with truck traffic, and air pollution and surface runoff issues, the principal environmental concerns associated with hydraulic fracturing projects are water and soil contamination that can result from the processes and handling and disposal of the fluids as well as the large quantities of water necessary to undertake fracking and seismic activity that might be induced. Large volumes of water are withdrawn from surface or groundwaters. They are mixed with sand and chemical additives including biocides, hydrochloric acid, corrosion inhibitors, borate salts, friction reducers, gelling agents, potassium chloride, oxygen scavengers, scale inhibitors, and surfactants. In addition to the predominant sodium and chloride, the salts content can include elevated concentrations of bromide, bicarbonate, sulfate, calcium, magnesium, barium, strontium, radium, organic chemicals, and heavy metals. The management challenge is to safely dispose, treat, or reuse those waters without damaging the local groundwater or downstream surface waters and potential drinking water sources.

Hundreds of thousands of gallons of water may be injected and withdrawn per site, and great volumes of flowback and produced waters are generated. Flowback waters are those that return to the surface after the pressure is released. They consist of hydrolytic fracturing fluids, water from the natural formation, chemical additives that were injected and the recovered hydrocarbons from the deep formations. The fracking fluids contain many additives, which if not controlled can result in releases and environmental damage. Air quality degradation can occur in the vicinity of drilling sites because of engine exhaust and from flaring or venting of natural gas as well as from particulate releases.

There are water quality risks from contamination of ground and surface waters from spills and releases. Freshwater used in drilling could range from 100,000 to 600,000 gallons, or more, per well. The hydraulic fracturing could consume 5,000,000 gallons per site. The sources could include local streams and groundwater, municipal water, reused industrial or municipal wastewater, or water recycled from the process.

Some fracking locations require transport to a central location for water treatment prior to surface environmental releases. Onsite water treatment is being practiced to a somewhat greater degree, although the least costly and predominant disposal method by far is reinjection of the fluids into the subzone where the hydrocarbons have been removed.

Increased seismic activity has been suggested as a problem from fracking operations; however, others have suggested that other waste disposal wells are more likely causes.

Water Treatment Technology

Numerous water treatment processes can be employed to render the wastewaters usable on-site and others to upgrade it so it can be discharged to surface waters. Some remove residual oil, others separate solids that can be disposed of in landfills.

The wastewater management procedures utilized are consistent with the contaminants to be managed as well as the economics of the options available by regulations and guidelines that apply at the project site. Among the most frequently used approaches are disposal by deep-well injection, treatment on-site, several reuse possibilities, including as an injection fluid, and sometimes transport to a centralized wastewater treatment facility (CWTF) or a publicly owned treatment works (POTWs).

Disposal of treatment concentrates creates another management issue. There are applicable controlling national regulations under the Clean Water Act and Underground Injection Control provisions under the SDWA, but states are actually even more active in determining the acceptable environmental protection requirements and options.

Deep-Well Injection

When possible, underground injection is the primary method for management and disposal of wastewaters from oil and gas producing facilities. These are regulated by the Underground Injection Control provisions of the 1974 SDWA and implemented by states along with their additional provisions. Enhanced oil recovery, disposal and hydrocarbon storage are covered in the Class II well designations. Class II fluids are primarily brines (salt water) that are generated while producing oil and gas.

Deep underground injection of brines in formations isolated from underground sources of drinking water prevents soil and ground and surface water contamination. These are usually the formations in which the brines originated or similar formations. Deep-well injection is usually the least expensive management strategy unless trucking is needed to transport the brine to a disposal well. Over 2 billion gallons of brine are injected underground in the United States every day, mostly in Texas, California, Oklahoma, and Kansas. About 27,000 Class IID disposal wells are in use exclusively to inject fluids from oil and gas production. Because of the geology and other restrictions, relatively few Class IID wells are operative in the Marcellus Shale areas of the northeastern United States.

More than 98 percent of an estimated 882 billion gallons of produced water from oil and gas extraction facilities in 2007 was managed by some form of underground injection with 40 percent in Class II wells. Average disposal rates per well are somewhat regionally diverse and range from about 1,750 GPD/well in Illinois to over 50,000 GPD/well in Texas and Colorado, to 182,000 GPD/well in the North Slope basin in Arkansas. There have been indications of seismic activity, in Oklahoma, e.g., which could result in greater restrictions on underground injection.

High concentrations of TDS in brines will require some level of treatment if disposal will be above ground or by transport to a treatment facility. Treatment processes used by POTWs and centralized wastewater treatment facilities are not generally amenable to significant removals of salts. High-strength wastes will disrupt biological processes in POTWs. Those options are in decline because of the expense of transport and the frequent need for some kind of pretreatment before the wastewater is acceptable to the treatment works—so it will not disrupt its system performance and so the facility will be able to meet its own NPDES permit discharge requirements.

Standard treatment processes when deep well reinjection is not applied include the following:

Media filtration
Separation of oil and grease
Biological and aerated filters

Membrane processes may include the following:

Microfiltration, ultrafiltration, nanofiltration, and reverse osmosis
Distillation (e.g., vapor compression)
Evaporation ponds
Chemical precipitation
Evaporation ponds
Anion and cation exchange processes
Electrocoagulation (emerging process)

Some types of contaminants create unique problems. Radionuclides, such as radium, are common in deep groundwaters in some regions. When surfaced in flowback and produced waters their presence restricts opportunities for discharges to treatment plants and surface waters and some of the potential end uses.

Radium is removable by cation exchange, RO membranes, and co-precipitation with barium. However, the concentrates then create another disposal problem and might require disposal in radioactive waste landfills.

Bromide is a common anion, but it is usually not present in significant amounts in surface waters. It is not easily removed by technologies other than RO membranes. When the bromide concentration in surface streams is increased by conventionally treated brine discharges, the concentrations of brominated DBPs will be increased in downstream drinking waters that chlorinate. Chlorine oxidizes bromide to brominating species that react with natural organic chemicals also present in the water. There are some concerns that brominated organics may be the more hazardous fractions of the DBPs in drinking water.

Organic Chemicals

Organic chemicals in fracking wastewater can include light petroleum hydrocarbons, diesel range organics, oil and grease, volatile organics such as benzene and toluene, and semivolatile organics as well as chemical additives that are formulated in the hydraulic fracturing injection fluids. Treatment processes are available to manage those chemicals including adsorption, biological treatment, conventional coagulation, flocculation, flotation, skimming, and several others depending upon the specific chemical types and their physical and chemical properties.

Residuals management is an important factor in fracking wastewater management. Some residuals are concentrated toxins such as radionuclides, and some are regulated inorganic species or just highly saline brines that require additional reuse or disposal limitations.

Reuse Possibilities

Reuse of wastewater brines in the hydraulic fracturing process would be an ideal practice, and it is increasing, especially in the Marcellus Shale region, because no or minimal treatment might be necessary, and the amounts of freshwater needed are reduced as well as less total wastewater to be treated and disposed of at the surface. However, repeated use may accumulate the contaminants to ultimately be managed either by treatment, injection, or disposal.

Other kinds of reuse that are allowed in some jurisdictions depend upon the composition and concentrations of the brines and state regulations and may or may not require some level of pretreatment depending upon the intended end use. These can include land application, road spreading for dust control and de-icing, livestock watering, irrigation, and even stream flow augmentation, fire protection, and industrial uses.

Regulations

Most aspects of oil and gas development, including well siting, drilling, casing, cementing, etc., are covered by state laws. Many activities are exempted from the Clean Water Act National Pollutant Discharge Elimination System (NPDES) storm water permits for uncontaminated runoff. However, many states regulate those more stringently than federal requirements. In general, fracking can be carried out without causing environmental damage. Oil and gas production activities are regulated, and considering the extent and diversity of those activities the record of performance appears to be fairly good.

Fracking is indirectly regulated to some degree by the Underground Injection Control requirements under the SDWA, but the Energy Policy Act of 2005 excluded hydraulic fracking per se from underground injection. Disposals of oil and gas wastewaters are regulated by NPDES standards for discharges to surface waters. Pretreatment is often required at an industrial treatment site.

Many or most oil and gas wastewaters are disposed of by underground reinjection and these are covered by the Underground Injection Control programs by states and EPA regions if the state does not have enforcement primacy.

The federal government is considering new legislation to provide additional safeguards, but the need for more federal legislation will surely be debated in Congress.

Conclusions

Hydraulic fracturing wastewaters are complex saline and organic chemical mixtures, and they create treatment and disposal challenges that can, however, be met when economics permit. This very brief summary is derived extensively from the USEPA's 600-page draft report along with hundreds of pages of Appendices from the review process that was initiated in 2009, as well as numerous related technical publications.

The draft EPA report generally concluded that it did not find evidence of "widespread systemic impacts on drinking water resources in the United States." The longstanding federal and state control requirements, as well as increased sensitivity by drillers, are the likely principal reasons why that positive statement can be made.

EPA's Science Advisory Board (SAB) produced a 160-page review of the draft that was partly in disagreement and particularly asked for more analyses and quantitative support for the draft report's conclusions, including more discussion of local impacts, carrying out of prospective case studies, probabilities and risks of failure scenarios, chemical and toxicity and hazards, more characteristics of fracking fluid composition, and several other assessments. Some other SAB members filed dissenting opinions that disagreed with the SAB's majority recommendations.

The final revised report states, "EPA found scientific evidence that hydraulic fracturing activities can impact drinking water resources under some circumstances. The report identifies certain conditions under which impacts from hydraulic fracturing activities can be more frequent or severe:

- Water withdrawals for hydraulic fracturing in times or areas of low water availability, particularly in areas with limited or declining groundwater resources
- Spills during the handling of hydraulic fracturing fluids and chemicals or produced water that result in large volumes or high concentrations of chemicals reaching groundwater resources
- Injection of hydraulic fracturing fluids into wells with inadequate mechanical integrity, allowing gases or liquids to move to groundwater resources
- Injection of hydraulic fracturing fluids directly into groundwater resources
- Discharge of inadequately treated hydraulic fracturing wastewater to surface water
- Disposal or storage of hydraulic fracturing wastewater in unlined pits resulting in contamination of groundwater resources

Data gaps and uncertainties limited EPA's ability to fully assess the potential impacts on drinking water resources locally and nationally."

All of the above are true, of course, and obvious and those possibilities were well known prior to the EPA study, and undoubtedly the reasons that the study was undertaken. However, the original conclusion in the draft report that did not find evidence of "widespread systemic impacts on drinking water resources in the United States" is also true and probably the more significant public policy outcome. It indicates that the long history of drinking water aquifer protections at the state and federal levels have been quite successful in spite of the perhaps millions of fracking applications, and the potential for adverse outcomes. One could speculate on the motivations and drivers for the changed emphasis in the conclusion.

The government's issue is whether to produce additional regulations. The SAB review and the final revised report encouraged anti-fracking organizations, and certainly will extend the time frame for reaching some kind of technical and political conclusion on the issue, if it ever occurs. In the meantime, it will always be necessary to continue to manage and treat the wastewaters generated from the fracking and other drilling processes and to try to minimize the quantities of good surface and groundwaters that are injected.

SOURCES

AWWA White Paper: Hydraulic Fracturing. www.awwa.org/legislation-regulation/issues/hydraulic-fracturing.aspx.

Cotruvo JA (2014). Contaminant of the Month: Fracking—Water Technology. www.watertechonline.com/contaminant-of-the-month-fracking/.

Cotruvo JA (2016). Fracking Water Treatment Technologies. Water Technology on Line. www.watertechonline.com/author/dr-joseph-cotruvo-technical-editor/.

EPA Assessment of the Potential Impacts of Hydraulic Fracturing for Oil and Gas on Drinking Water Resources (External Review Draft, EPA/600/R-15/047, June 2015).

EPA (2016). Hydraulic Fracturing Study—Final Assessment. Hydraulic Fracturing for Oil and Gas: Impacts from the Hydraulic Fracturing Water Cycle on Drinking Water Resources in the United States, Main Report & Appendices (EPA/600/R-16/236).

GAO (2012). General Accounting Office. Report to Congress, GAO-12–732. September 2012.

Hydraulic Fracturing & Water Stress: Growing Competitive Pressures for Water. www.ceres.org/resources/reports/hydraulic-fracturing-water-stress-growing-competitive-pressures-for-water/view.

McMahon PB. et al (2017). Methane and Benzene in Drinking Water Wells Overlying the Eagle Ford, Fayetteville, and Hanesville Shale Hydrocarbon Production Areas. *Environmental Science and Technology.* 51(12): pp. 6727–6734.

NETL (2014). NETL Releases Hydraulic Fracturing Study. www.energy.gov/fe/articles/netl-releases-hydraulic-fracturing-study.

RECYCLED WASTEWATER AND POTABLE WATER REUSE

Introduction

All water has always been reused. In the natural cycle, water evaporates to the atmosphere from the Earth's surface; it ultimately falls as rain and snow, some of which runs off from land and collects in rivers and lakes and oceans, and some of which percolates into underground aquifers. Shallow aquifers and surface waters are often interconnected. Increasingly, the water is being withdrawn and used for irrigation, industrial processes, or drinking water and then the resultant wastewater is usually treated and discharged back to the environment to reenter the cycle. Although it is estimated that there are at least 326 million trillion gallons of water in or on the earth, 98 percent is brackish or in the oceans. Of the remaining 2 percent freshwater, most is locked in polar icecaps and glaciers, about 0.36 percent is in the ground and only about 0.036 percent is in lakes and rivers. The rest is in transition in the atmosphere as water vapor. The problem is that the available freshwater isn't always located in sufficient quantities where people who need it live.

Human technology has stepped into make more water available. Dams have been built to store it and canals and pipelines to move it. Water treatment technology is now available to take water of any quality from any source and convert it into water of necessary quality for any purpose, including drinking.

Water Reuse

Sanitary wastewater is available as a source for essentially 100 percent reuse. It contains recoverable nitrogen and phosphorus nutrients, and biosolids for agriculture, and oils and grease as potential biofuels. It can be fermented anaerobically to produce methane for energy. The treated water can be produced for crop irrigation and cooling water and high-quality drinking water, depending upon the level of treatment that is provided.

The goal is to change the identity of the water from wastewater to water of appropriate quality for the intended use, be it for potable or non-potable applications, so that it is acceptable and safe for human contact. The natural water cycle does this by biological degradation of contaminants and sedimentation in rivers and lakes, evaporation and precipitation and by filtration and storage time in groundwater. These remove many minerals, chemicals, and microbial contaminants by several mechanisms. Water treatment processes simulate and accelerate the natural purification processes (for a price), but they can also provide a supplement for more reliable, efficient, and environmental friendly supply.

Direct and Indirect Potable Reuse

There are two general categories of potable reuse water: indirect potable reuse(IPR) and direct potable reuse (DPR). The essential difference between IPR and DPR is the lack of an environmental phase before or after treatment prior to delivery to consumers.

WHO paraphrased definitions are as follows:

Wastewater is liquid waste discharged from homes and other residential premises, commercial and industrial premises and similar sources, to municipal sewers. In properly regulated municipal sewerage systems, contributions of industrial contaminants are reduced by management (e.g., through pretreatment requirements) and prevention of refractory industrial waste discharges.

IPR involves the planned addition of treated wastewater into water bodies used as sources of drinking water. Those rivers, lakes, reservoirs, and aquifers are referred to as environmental buffers. Water containing a proportion of treated wastewater is taken from the environmental buffer and further treated to provide drinking water.

DPR involves the introduction of treated wastewater (with or without retention in an engineered storage facility) into a drinking water supply without passage through an environmental buffer. The treated wastewater may be blended with raw water from a river, lake, reservoir, or aquifer immediately before a drinking water treatment plant (although this borders on IPR); blended with treated water downstream of a conventional drinking water treatment plant; or introduced directly into a drinking water distribution system.

Unplanned potable reuse (de facto potable reuse) represents various descriptions of the practice of producing drinking water from water sources impacted by wastewater discharges. This is particularly common in river systems serving multiple urban centers where discharged wastewater (treated or untreated) becomes part of the water resource used by downstream communities. Providing that appropriate control measures, including water treatment are applied, unplanned potable reuse drinking water supplies produce safe drinking water.

Either deliberate (planned) or inadvertent (unplanned) IPR has been practiced since the beginning of civilization particularly with respect to withdrawals from surface waters. Natural runoff and animal human waste discharges into upstream surface waters are diluted and transported downstream to be withdrawn and put to use for irrigation or human consumption, usually with subsequent treatment in the last approximately 150 years. Most river surface water supplies in the United States have been treating more or less contaminated upstream water by "conventional processes" to produce safe drinking water that meets national drinking water quality standards. Only about 1 percent of that municipal water is used for human consumption for food preparation and drinking water, but all is treated to drinking water specifications. There are alternatives of dual water supplies and decentralized treatment water supplies that are worthy of considered in specific circumstances.

IPR and DPR Recent History

The Montebello Forebay Groundwater Recharge Project has been in operation in Los Angeles, California since 1962. It is a planned IPR project where 50,000 acre feet (16.3 billion gallons) per year of now tertiary treated wastewater is spread and percolated to an aquifer where it is stored and withdrawn for drinking water. This is a soil aquifer treatment (SAT) process. Several other more recent spreading or injection projects have been in successful operation in many locations.

A fairly recent (since the 1990s) is the IPR facility of the Orange County (CA) Water District where half of the 130 million gallons per day of production of advanced treated water is injected as a salt water intrusion barrier. The remainder is percolated from lakes into the groundwater where it is stored and transported and subsequently withdrawn by water suppliers and distributed often without further treatment. The plant receives secondary treated municipal wastewater, and provides microfiltration, RO, advanced oxidation, stabilization by partial decarbonation, and lime addition. The Orange County process consistently produces water with TOC levels in the range of 0.15 mg/L and removes dioxane that is probably the most difficult organic chemical to treat, to non-detect, or less than 1 ppb. A low TOC means that the ultimate production of DBPs would also be low. This low TOC would also cap the potential for contaminants that would be present at levels of concern. The treatment process is carefully managed and produces water that meets all federal and California regulations and WHO Guidelines.

The first large-scale DPR project was initiated in Windhoek, Namibia, South Africa, in 1968—it has been modified and expanded since then. Singapore has had an IPR/DPR "NEWater" project in operation for more than 10 years and is expanding its production. Singapore's Public Utilities Board also bottles its NEWater and provides it at no cost for plant visitors and at public events. DPR processes are being considered in several locations in the United States.

Treatment Processes

There are many large-scale potable reuse projects being developed and already underway aimed at converting wastewater into drinking water. The historic droughts in Texas and the Southwest have triggered much interest in recovering wastewater, especially because populations have been increasing so that the demand for public water has increased.

Conventional drinking water treatment processes for surface waters in the United States consist of coagulation, flocculation, sedimentation, sand filtration, and disinfection by a form of chlorine. Conventional treatment is very good at removing particulates and some chemicals and bacteria and viruses and protozoa. Typical TOC levels of conventional finished water are at the several mg/L level. Conventional treatment is not designed to effectively remove many industrial chemicals. It will produce DBPs, and protozoa removal requires very effective filtration or disinfection modifications because chlorine is not totally effective for protozoa, especially cryptosporidium.

Planned potable reuse technologies are more intensive than conventional treatments because they begin with sanitary wastewater, which is a frankly contaminated source. However, they are capable of ultimately producing even higher quality drinking water than surface water conventional treatment systems. They are specifically designed to remove essentially all microbial and chemical contaminants with very high effectiveness and they rely on multiple barrier treatment trains to assure excellent reliability even in the event of diminished performance of one of the barriers. Real-time monitoring is a key element of an IPR or DPR system to assure that any deviations from unit process performance specifications are rapidly identified and corrected.

There are multiple treatment configurations that can be used to produce high-quality potable drinking water from impaired sources. The components can include several of the following technologies: Starting with secondary or tertiary treated wastewater, SAT, granular and biologically activated carbon, sequences of membrane treatments including microfiltration, ultrafiltration, or NF with RO, and disinfection systems including chlorine, ozone, chlorine dioxide, and UV light. NF or RO membrane processes are useful when higher salinity requires reduction of TDS.

The more costly advanced oxidation technologies can be used to remove trace organic chemicals like some refractory residual pharmaceuticals or recalcitrant chemicals like 1,4-dioxane. Advanced oxidation involves technologies that produce hydroxyl free radicals from hydrogen peroxide or ozone and UV light, or chlorine and UV light. Hydroxyl-free radicals have a free electron and they are the most reactive free radicals available in water. With higher costs, they have the capability of destroying essentially any organic chemical and mineralizing it to carbon dioxide and water if a sufficiently high dosage is produced. They are, however, inefficient because the hydroxyl radicals are indiscriminant and most are consumed by reactions with TOC of no health concern in order to decompose the fraction of a percent of trace (ppb or ppt) chemicals in the TOC of potential concern.

Health Implications

The principal concern in any water system is eliminating acute microbial risks, so IPR and DPR must be designed to reliably produce microbiologically safe drinking water with a sufficient margin. Drinking water regulations and guidelines provide target specifications for contaminants. Trace chemical removal is also highly desirable and practiced, but it is usually understood that those more hypothetical risks, if any, of consumption of low ppb and ppt of a few residual organics are not as significant. Planned reuse projects are designed to consistently achieve these results so they can produce water that is at least as safe as and probably better than conventional drinking water that meets drinking water regulations.

WHO Potable Reuse Guidelines

In response to growing pressures on available water resources, potable reuse represents a practical source of drinking water in specific circumstances.

The WHO document describes how to apply appropriate management systems to produce safe drinking water from municipal wastewater. Information is provided on specific aspects of potable reuse including the quality and protection of source wastewaters, types of control measures, challenge testing, log removal targets for microbial indicators and specific microbes, use of a Disability Adjusted Life Year methodology for microbial specifications, monitoring considerations, and public acceptance. Several functioning potable reuse projects are also described through a number of case studies.

Some of the key messages derived from the WHO Guidelines and other sources are summarized here.

The scientific and technological basis for implementing potable and non-potable reuse has been demonstrated in numerous functioning projects. Well-designed potable reuse schemes, managed in accord with Water Safety Plans as a management structure will be successful.

Potable and non-potable reuse should be among the options for developing new drinking water supplies or when expanding or replacing existing supplies, especially in water limited areas. Major advantages of potable and non-potable reuse are that they are virtually climate-independent and they actually increase the availability of water for the locality because they allow multiple use rather than one pass use. It is important to coordinate wastewater management and drinking water production because of their interdependence in the quantity and quality of water that will be available. Potable reuse also reduces undesirable environmental impacts from wastewater discharges

The principles and health-based targets in the Guidelines for Drinking Water Quality (WHO, 2017) apply to potable reuse as well as for traditional drinking water supplies, because the end product water must meet all quality and safety specifications. Where source water surveys indicate a potential for elevated levels of a chemical without a guideline value (e.g., due to poorly managed discharges from manufacturing facilities) screening or performance target values should be developed by qualified health and technology experts. Development of a single set of specifications for drinking water including potable reuse should be considered by national regulatory agencies and the content of regulations should be consistent with those developed for other types of drinking water supplies.

Management and control measures should operate from introduction and collection of wastewater to the delivery of treated drinking water. Appropriate chemical and indicator monitoring should be carried out consistent with the water management plan that has been developed that is reflective of health, technology, and regulatory considerations.

Log removal values for microbial contaminants and indicators should be based on challenge testing and the monitoring capabilities and plan requirements. Pilot studies should be conducted as needed to assure that the final multi-barrier treatment scheme will perform satisfactorily. Technically feasible real-time continuous monitoring with alarms should be utilized to assure that deviations from performance specifications will be rapidly detected and corrected to avoid any risks to consumers.

Public Concerns and Reactions

In spite of the proven successes of planned IPR and DPR technologies and the high-quality product water that they produce, it is natural for many consumers to have some misgivings because of the sanitary wastewater source, i.e., the "yuck factor." Planned IPR systems also provide a greater perception that the treated water has lost its original wastewater identity because there has been an intervening environmental phase, such as storage in the ground, or placement in a surface reservoir prior to being retreated in a conventional drinking water plant. It would not be surprising that some consumers who are supportive of the IPR and DPR reuse project and intellectually satisfied that the water is safe to drink, might be reluctant to do so and would gravitate to POU treated water or to bottled drinking water.

In fact, this is not an unusual situation among some consumers in many conventional public systems, either because of undesirable taste or media-based perceived, although unlikely, risks from the public water supply. One small poll in an IPR location indicated that among strong supporters, about 40 percent of respondents stated that they were drinking bottled water and another 40 percent stated that they had a POU device in their home. The types of devices were not specified, but it is likely that many of them were just taste and odor carbon filters so they would not have much of an effect on the finished water composition. So, clearly the IPR/DPR issues are of perception rather than actual water quality and safety.

Conclusions

All water is recycled either in the natural cycle or via human technological intervention. Potable and other forms of wastewater reuse are truly sustainable concepts and make efficient use of the available water resources. The treated water otherwise would be discharged to a river or the sea. Indirect (unplanned) wastewater reuse is routine; direct (planned) potable reuse is now viable as demonstrated by several successful projects with appropriate technologies. The key elements are multiple barrier treatment designs, real-time monitoring for meeting performance expectations, and assuring reliability and safety. The WHO Guidelines provide pragmatic recommendations that should facilitate additional applications of reuse opportunities of all types. There are several successful technological approaches, so no single approach should be mandated. The regulatory acceptance decisions should be based upon water quality performance.

Several options should be considered for increasing access to water in a locality including IPR and DPR systems, and lower cost non-potable reuse offset options should be explored. The needs for additional water resources are increasing, because the need for high-quality water is increasing in parts of the United States and the word experiencing shortages, often due to population shifts to areas that are short of natural water or experiencing droughts. The technologies for IPR and DPR are proven to be successful and reliable and drinking water quality is at least as good as or better than from conventional surface water supplies. Real-time monitoring is a key element of an IPR or DPR system to assure that any deviations from unit process performance specifications are rapidly identified and corrected.

The last barrier to potable reuse is public acceptance. Consumers are supportive when they understand the need for an adequate and reliable water supply. Additionally, more intensive treatment of wastewater protects the environment by reducing the waste discharges to surface waters. Nonetheless, some consumers will be reluctant to drink the water in their homes because of concerns about the history and proximity of the impaired source water, but that should not be the determining factor of whether to implement a DPR or IPR project. These concerns may subside in time with familiarity, but it is not surprising that although supportive of the concept or project, some people then will opt to consume POU or bottled water.

Sources

Cotruvo JA (2014). Recycled Wastewater and Potable Water Reuse. Water Technology on Line. www.watertechonline.com/professor-poupoe-february-2014/.

Cotruvo JA (2015). Potable Reuse History and a New Framework for Decision Making. *International Journal of Water Resources Development.* DOI: 10.1080/07900627.2015.1099520.

Cotruvo JA (2014). Direct Potable Reuse: Then and Now. World Water: Reuse & Desalination. 5: pp. 1, 10–13, Spring 2014. http://edition.pagesuite-professional.co.uk/Launch.aspx?EID=192226ee-85e9-4277-9129-9ff8272ac622.

EPA (2017). Potable Reuse Compendium. www.epa.gov/ground-water-and-drinking-water/2017-potable-reuse-compendium.

EPA (2012). Guidelines for Potable Reuse. www.epa.gov/ground-water-and-drinking-water/potable-water-reuse-and-drinking-water.

ILSI (2013). *Water Recovery and Reuse: Guideline for Safe Application of Water Conservation Methods in Beverage Production and Food Processing.* International Life Sciences Institute, Washington, DC, USA. http://ilsi.org/wp-content/uploads/2016/05/Guideline-for-Water-ReUse-in-Beverage-Production-and-Food-Processing.pdf.

Leddy M (2017). Characterization of microbial signatures from advanced treated wastewater biofilms. *American Water Works Association Journal.* www.awwa.org/publications/journal-awwa/abstract/articleid/66240693.aspx.

WHO (2017). Potable Reuse: Guidance for producing safe drinking-water. Cunliffe D, Cotruvo J, DuPisani P, Limm MH, Menge J, Ong CN, Raschid Sally L, Snyder S. World Health Organization. ISBN 978-92-4-151277-0. www.who.int/water_sanitation_health/publications/potable-reuse-guidelines/en/.

Index

I

J

K

L

M

Printed in the United States
by Baker & Taylor Publisher Services

Printed in the United States
by Baker & Taylor Publisher Services